THE BOOK OF PROBLEMS:

ALGEBRA

Brian K. Saltzer

Eric Stimmel

The Book of Problems Series

QUANTUM SCIENTIFIC PUBLISHING

Pittsburgh

PEARSON

Custom
Publishing

Printed in the United States of America

10 9 8 7 6 5 4 3 2 1

Please visit our web site at *www.pearsoncustom.com*

ISBN 0-536-86211-7

2004360488

JE

PEARSON CUSTOM PUBLISHING
75 Arlington Street, Suite 300, Boston, MA 02116
A Pearson Education Company

About This Book

The Book of Problems series originated in the fact that students simply don't need another textbook on Algebra, Calculus, etc. There are already wonderful textbooks on the market in almost every area of mathematics and science. What struggling students do need, however, are more detailed worked examples than are normally found in even the best textbooks. To solve this problem, every book in the Book of Problems series contains hundreds of problems with both answers and detailed, worked solutions.

In this volume, *The Book of Problems - Algebra*, each of the major concepts in a standard Algebra course is given its own section and problems. After a list of the problems for a concept, the answers are given so that students can compare their answers to the correct ones. Following the answers are detailed worked solutions to each problem. The answers are given first because many students do not want to see a detailed worked solution immediately upon finding that their answer is not the correct one.

At the end of the book are two Final Exams that test whether or not the student has grasped all of the concepts in the book. Because students must be able to solve problems regardless of the order that they appear on their college/high school exams, the Finals are not in the same concept order as that given in the Table of Contents. The first Final Exam groups concepts that are similar (although not it the same order as presented in the book) and the second Final Exam completely randomizes the concepts and problems. As with every other problem in the Book of Problems series, both answers and detailed, worked solutions to all Final Exam questions are included in the book.

Our sincere hope is that this book will aid you in your goal of attaining both a higher course grade and a deeper understanding of Algebra.

BKS
EPS

$$x^{\frac{a}{b}} = \sqrt[b]{x^a}$$

TABLE OF CONTENTS

In each of the following:
   a) Identify the base and the exponent.
   b) Write out the repeated multiplication indicated by the expression.

1. x^2

2. b^3

3. 5^4

4. $\left(\dfrac{1}{2}\right)^3$

5. $(0.7)^6$

6. $(2.4)^3$

7. $(x+1)^4$

8. $(2x-y)^3$

9. $\left(\sqrt{x-1}\right)^2$

10. $\left(\dfrac{1}{x}\right)^5$

Notes

1. $x^2 = \underbrace{x \cdot x}_{2\,\text{copies}}$, exponent, base

2. $b^3 = \underbrace{b \cdot b \cdot b}_{3\,\text{copies}}$, exponent, base

3. $5^4 = \underbrace{5 \cdot 5 \cdot 5 \cdot 5}_{4\,\text{copies}}$, exponent, base

4. $\underbrace{\left(\dfrac{1}{2}\right)}_{\text{base}}^{3} = \underbrace{\left(\dfrac{1}{2}\right) \cdot \left(\dfrac{1}{2}\right) \cdot \left(\dfrac{1}{2}\right)}_{3\,\text{copies}}$, exponent

5. $\underbrace{\left(0.7\right)}_{\text{base}}^{6} = \underbrace{\left(0.7\right) \cdot \left(0.7\right) \cdot \left(0.7\right) \cdot \left(0.7\right) \cdot \left(0.7\right) \cdot \left(0.7\right)}_{6\,\text{copies}}$, exponent

6. $\underbrace{\left(2.4\right)}_{\text{base}}^{3} = \underbrace{\left(2.4\right) \cdot \left(2.4\right) \cdot \left(2.4\right)}_{3\,\text{copies}}$, exponent

7. $\underbrace{\left(x+1\right)}_{\text{base}}^{4} = \underbrace{\left(x+1\right) \cdot \left(x+1\right) \cdot \left(x+1\right) \cdot \left(x+1\right)}_{4\,\text{copies}}$, exponent

8. $\underbrace{\left(2x-y\right)}_{\text{base}}^{3} = \underbrace{\left(2x-y\right) \cdot \left(2x-y\right) \cdot \left(2x-y\right)}_{3\,\text{copies}}$, exponent

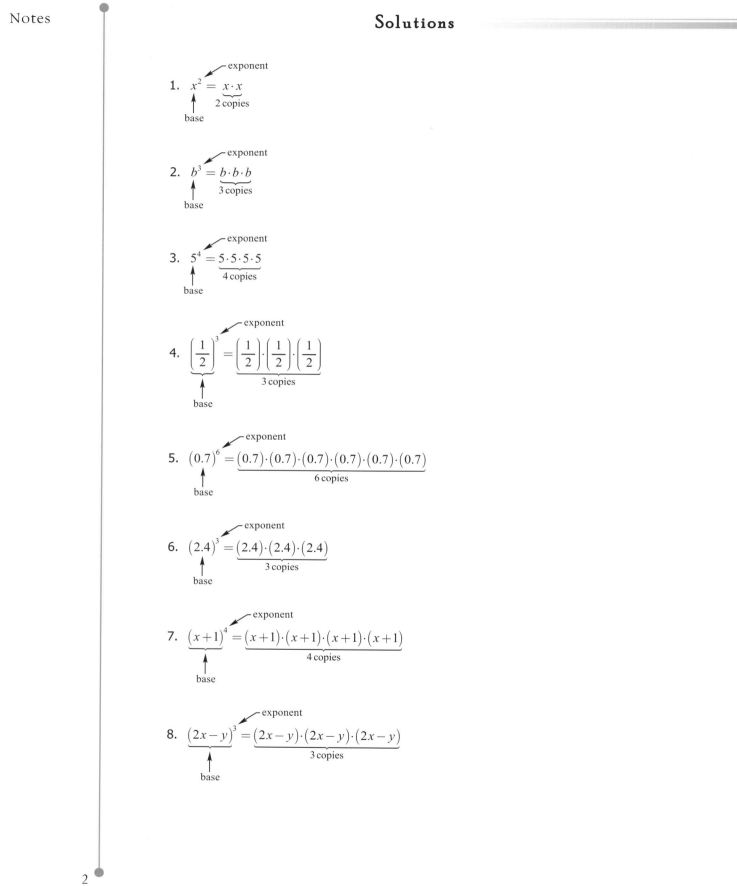

9.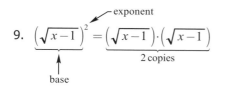

10.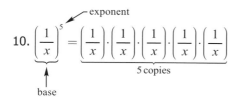

4

PROPERTIES OF EXPONENTS

Simplify each of the following.

$$x^a \cdot x^b = x^{a+b}, \quad \frac{x^a}{x^b} = x^{a-b}, \quad \left(x^a\right)^b = x^{ab}$$

1. $x^2 \cdot x^4$

2. $x^3 \cdot x^5$

3. $x \cdot x$

4. $x^2 \cdot x^3 \cdot x^6$

5. $\dfrac{x^9}{x^2}$

6. $\dfrac{x^5}{x}$

7. $\dfrac{x^2 \cdot x^4}{x}$

8. $\dfrac{x^3 \cdot x}{x^4 \cdot x^2}$

9. $x^{\frac{1}{2}} \cdot x^{\frac{2}{3}}$

10. $\left(x^2\right)^3$

11. $\left(x^3\right)^5$

12. $\left(x^2 \cdot x\right)^4$

13. $\left(\sqrt{x}\right)^4$

14. $\left(\sqrt[3]{x}\right)^2$

15. $\left(x^2 \sqrt{x}\right)^3$

Solutions

1. $x^2 \cdot x^4 = x^6$

2. $x^3 \cdot x^5 = x^8$

3. $x \cdot x = x^2$

4. $x^2 \cdot x^3 \cdot x^6 = x^{11}$

5. $\dfrac{x^9}{x^2} = x^7$

6. $\dfrac{x^5}{x} = x^4$

7. $\dfrac{x^2 \cdot x^4}{x} = \dfrac{x^6}{x} = x^5$

8. $\dfrac{x^3 \cdot x}{x^4 \cdot x^2} = \dfrac{x^4}{x^6} = \dfrac{1}{x^2}$

9. $x^{\frac{1}{2}} \cdot x^{\frac{2}{3}} = x^{\frac{3}{6}} \cdot x^{\frac{4}{6}} = x^{\frac{7}{6}}$

10. $\left(x^2\right)^3 = x^6$

11. $\left(x^3\right)^5 = x^{15}$

12. $\left(x^2 \cdot x\right)^4 = \left(x^3\right)^4 = x^{12}$

13. $\left(\sqrt{x}\right)^4 = \left(x^{\frac{1}{2}}\right)^4 = x^2$

14. $\left(\sqrt[3]{x}\right)^2 = \left(x^{\frac{1}{3}}\right)^2 = x^{\frac{2}{3}}$

15. $\left(x^2 \sqrt{x}\right)^3 = \left(x^2 \cdot x^{\frac{1}{2}}\right)^3 = \left(x^{\frac{5}{2}}\right)^3 = x^{\frac{15}{2}}$

ADDITION, SUBTRACTION, AND MULTIPLICATION OF RADICAL EXPRESSIONS

Perform the following operations.

1. $\sqrt{x} + \sqrt{x}$

2. $\sqrt[3]{xy} + \sqrt[3]{xy}$

3. $\sqrt[3]{x^2 y} + \sqrt[3]{xy^2} + \sqrt[3]{x^2 y}$

4. $3\sqrt{x} - 2\sqrt{x}$

5. $6\sqrt{y} + 2\sqrt{y} - 5\sqrt{y}$

6. $\sqrt{x} \cdot \sqrt{y}$

7. $\sqrt{x} \cdot \sqrt{y} \cdot \sqrt{z}$

8. $\sqrt{2} \cdot \sqrt{50}$

9. $\sqrt[3]{2} \cdot \sqrt[3]{4}$

10. $\dfrac{\sqrt{x}}{\sqrt{y}}$

11. $\dfrac{\sqrt[3]{x}}{\sqrt[3]{y}}$

12. $\dfrac{\sqrt{1000}}{\sqrt{10}}$

13. $\sqrt[3]{x} \cdot \sqrt[3]{x} \cdot \sqrt[3]{x}$

14. $\sqrt{x} \cdot \sqrt{y} + \sqrt{x} \cdot \sqrt{y}$

15. $\dfrac{\sqrt[3]{2}}{\sqrt[3]{16}}$

16. $\sqrt{x^3} \cdot \sqrt{x}$

17. $\sqrt[3]{x^2} \cdot \sqrt[3]{x^2}$

18. $2\sqrt{x} + 3\sqrt[3]{x} + 5\sqrt{x}$

19. $\dfrac{\sqrt{x} \cdot \sqrt{y}}{\sqrt{z}}$

20. $\dfrac{\dfrac{\sqrt[3]{x}}{\sqrt[3]{y}}}{\sqrt[3]{z}}$

Solutions

1. $\sqrt{x} + \sqrt{x} = 2\sqrt{x}$

2. $\sqrt[3]{xy} + \sqrt[3]{xy} = 2\sqrt[3]{xy}$

3. $\sqrt[3]{x^2 y} + \sqrt[3]{xy^2} + \sqrt[3]{x^2 y} = 2\sqrt[3]{x^2 y} + \sqrt[3]{xy^2}$

4. $3\sqrt{x} - 2\sqrt{x} = \sqrt{x}$

5. $6\sqrt{y} + 2\sqrt{y} - 5\sqrt{y} = 3\sqrt{y}$

6. $\sqrt{x} \cdot \sqrt{y} = \sqrt{xy}$

7. $\sqrt{x} \cdot \sqrt{y} \cdot \sqrt{z} = \sqrt{xyz}$

8. $\sqrt{2} \cdot \sqrt{50} = \sqrt{2(50)} = \sqrt{100} = 10$

9. $\sqrt[3]{2} \cdot \sqrt[3]{4} = \sqrt[3]{8} = 2$

10. $\dfrac{\sqrt{x}}{\sqrt{y}} = \sqrt{\dfrac{x}{y}}$

11. $\dfrac{\sqrt[3]{x}}{\sqrt[3]{y}} = \sqrt[3]{\dfrac{x}{y}}$

12. $\dfrac{\sqrt{1000}}{\sqrt{10}} = \sqrt{\dfrac{1000}{10}} = \sqrt{100} = 10$

13. $\sqrt[3]{x} \cdot \sqrt[3]{x} \cdot \sqrt[3]{x} = \sqrt[3]{x \cdot x \cdot x} = \sqrt[3]{x^3} = x$

14. $\sqrt{x} \cdot \sqrt{y} + \sqrt{x} \cdot \sqrt{y} = \sqrt{xy} + \sqrt{xy} = 2\sqrt{xy}$

15. $\dfrac{\sqrt[3]{2}}{\sqrt[3]{16}} = \sqrt[3]{\dfrac{2}{16}} = \sqrt[3]{\dfrac{1}{8}} = \dfrac{1}{2}$

16. $\sqrt{x^3} \cdot \sqrt{x} = \sqrt{x^3 \cdot x} = \sqrt{x^4} = x^2$

17. $\sqrt[3]{x^2} \cdot \sqrt[3]{x^2} = \sqrt[3]{x^2 \cdot x^2} = \sqrt[3]{x^4} = x\sqrt[3]{x}$

18. $2\sqrt{x} + 3\sqrt[3]{x} + 5\sqrt{x} = 7\sqrt{x} + 3\sqrt[3]{x}$

19. $\dfrac{\sqrt{x} \cdot \sqrt{y}}{\sqrt{z}} = \dfrac{\sqrt{xy}}{\sqrt{z}} = \sqrt{\dfrac{xy}{z}}$

20. $\dfrac{\dfrac{\sqrt[3]{x}}{\sqrt[3]{y}}}{\sqrt[3]{z}} = \dfrac{\sqrt[3]{x}}{\sqrt[3]{y}} \cdot \dfrac{1}{\sqrt[3]{z}} = \dfrac{\sqrt[3]{x}}{\sqrt[3]{y} \cdot \sqrt[3]{z}} = \dfrac{\sqrt[3]{x}}{\sqrt[3]{yz}} = \sqrt[3]{\dfrac{x}{yz}}$

PERMUTATIONS AND COMBINATIONS

Calculate each of the following permutations and calculations.

> The number of *permutations* of n objects taken r at a time:
>
> $$_nP_r = \frac{n!}{(n-r)!}$$
>
> The number of *combinations* of n objects taken r at a time:
>
> $$_nC_r = \frac{n!}{(n-r)!\,r!}$$

1.
   a) $_5P_2$

   b) $_5C_2$

2.
   a) $_4P_3$

   b) $_4C_3$

3.
   a) $_{26}P_5$

   b) $_{26}C_5$

4.
   a) $_8P_1$

   b) $_8C_1$

5.
   a) $_7P_7$

   b) $_7C_7$

Notes

Answer Key

1.

a) $_5P_2 = 20$

b) $_5C_2 = 10$

2.

a) $_4P_3 = 24$

b) $_4C_3 = 4$

3.

a) $_{26}P_5 = 7,893,600$

b) $_{26}C_5 = 65,780$

4.

a) $_8P_1 = 8$

b) $_8C_1 = 8$

5.

a) $_7P_7 = 5040$

b) $_7C_7 = 1$

Solutions

1.

a) $_5P_2 = \dfrac{5!}{(5-2)!} = \dfrac{5!}{3!} = \dfrac{5 \cdot 4 \cdot 3 \cdot 2 \cdot 1}{3 \cdot 2 \cdot 1} = 5(4) = 20$

b) $_5C_2 = \dfrac{5!}{(5-2)!2!} = \dfrac{5!}{3!2!} = \dfrac{120}{6(2)} = \dfrac{120}{12} = 10$

2.

a) $_4P_3 = \dfrac{4!}{(4-3)!} = \dfrac{4!}{1!} = \dfrac{24}{1} = 24$

b) $_4C_3 = \dfrac{4!}{(4-3)!3!} = \dfrac{4!}{1!3!} = \dfrac{4!}{3!} = \dfrac{4 \cdot 3 \cdot 2 \cdot 1}{3 \cdot 2 \cdot 1} = 4$

3.

a) $_{26}P_5 = \dfrac{26!}{(26-5)!} = \dfrac{26!}{21!} = 26(25)(24)(23)(22) = 7,893,600$

b) $_{26}C_5 = \dfrac{26!}{(26-5)!5!} = \dfrac{26!}{21!5!} = \dfrac{26(25)(24)(23)(22)}{5!} = \dfrac{7,893,600}{120} = 65,780$

4.

a) $_8P_1 = \dfrac{8!}{(8-1)!} = \dfrac{8!}{7!} = \dfrac{8 \cdot 7 \cdot 6 \cdot 5 \cdot 4 \cdot 3 \cdot 2 \cdot 1}{7 \cdot 6 \cdot 5 \cdot 4 \cdot 3 \cdot 2 \cdot 1} = 8$

b) $_8C_1 = \dfrac{8!}{(8-1)!1!} = \dfrac{8!}{7!1!} = \dfrac{8 \cdot 7 \cdot 6 \cdot 5 \cdot 4 \cdot 3 \cdot 2 \cdot 1}{7 \cdot 6 \cdot 5 \cdot 4 \cdot 3 \cdot 2 \cdot 1} = 8$

5.

a) $_7P_7 = \dfrac{7!}{(7-7)!} = \dfrac{7!}{0!} = \dfrac{7!}{1} = 5040$

b) $_7C_7 = \dfrac{7!}{(7-7)!7!} = \dfrac{7!}{0!7!} = \dfrac{7!}{1 \cdot 7!} = \dfrac{7!}{7!} = 1$

ADDING AND SUBTRACTING POLYNOMIALS

Add or subtract the following polynomials.

1. $\left(3x^2 + 2x + 5\right) + \left(4x^2 + 6x + 7\right)$

2. $\left(7x^3 - 9x^2 + 8\right) + \left(5x^2 + 3x + 2\right)$

3. $\left(8x^2 + 5x - 2\right) - \left(6x^2 - 3x - 4\right)$

4. $\left(3x + 9\right) - \left(x^2 - x^3\right)$

5. $\left(7x^2 - 4x + 3\right) + \left(-x^3 + x^4\right)$

6. $3\left(2x + 1\right) + 5\left(2x^2 + 3x + 6\right)$

7. $-5\left(4x^3 - 2x^2 + 3x\right) - 2\left(7x^2 + 8x - 1\right)$

8. $\left(3.2x^2 + 4.1x + 6.3\right) + \left(5.1x^2 + 7.8x - 2.1\right)$

9. $\frac{1}{2}\left(4x^2 + 8x + 6\right) - \frac{1}{3}\left(6x^2 - 9x - 12\right)$

10. $\left(7x^3 + 8x^2 + 5x - 9\right) - \left(6x^2 - 4x + 2\right) + \left(10x^3 + 4x^2 - 3\right)$

11. $\left(\frac{1}{2}x^3 + \frac{4}{5}x\right) + \left(\frac{1}{3}x^3 - \frac{2}{5}x^2 + \frac{1}{3}x\right)$

12. $\left(6x^7 + 5x^4 - 9x^3 - 3x^2 + 4x + 6\right) - \left(x^8 - 5x^7 - 4x^6 - 2x^5 - 7x^4 - 8x^3 - 5x^2 - 7\right)$

13. $\left(3 + x + x^2 + 6x^3\right) + \left(4x^3 + 5x^2 + 3x + 9\right)$

14. $\left(\frac{x^2}{2} + \frac{x}{3} - 5\right) + \left(\frac{1}{2}x^2 + \frac{1}{3}x + 2\right)$

15. $a\left(x^2 + 3x + 2\right) + b\left(2x^2 + x + 5\right)$

Answer Key

1. $\left(3x^2+2x+5\right)+\left(4x^2+6x+7\right)=7x^2+8x+12$

2. $\left(7x^3-9x^2+8\right)+\left(5x^2+3x+2\right)=7x^3-4x^2+3x+10$

3. $\left(8x^2+5x-2\right)-\left(6x^2-3x-4\right)=2x^2+8x+2$

4. $\left(3x+9\right)-\left(x^2-x^3\right)=-x^3+x^2+3x+9$

5. $\left(7x^2-4x+3\right)+\left(-x^3+x^4\right)=x^4-x^3+7x^2-4x+3$

6. $3\left(2x+1\right)+5\left(2x^2+3x+6\right)=10x^2+21x+33$

7. $-5\left(4x^3-2x^2+3x\right)-2\left(7x^2+8x-1\right)=-20x^3-4x^2-31x+2$

8. $\left(3.2x^2+4.1x+6.3\right)+\left(5.1x^2+7.8x-2.1\right)=8.3x^2+11.9x+4.2$

9. $\dfrac{1}{2}\left(4x^2+8x+6\right)-\dfrac{1}{3}\left(6x^2-9x-12\right)=7x+7$

10. $\left(7x^3+8x^2+5x-9\right)-\left(6x^2-4x+2\right)+\left(10x^3+4x^2-3\right)=17x^3+6x^2+9x-14$

11. $\left(\dfrac{1}{2}x^3+\dfrac{4}{5}x\right)+\left(\dfrac{1}{3}x^3-\dfrac{2}{5}x^2+\dfrac{1}{3}x\right)=\dfrac{5}{6}x^3-\dfrac{2}{5}x^2+\dfrac{17}{15}x$

12. $\left(6x^7+5x^4-9x^3-3x^2+4x+6\right)-\left(x^8-5x^7-4x^6-2x^5-7x^4-8x^3-5x^2-7\right)$

    $=-x^8+11x^7+4x^6+2x^5+12x^4-x^3+2x^2+4x+13$

13. $\left(3+x+x^2+6x^3\right)+\left(4x^3+5x^2+3x+9\right)=10x^3+6x^2+4x+12$

14. $\left(\dfrac{x^2}{2}+\dfrac{x}{3}-5\right)+\left(\dfrac{1}{2}x^2+\dfrac{1}{3}x+2\right)=x^2+\dfrac{2}{3}x-3$

15. $a\left(x^2+3x+2\right)+b\left(2x^2+x+5\right)=(a+2b)x^2+(3a+b)x+2a+5b$

Solutions

1. $\left(3x^2 + 2x + 5\right) + \left(4x^2 + 6x + 7\right) = 3x^2 + 2x + 5 + 4x^2 + 6x + 7$

$$= 7x^2 + 8x + 12$$

2. $\left(7x^3 - 9x^2 + 8\right) + \left(5x^2 + 3x + 2\right) = 7x^3 - 9x^2 + 8 + 5x^2 + 3x + 2$

$$= 7x^3 - 4x^2 + 3x + 10$$

3. $\left(8x^2 + 5x - 2\right) - \left(6x^2 - 3x - 4\right) = 8x^2 + 5x - 2 - 6x^2 + 3x + 4$

$$= 2x^2 + 8x + 2$$

4. $\left(3x + 9\right) - \left(x^2 - x^3\right) = 3x + 9 + x^2 - x^3$

$$= -x^3 + x^2 + 3x + 9$$

5. $\left(7x^2 - 4x + 3\right) + \left(-x^3 + x^4\right) = 7x^2 - 4x + 3 - x^3 + x^4$

$$= x^4 - x^3 + 7x^2 - 4x + 3$$

6. $3\left(2x + 1\right) + 5\left(2x^2 + 3x + 6\right) = 6x + 3 + 10x^2 + 15x + 30$

$$= 10x^2 + 21x + 33$$

7. $-5\left(4x^3 - 2x^2 + 3x\right) - 2\left(7x^2 + 8x - 1\right) = -20x^3 + 10x^2 - 15x - 14x^2 - 16x + 2$

$$= -20x^3 - 4x^2 - 31x + 2$$

8. $\left(3.2x^2 + 4.1x + 6.3\right) + \left(5.1x^2 + 7.8x - 2.1\right) = 3.2x^2 + 4.1x + 6.3 + 5.1x^2 + 7.8x - 2.1$

$$= 8.3x^2 + 11.9x + 4.2$$

9. $\frac{1}{2}\left(4x^2 + 8x + 6\right) - \frac{1}{3}\left(6x^2 - 9x - 12\right) = \frac{1}{2}\left(4x^2\right) + \frac{1}{2}\left(8x\right) + \frac{1}{2}\left(6\right) - \frac{1}{3}\left(6x^2\right) - \frac{1}{3}\left(-9x\right) - \frac{1}{3}\left(-12\right)$

$$= 2x^2 + 4x + 3 - 2x^2 + 3x + 4$$

$$= 7x + 7$$

10. $\left(7x^3 + 8x^2 + 5x - 9\right) - \left(6x^2 - 4x + 2\right) + \left(10x^3 + 4x^2 - 3\right)$

$$= 7x^3 + 8x^2 + 5x - 9 - 6x^2 + 4x - 2 + 10x^3 + 4x^2 - 3$$

$$= 17x^3 + 6x^2 + 9x - 14$$

11. $\left(\frac{1}{2}x^3 + \frac{4}{5}x\right) + \left(\frac{1}{3}x^3 - \frac{2}{5}x^2 + \frac{1}{3}x\right) = \frac{1}{2}x^3 + \frac{4}{5}x + \frac{1}{3}x^3 - \frac{2}{5}x^2 + \frac{1}{3}x$

$$= \frac{3}{6}x^3 + \frac{2}{6}x^3 - \frac{2}{5}x^2 + \frac{12}{15}x + \frac{5}{15}x$$

$$= \frac{5}{6}x^3 - \frac{2}{5}x^2 + \frac{17}{15}x$$

12. $\left(6x^7 + 5x^4 - 9x^3 - 3x^2 + 4x + 6\right) - \left(x^8 - 5x^7 - 4x^6 - 2x^5 - 7x^4 - 8x^3 - 5x^2 - 7\right)$

$\quad = 6x^7 + 5x^4 - 9x^3 - 3x^2 + 4x + 6 - x^8 + 5x^7 + 4x^6 + 2x^5 + 7x^4 + 8x^3 + 5x^2 + 7$

$\quad = -x^8 + 11x^7 + 4x^6 + 2x^5 + 12x^4 - x^3 + 2x^2 + 4x + 13$

13. $\left(3 + x + x^2 + 6x^3\right) + \left(4x^3 + 5x^2 + 3x + 9\right) = 3 + x + x^2 + 6x^3 + 4x^3 + 5x^2 + 3x + 9$

$\qquad\qquad\qquad\qquad\qquad\qquad\quad = 10x^3 + 6x^2 + 4x + 12$

14. $\left(\dfrac{x^2}{2} + \dfrac{x}{3} - 5\right) + \left(\dfrac{1}{2}x^2 + \dfrac{1}{3}x + 2\right) = \dfrac{1}{2}x^2 + \dfrac{1}{3}x - 5 + \dfrac{1}{2}x^2 + \dfrac{1}{3}x + 2$

$\qquad\qquad\qquad\qquad\qquad\qquad = x^2 + \dfrac{2}{3}x - 3$

15. $a\left(x^2 + 3x + 2\right) + b\left(2x^2 + x + 5\right) = ax^2 + 3ax + 2a + 2bx^2 + bx + 5b$

$\qquad\qquad\qquad\qquad\qquad\quad = \left(a + 2b\right)x^2 + \left(3a + b\right)x + 2a + 5b$

MULTIPLYING POLYNOMIALS

Execute each of the following multiplications.

1. $2(x+3)$

2. $x(x+4)$

3. $x^3(x^2+5x)$

4. $3x(7x^2+4x-6)$

5. $(x+2)(x+3)$

6. $(2+x)(x-3)$

7. $(4x-1)(x+6)$

8. $(x^2+2x+3)(x+4)$

9. $(3x^4-7x^2)(x^2+x+1)$

10. $x(x+3)(x-1)$

11. $(x+2)(x-2)$

12. $(x-3)(x^2+3x+9)$

13. $\left(\dfrac{1}{x}+2\right)(x^2+x^3)$

14. $(\sqrt{x}+4)(\sqrt{x}+1)$

15. $(x+\sqrt{x})(x-\sqrt{x})$

Notes

Answer Key

1. $2(x+3) = 2x+6$

2. $x(x+4) = x^2 + 4x$

3. $x^3(x^2 + 5x) = x^5 + 5x^4$

4. $3x(7x^2 + 4x - 6) = 21x^3 + 12x^2 - 18x$

5. $(x+2)(x+3) = x^2 + 5x + 6$

6. $(2+x)(x-3) = x^2 - x - 6$

7. $(4x-1)(x+6) = 4x^2 + 23x - 6$

8. $(x^2 + 2x + 3)(x+4) = x^3 + 6x^2 + 11x + 12$

9. $(3x^4 - 7x^2)(x^2 + x + 1) = 3x^6 + 3x^5 - 4x^4 - 7x^3 - 7x^2$

10. $x(x+3)(x-1) = x^3 + 2x^2 - 3x$

11. $(x+2)(x-2) = x^2 - 4$

12. $(x-3)(x^2 + 3x + 9) = x^3 - 27$

13. $\left(\dfrac{1}{x} + 2\right)(x^2 + x^3) = 2x^3 + 3x^2 + x$

14. $(\sqrt{x} + 4)(\sqrt{x} + 1) = x + 5\sqrt{x} + 4$

15. $(x + \sqrt{x})(x - \sqrt{x}) = x^2 - x$

Solutions

1. $2(x+3)=2x+2(3)$

   $=2x+6$

2. $x(x+4)=x \cdot x+x \cdot 4$

   $=x^2+4x$

3. $x^3(x^2+5x)=x^3 \cdot x^2+x^3(5x)$

   $=x^5+5x^4$

4. $3x(7x^2+4x-6)=3x(7x^2)+3x(4x)+3x(-6)$

   $=21x^3+12x^2-18x$

5. $(x+2)(x+3)=x \cdot x+x(3)+2(x)+2(3)$

   $=x^2+3x+2x+6$

   $=x^2+5x+6$

6. $(2+x)(x-3)=2x+2(-3)+x \cdot x+x(-3)$

   $=2x-6+x^2-3x$

   $=x^2-x-6$

7. $(4x-1)(x+6)=4x(x)+4x(6)+(-1)(x)+(-1)(6)$

   $=4x^2+24x-x-6$

   $=4x^2+23x-6$

8. $(x^2+2x+3)(x+4)=x^2 \cdot x+x^2(4)+2x(x)+2x(4)+3x+3(4)$

   $=x^3+4x^2+2x^2+8x+3x+12$

   $=x^3+6x^2+11x+12$

9. $(3x^4-7x^2)(x^2+x+1)=3x^4(x^2)+3x^4(x)+3x^4(1)+(-7x^2)(x^2)+(-7x^2)(x)+(-7x^2)(1)$

   $=3x^6+3x^5+3x^4-7x^4-7x^3-7x^2$

   $=3x^6+3x^5-4x^4-7x^3-7x^2$

10. $x(x+3)(x-1)=[x \cdot x+x(3)](x-1)$

    $=(x^2+3x)(x-1)$

    $=x^2 \cdot x+x^2(-1)+3x(x)+3x(-1)$

    $=x^3-x^2+3x^2-3x$

    $=x^3+2x^2-3x$

11. $(x+2)(x-2) = x \cdot x + x(-2) + 2(x) + 2(-2)$

$$= x^2 - 2x + 2x - 4$$

$$= x^2 - 4$$

12. $(x-3)(x^2 + 3x + 9) = x \cdot x^2 + x(3x) + x(9) + (-3)(x^2) + (-3)(3x) + (-3)(9)$

$$= x^3 + 3x^2 + 9x - 3x^2 - 9x - 27$$

$$= x^3 - 27$$

13. $\left(\dfrac{1}{x} + 2\right)(x^2 + x^3) = \left(\dfrac{1}{x}\right)x^2 + \left(\dfrac{1}{x}\right)x^3 + 2 \cdot x^2 + 2 \cdot x^3$

$$= x + x^2 + 2x^2 + 2x^3$$

$$= 2x^3 + 3x^2 + x$$

14. $\left(\sqrt{x} + 4\right)\left(\sqrt{x} + 1\right) = \sqrt{x} \cdot \sqrt{x} + \sqrt{x}(1) + 4 \cdot \sqrt{x} + 4(1)$

$$= x + \sqrt{x} + 4\sqrt{x} + 4$$

$$= x + 5\sqrt{x} + 4$$

15. $\left(x + \sqrt{x}\right)\left(x - \sqrt{x}\right) = x \cdot x + x\left(-\sqrt{x}\right) + \sqrt{x}(x) + \sqrt{x}\left(-\sqrt{x}\right)$

$$= x^2 - x\sqrt{x} + x\sqrt{x} - x$$

$$= x^2 - x$$

METHODS OF FACTORING POLYNOMIALS

Factor each of the following:

Common factors

1. $4x + 4y$

2. $3x^2y + 6xy^2$

3. $ax + ay - az$

4. $x^2(y-1) + z^2(y-1)$

Difference of two squares

5. $x^2 - 1$

6. $x^2 - 25$

7. $t^2 - 36$

8. $4x^2 - 100$

9. $m^2 - n^2$

10. $16x^2 - 4y^2$

Difference of two cubes

11. $x^3 - y^3$

12. $x^3 - 8$

13. $y^3 - 1$

14. $8x^3 - 27$

15. $125 - t^3$

Sum of two cubes

16. $x^3 + y^3$

17. $x^3 + 8$

18. $x^3 + 64$

19. $27y^3 + 1$

20. $8x^3 + 125$

Answer Key

1. $4x + 4y = 4(x + y)$

2. $3x^2 y + 6xy^2 = 3xy(x + 2y)$

3. $ax + ay - az = a(x + y - z)$

4. $x^2(y-1) + z^2(y-1) = (x^2 + z^2)(y-1)$

5. $x^2 - 1 = (x+1)(x-1)$

6. $x^2 - 25 = (x+5)(x-5)$

7. $t^2 - 36 = (t+6)(t-6)$

8. $4x^2 - 100 = 4(x+5)(x-5)$

9. $m^2 - n^2 = (m+n)(m-n)$

10. $16x^2 - 4y^2 = 4(2x+y)(2x-y)$

11. $x^3 - y^3 = (x-y)(x^2 + xy + y^2)$

12. $x^3 - 8 = (x-2)(x^2 + 2x + 4)$

13. $y^3 - 1 = (y-1)(y^2 + y + 1)$

14. $8x^3 - 27 = (2x-3)(4x^2 + 6x + 9)$

15. $125 - t^3 = (5-t)(25 + 5t + t^2)$

16. $x^3 + y^3 = (x+y)(x^2 - xy + y^2)$

17. $x^3 + 8 = (x+2)(x^2 - 2x + 4)$

18. $x^3 + 64 = (x+4)(x^2 - 4x + 16)$

19. $27y^3 + 1 = (3y+1)(9y^2 - 3y + 1)$

20. $8x^3 + 125 = (2x+5)(4x^2 - 10x + 25)$

Solutions

Common factors

1. $4x + 4y = 4(x + y)$

2. $3x^2 y + 6xy^2 = 3xy(x + 2y)$

3. $ax + ay - az = a(x + y - z)$

4. $x^2(y-1) + z^2(y-1) = (x^2 + z^2)(y-1)$

Difference of two squares

5. $x^2 - 1 = x^2 - 1^2$
$$= (x+1)(x-1)$$

6. $x^2 - 25 = x^2 - 5^2$
$$= (x+5)(x-5)$$

7. $t^2 - 36 = t^2 - 6^2$
$$= (t+6)(t-6)$$

8. $4x^2 - 100 = 4(x^2 - 25)$
$$= 4(x^2 - 5^2)$$
$$= 4(x+5)(x-5)$$

9. $m^2 - n^2 = (m+n)(m-n)$

10. $16x^2 - 4y^2 = 4(4x^2 - y^2)$
$$= 4(2x+y)(2x-y)$$

Difference of two cubes

11. $x^3 - y^3 = (x-y)(x^2 + xy + y^2)$

12. $x^3 - 8 = x^3 - 2^3$
$$= (x-2)(x^2 + 2x + 2^2)$$
$$= (x-2)(x^2 + 2x + 4)$$

13. $y^3 - 1 = y^3 - 1^3$
$$= (y-1)(y^2 + y + 1^2)$$
$$= (y-1)(y^2 + y + 1)$$

Difference of two cubes cont...

14. $8x^3 - 27 = (2x)^3 - 3^3$

$$= (2x-3)\left[(2x)^2 + (2x)(3) + 3^2\right]$$

$$= (2x-3)(4x^2 + 6x + 9)$$

15. $125 - t^3 = 5^3 - t^3$

$$= (5-t)(5^2 + 5t + t^2)$$

$$= (5-t)(25 + 5t + t^2)$$

Sum of two cubes

16. $x^3 + y^3 = (x+y)(x^2 - xy + y^2)$

17. $x^3 + 8 = x^3 + 2^3$

$$= (x+2)(x^2 - 2x + 2^2)$$

$$= (x+2)(x^2 - 2x + 4)$$

18. $x^3 + 64 = x^3 + 4^3$

$$= (x+4)(x^2 - 4x + 4^2)$$

$$= (x+4)(x^2 - 4x + 16)$$

19. $27y^3 + 1 = (3y)^3 + 1^3$

$$= (3y+1)\left[(3y)^2 - 3y + 1^2\right]$$

$$= (3y+1)(9y^2 - 3y + 1)$$

20. $8x^3 + 125 = (2x)^3 + 5^3$

$$= (2x+5)\left[(2x)^2 - (2x)(5) + 5^2\right]$$

$$= (2x+5)(4x^2 - 10x + 25)$$

SOLVING LINEAR EQUATIONS

Solve the following equations.

1. $x + 2 = 5$

2. $x + 3 = 7$

3. $x - 2 = 10$

4. $x - 6 = 3$

5. $x + \dfrac{1}{2} = 2$

6. $x - \dfrac{1}{3} = 5$

7. $2x = 10$

8. $3x = 12$

9. $5x = 6$

10. $\dfrac{x}{2} = 3$

11. $\dfrac{x}{5} = 1$

12. $\dfrac{x}{4} = 2$

13. $2x + 1 = 7$

14. $3x - 5 = 2$

15. $\dfrac{x + 2}{3} = 4$

16. $\dfrac{x - 1}{2} = 4$

17. $\dfrac{x + 2}{4} - 3 = 1$

18. $\dfrac{5}{x} = 10$

19. $\dfrac{6}{x} = 18$

20. $2(x + 1) = 10$

21. $3(x - 1) = 12$

22. $\dfrac{5(x + 2)}{2} = 3$

23. $\dfrac{4}{x + 1} = 2$

24. $\dfrac{6}{x - 3} = 12$

25. $\dfrac{4x + 1}{3} + 2 = 14$

Answer Key

1. $x = 3$

2. $x = 4$

3. $x = 12$

4. $x = 9$

5. $x = 1\frac{1}{2}$

6. $x = 5\frac{1}{3}$

7. $x = 5$

8. $x = 4$

9. $x = 1\frac{1}{5}$

10. $x = 6$

11. $x = 5$

12. $x = 8$

13. $x = 3$

14. $x = 2\frac{1}{3}$

15. $x = 10$

16. $x = 9$

17. $x = 14$

18. $x = \frac{1}{2}$

19. $x = \frac{1}{3}$

20. $x = 4$

21. $x = 5$

22. $x = -\frac{4}{5}$

23. $x = 1$

24. $x = 3\frac{1}{2}$

25. $x = 8\frac{3}{4}$

Solutions

1. $x + 2 = 5$

   $x + 2 - 2 = 5 - 2$

   $x = 3$

2. $x + 3 = 7$

   $x + 3 - 3 = 7 - 3$

   $x = 4$

3. $x - 2 = 10$

   $x - 2 + 2 = 10 + 2$

   $x = 12$

4. $x - 6 = 3$

   $x - 6 + 6 = 3 + 6$

   $x = 9$

5. $x + \dfrac{1}{2} = 2$

   $x + \dfrac{1}{2} - \dfrac{1}{2} = 2 - \dfrac{1}{2}$

   $x = 1\dfrac{1}{2}$

6. $x - \dfrac{1}{3} = 5$

   $x - \dfrac{1}{3} + \dfrac{1}{3} = 5 + \dfrac{1}{3}$

   $x = 5\dfrac{1}{3}$

7. $2x = 10$

   $\dfrac{2x}{2} = \dfrac{10}{2}$

   $x = 5$

8. $3x = 12$

   $\dfrac{3x}{3} = \dfrac{12}{3}$

   $x = 4$

9. $5x = 6$

   $\dfrac{5x}{5} = \dfrac{6}{5}$

   $x = 1\dfrac{1}{5}$

10. $\dfrac{x}{2} = 3$

    $\dfrac{x}{2}(2) = 3(2)$

    $x = 6$

11. $\dfrac{x}{5} = 1$

    $\dfrac{x}{5}(5) = 1(5)$

    $x = 5$

12. $\dfrac{x}{4} = 2$

    $\dfrac{x}{4}(4) = 2(4)$

    $x = 8$

13. $2x + 1 = 7$

    $2x + 1 - 1 = 7 - 1$

    $2x = 6$

    $\dfrac{2x}{2} = \dfrac{6}{2}$

    $x = 3$

14. $3x - 5 = 2$

    $3x - 5 + 5 = 2 + 5$

    $3x = 7$

    $\dfrac{3x}{3} = \dfrac{7}{3}$

    $x = 2\dfrac{1}{3}$

15. $\dfrac{x+2}{3} = 4$

$\dfrac{x+2}{3}(3) = 4(3)$

$x+2 = 12$

$x+2-2 = 12-2$

$x = 10$

16. $\dfrac{x-1}{2} = 4$

$\dfrac{x-1}{2}(2) = 4(2)$

$x-1 = 8$

$x-1+1 = 8+1$

$x = 9$

17. $\dfrac{x+2}{4} - 3 = 1$

$\dfrac{x+2}{4} - 3 + 3 = 1 + 3$

$\dfrac{x+2}{4} = 4$

$\dfrac{x+2}{4}(4) = 4(4)$

$x+2 = 16$

$x+2-2 = 16-2$

$x = 14$

18. $\dfrac{5}{x} = 10$

$\dfrac{5}{x}(x) = 10(x)$

$5 = 10x$

$\dfrac{5}{10} = \dfrac{10x}{10}$

$\dfrac{1}{2} = x$

19. $\dfrac{6}{x} = 18$

$\dfrac{6}{x}(x) = 18x$

$6 = 18x$

$\dfrac{6}{18} = \dfrac{18x}{18}$

$\dfrac{1}{3} = x$

20. $2(x+1) = 10$

$\dfrac{2(x+1)}{2} = \dfrac{10}{2}$

$x+1 = 5$

$x+1-1 = 5-1$

$x = 4$

21. $3(x-1) = 12$

$\dfrac{3(x-1)}{3} = \dfrac{12}{3}$

$x-1 = 4$

$x-1+1 = 4+1$

$x = 5$

22. $\dfrac{5(x+2)}{2} = 3$

$\dfrac{5(x+2)}{2}(2) = 3(2)$

$5(x+2) = 6$

$\dfrac{5(x+2)}{5} = \dfrac{6}{5}$

$x+2 = \dfrac{6}{5}$

$x+2-2 = \dfrac{6}{5} - 2$

$x = \dfrac{6}{5} - \dfrac{10}{5}$

$x = -\dfrac{4}{5}$

23. $\dfrac{4}{x+1} = 2$

$\dfrac{4}{x+1}(x+1) = 2(x+1)$

$4 = 2(x+1)$

$\dfrac{4}{2} = \dfrac{2(x+1)}{2}$

$2 = x+1$

$2-1 = x+1-1$

$1 = x$

24. $\dfrac{6}{x-3} = 12$

$\dfrac{6}{x-3}(x-3) = 12(x-3)$

$6 = 12(x-3)$

$\dfrac{6}{12} = \dfrac{12(x-3)}{12}$

$\dfrac{1}{2} = x-3$

$\dfrac{1}{2}+3 = x-3+3$

$3\dfrac{1}{2} = x$

25. $\dfrac{4x+1}{3} + 2 = 14$

$\dfrac{4x+1}{3} + 2 - 2 = 14 - 2$

$\dfrac{4x+1}{3} = 12$

$\dfrac{4x+1}{3}(3) = 12(3)$

$4x+1 = 36$

$4x+1-1 = 36-1$

$4x = 35$

$x = \dfrac{35}{4}$

$x = 8\dfrac{3}{4}$

SOLVING LINEAR
INEQUALITIES

Solve the following linear inequalities.

1. $x + 3 < 7$

2. $x - 4 < 2$

3. $2 - 5x \leq 6$

4. $3x + 7 > 5$

5. $2(x - 1) < 10$

6. $3x + 2x \geq 15$

7. $\dfrac{x}{3} > 9$

8. $-5x + 1 < 6$

9. $3x > 1 + 6x$

10. $0 \leq 5x - 1 \leq 10$

Notes

1. $x < 4$

2. $x < 6$

3. $x \geq -\dfrac{4}{5}$

4. $x > -\dfrac{2}{3}$

5. $x < 6$

6. $x \geq 3$

7. $x > 27$

8. $x > -1$

9. $x < -\dfrac{1}{3}$

10. $\dfrac{1}{5} \leq x \leq \dfrac{11}{5}$

Solutions

1. $x + 3 < 7$

   $x + 3 - 3 < 7 - 3$

   $x < 4$

2. $x - 4 < 2$

   $x - 4 + 4 < 2 + 4$

   $x < 6$

3. $2 - 5x \leq 6$

   $2 - 5x - 2 \leq 6 - 2$

   $-5x \leq 4$

   $\dfrac{-5x}{-5} \geq \dfrac{4}{-5}$

   $x \geq -\dfrac{4}{5}$

4. $3x + 7 > 5$

   $3x + 7 - 7 > 5 - 7$

   $3x > -2$

   $\dfrac{3x}{3} > \dfrac{-2}{3}$

   $x > -\dfrac{2}{3}$

5. $2(x - 1) < 10$

   $\dfrac{2(x - 1)}{2} < \dfrac{10}{2}$

   $x - 1 < 5$

   $x - 1 + 1 < 5 + 1$

   $x < 6$

6. $3x + 2x \geq 15$

   $5x \geq 15$

   $\dfrac{5x}{5} \geq \dfrac{15}{5}$

   $x \geq 3$

7. $\dfrac{x}{3} > 9$

   $\dfrac{x}{3}(3) > 9(3)$

   $x > 27$

8. $-5x + 1 < 6$

   $-5x + 1 - 1 < 6 - 1$

   $-5x < 5$

   $\dfrac{-5x}{-5} > \dfrac{5}{-5}$

   $x > -1$

9. $3x > 1 + 6x$

   $3x - 6x > 1 + 6x - 6x$

   $-3x > 1$

   $\dfrac{-3x}{-3} < \dfrac{1}{-3}$

   $x < -\dfrac{1}{3}$

10. $0 \leq 5x - 1 \leq 10$

    $0 + 1 \leq 5x - 1 + 1 \leq 10 + 1$

    $1 \leq 5x \leq 11$

    $\dfrac{1}{5} \leq \dfrac{5x}{5} \leq \dfrac{11}{5}$

    $\dfrac{1}{5} \leq x \leq \dfrac{11}{5}$

QUADRATIC EQUATIONS I: THE SQUARE ROOT METHOD

Solve the following quadratic equations using the square root method.

1. $x^2 = 25$

2. $x^2 = 49$

3. $x^2 - 36 = 0$

4. $x^2 - 100 = 0$

5. $(x-1)^2 = 4$

6. $(x+2)^2 = 16$

7. $x^2 - 3 = 61$

8. $x^2 + 5 = 86$

9. $\dfrac{x^2+1}{5} = 4$

10. $\dfrac{x^2}{4} - 6 = 8$

11. $\dfrac{16}{x^2} = 4$

12. $3x^2 = 27$

13. $4x^2 - 1 = 35$

14. $\dfrac{5x^2-1}{6} = 4$

15. $\dfrac{64}{x^2} = 4$

Notes

Answer Key

1. $x = \pm 5$

2. $x = \pm 7$

3. $x = \pm 6$

4. $x = \pm 10$

5. $x = 3$ and $x = -1$

6. $x = 2$ and $x = -6$

7. $x = \pm 8$

8. $x = \pm 9$

9. $x = \pm \sqrt{19}$

10. $x = \pm \sqrt{56}$

11. $x = \pm 2$

12. $x = \pm 3$

13. $x = \pm 3$

14. $x = \pm \sqrt{5}$

15. $x = \pm 4$

Solutions

1. $x^2 = 25$

   $\sqrt{x^2} = \sqrt{25}$

   $x = \pm 5$

2. $x^2 = 49$

   $\sqrt{x^2} = \sqrt{49}$

   $x = \pm 7$

3. $x^2 - 36 = 0$

   $x^2 - 36 + 36 = 0 + 36$

   $x^2 = 36$

   $\sqrt{x^2} = \sqrt{36}$

   $x = \pm 6$

4. $x^2 - 100 = 0$

   $x^2 - 100 + 100 = 0 + 100$

   $x^2 = 100$

   $\sqrt{x^2} = \sqrt{100}$

   $x = \pm 10$

5. $(x-1)^2 = 4$

   $\sqrt{(x-1)^2} = \sqrt{4}$

   $x - 1 = \pm 2$

$x - 1 = 2$	$x - 1 = -2$
$x - 1 + 1 = 2 + 1$	$x - 1 + 1 = -2 + 1$
$x = 3$	$x = -1$

6. $(x+2)^2 = 16$

   $\sqrt{(x+2)^2} = \sqrt{16}$

   $x + 2 = \pm 4$

$x + 2 = 4$	$x + 2 = -4$
$x + 2 - 2 = 4 - 2$	$x + 2 - 2 = -4 - 2$
$x = 2$	$x = -6$

7. $x^2 - 3 = 61$

$x^2 - 3 + 3 = 61 + 3$

$x^2 = 64$

$\sqrt{x^2} = \sqrt{64}$

$x = \pm 8$

8. $x^2 + 5 = 86$

$x^2 + 5 - 5 = 86 - 5$

$x^2 = 81$

$\sqrt{x^2} = \sqrt{81}$

$x = \pm 9$

9. $\dfrac{x^2 + 1}{5} = 4$

$\dfrac{x^2 + 1}{5}(5) = 4(5)$

$x^2 + 1 = 20$

$x^2 + 1 - 1 = 20 - 1$

$x^2 = 19$

$\sqrt{x^2} = \sqrt{19}$

$x = \pm\sqrt{19}$

10. $\dfrac{x^2}{4} - 6 = 8$

$\dfrac{x^2}{4} - 6 + 6 = 8 + 6$

$\dfrac{x^2}{4} = 14$

$\dfrac{x^2}{4}(4) = 14(4)$

$x^2 = 56$

$\sqrt{x^2} = \sqrt{56}$

$x = \pm\sqrt{56}$

11. $\dfrac{16}{x^2} = 4$

$\dfrac{16}{x^2}\left(x^2\right) = 4\left(x^2\right)$

$16 = 4x^2$

$\dfrac{16}{4} = \dfrac{4x^2}{4}$

$4 = x^2$

$\sqrt{4} = \sqrt{x^2}$

$x = \pm 2$

12. $3x^2 = 27$

$\dfrac{3x^2}{3} = \dfrac{27}{3}$

$x^2 = 9$

$\sqrt{x^2} = \sqrt{9}$

$x = \pm 3$

13. $4x^2 - 1 = 35$

$4x^2 - 1 + 1 = 35 + 1$

$4x^2 = 36$

$\dfrac{4x^2}{4} = \dfrac{36}{4}$

$x^2 = 9$

$\sqrt{x^2} = \sqrt{9}$

$x = \pm 3$

Notes

14. $\dfrac{5x^2-1}{6}=4$

$\dfrac{5x^2-1}{6}(6)=4(6)$

$5x^2-1=24$

$5x^2-1+1=24+1$

$5x^2=25$

$\dfrac{5x^2}{5}=\dfrac{25}{5}$

$x^2=5$

$\sqrt{x^2}=\sqrt{5}$

$x=\pm\sqrt{5}$

15. $\dfrac{64}{x^2}=4$

$\dfrac{64}{x^2}\left(x^2\right)=4\left(x^2\right)$

$64=4x^2$

$\dfrac{64}{4}=\dfrac{4x^2}{4}$

$16=x^2$

$\sqrt{16}=\sqrt{x^2}$

$\pm4=x$

QUADRATIC EQUATIONS II: COMPLETING THE SQUARE

11

Solve the following quadratic equations by completing the square.

1. $x^2 + 6x = 2$

2. $x^2 + 8x = -12$

3. $x^2 + 5x = 0$

4. $x^2 - x - 6 = 0$

5. $x^2 + \dfrac{1}{2}x = 2$

6. $x^2 - \dfrac{2}{3}x - 1 = 0$

7. $2x^2 + 4x = 5$

8. $x^2 + \dfrac{1}{3}x = \dfrac{1}{2}$

9. $3x^2 + 2x - 5 = 0$

10. $4x^2 + \sqrt{3}\,x - 2 = 3$

Notes

Answer Key

1. $x = -3 + \sqrt{11}$ and $x = -3 - \sqrt{11}$

2. $x = -2$ and $x = -6$

3. $x = 0$ and $x = -5$

4. $x = 3$ and $x = -2$

5. $x = \dfrac{\sqrt{33} - 1}{4}$ and $x = -\dfrac{\sqrt{33} - 1}{4}$

6. $x = \dfrac{\sqrt{13} + 2}{3}$ and $x = -\dfrac{\sqrt{13} + 2}{3}$

7. $x = \dfrac{\sqrt{14} - 2}{2}$ and $x = -\dfrac{\sqrt{14} - 2}{2}$

8. $x = \dfrac{\sqrt{19} - 1}{6}$ and $x = -\dfrac{\sqrt{19} - 1}{6}$

9. $x = 1$ and $x = -\dfrac{5}{3}$

10. $x = \dfrac{\sqrt{83} - \sqrt{3}}{8}$ and $x = -\dfrac{\sqrt{83} - \sqrt{3}}{8}$

Solutions

1. $x^2 + 6x = 2$

   We begin by using the coefficient on x to find the term that must be added to both sides:

   $$\left(\frac{6}{2}\right)^2 = (3)^2 = 9$$

   Adding this term to both sides, we get:

   $$x^2 + 6x + 9 = 2 + 9$$
   $$x^2 + 6x + 9 = 11$$

   Since the left side of the equation is now a perfect square, we can solve the equation:

   $$x^2 + 6x + 9 = 11$$
   $$(x+3)^2 = 11$$
   $$\sqrt{(x+3)^2} = \sqrt{11}$$
   $$x + 3 = \pm\sqrt{11}$$

   Thus,

   $$x + 3 = \sqrt{11} \qquad\qquad x + 3 = -\sqrt{11}$$
   $$x = -3 + \sqrt{11} \qquad\qquad x = -3 - \sqrt{11}$$

2. $x^2 + 8x = -12$

   We begin by using the coefficient on x to find the term that must be added to both sides:

   $$\left(\frac{8}{2}\right)^2 = (4)^2 = 16$$

   Adding this term to both sides, we get:

   $$x^2 + 8x + 16 = -12 + 16$$
   $$x^2 + 8x + 16 = 4$$

   Since the left side of the equation is now a perfect square, we can solve the equation:

   $$x^2 + 8x + 16 = 4$$
   $$(x+4)^2 = 4$$
   $$\sqrt{(x+4)^2} = \sqrt{4}$$
   $$x + 4 = \pm 2$$

   Thus,

   $$x + 4 = 2 \qquad\qquad x + 4 = -2$$
   $$x = -2 \qquad\qquad x = -6$$

43

3. $x^2 + 5x = 0$

We begin by using the coefficient on x to find the term that must be added to both sides:

$$\left(\frac{5}{2}\right)^2 = \frac{25}{4}$$

Adding this term to both sides, we get:

$$x^2 + 5x + \frac{25}{4} = 0 + \frac{25}{4}$$

$$x^2 + 5x + \frac{25}{4} = \frac{25}{4}$$

Since the left side of the equation is now a perfect square, we can solve the equation:

$$x^2 + 5x + \frac{25}{4} = \frac{25}{4}$$

$$\left(x + \frac{5}{2}\right)^2 = \frac{25}{4}$$

$$\sqrt{\left(x + \frac{5}{2}\right)^2} = \sqrt{\frac{25}{4}}$$

$$x + \frac{5}{2} = \pm\frac{5}{2}$$

Thus,

$$x + \frac{5}{2} = \frac{5}{2} \qquad\qquad x + 5 = -\frac{5}{2}$$

$$x = 0 \qquad\qquad\qquad x = -\frac{5}{2} - \frac{5}{2}$$

$$x = -\frac{10}{2}$$

$$x = -5$$

4. $x^2 - x - 6 = 0$

First, we must add 6 to both sides to put the equation into the correct form to solve by completing the square:

$$x^2 - x - 6 + 6 = 0 + 6$$

$$x^2 - x = 6$$

Next, we use the coefficient on x, -1, to find the term that must be added to both sides:

$$\left(-\frac{1}{2}\right)^2 = \frac{1}{4}$$

calculation cont. on next page...

Solution #4 from previous page...

Adding this term to both sides of the equation, we get:

$$x^2 - x = 6$$

$$x^2 - x + \frac{1}{4} = 6 + \frac{1}{4}$$

$$x^2 - x + \frac{1}{4} = \frac{24}{4} + \frac{1}{4}$$

$$x^2 - x + \frac{1}{4} = \frac{25}{4}$$

Since the left side of the equation is now a perfect square, we can solve the equation:

$$x^2 - x + \frac{1}{4} = \frac{25}{4}$$

$$\left(x - \frac{1}{2}\right)^2 = \frac{25}{4}$$

$$\sqrt{\left(x - \frac{1}{2}\right)^2} = \sqrt{\frac{25}{4}}$$

$$x - \frac{1}{2} = \pm\frac{5}{2}$$

Thus,

$$x - \frac{1}{2} = \frac{5}{2} \qquad\qquad x - \frac{1}{2} = -\frac{5}{2}$$

$$x = \frac{5}{2} + \frac{1}{2} \qquad\qquad x = -\frac{5}{2} + \frac{1}{2}$$

$$x = \frac{6}{2} \qquad\qquad x = -\frac{4}{2}$$

$$x = 3 \qquad\qquad x = -2$$

5. $x^2 + \dfrac{1}{2}x = 2$

We begin by using the coefficient on x to find the term that must be added to both sides:

$$\left(\frac{\frac{1}{2}}{2}\right)^2 = \left(\frac{\frac{1}{2}}{\frac{2}{1}}\right)^2 = \left(\frac{1}{2} \cdot \frac{1}{2}\right)^2 = \left(\frac{1}{4}\right)^2 = \frac{1}{16}$$

Adding this term to both sides of the equation, we get:

$$x^2 + \frac{1}{2}x = 2$$

$$x^2 + \frac{1}{2}x + \frac{1}{16} = 2 + \frac{1}{16}$$

$$x^2 + \frac{1}{2}x + \frac{1}{16} = \frac{32}{16} + \frac{1}{16}$$

$$x^2 + \frac{1}{2}x + \frac{1}{16} = \frac{33}{16}$$

calculation cont. on next page...

Solution #5 from previous page...

Now that the left side of the equation is a perfect square, we can solve the equation:

$$x^2 + \frac{1}{2}x + \frac{1}{16} = \frac{33}{16}$$

$$\left(x + \frac{1}{4}\right)^2 = \frac{33}{16}$$

$$\sqrt{\left(x + \frac{1}{4}\right)^2} = \sqrt{\frac{33}{16}}$$

$$x + \frac{1}{4} = \pm\frac{\sqrt{33}}{4}$$

Thus,

$$x + \frac{1}{4} = \frac{\sqrt{33}}{4} \qquad\qquad x + \frac{1}{4} = -\frac{\sqrt{33}}{4}$$

$$x = \frac{\sqrt{33}}{4} - \frac{1}{4} \qquad\qquad x = -\frac{\sqrt{33}}{4} - \frac{1}{4}$$

$$x = \frac{\sqrt{33} - 1}{4} \qquad\qquad x = -\frac{\sqrt{33} - 1}{4}$$

6. $x^2 - \frac{2}{3}x - 1 = 0$

First, we must add 1 to both sides to put the equation into the correct form to solve by completing the square:

$$x^2 - \frac{2}{3}x - 1 + 1 = 0 + 1$$

$$x^2 - \frac{2}{3}x = 1$$

Next, we use the coefficient on x to find the term that must be added to both sides:

$$\left(-\frac{2}{3}\right)^2 = \frac{4}{9}$$

Adding this term to both sides of the equation, we get:

$$x^2 - \frac{2}{3}x + \frac{4}{9} = 1 + \frac{4}{9}$$

$$x^2 - \frac{2}{3}x + \frac{4}{9} = \frac{9}{9} + \frac{4}{9}$$

$$x^2 - \frac{2}{3}x + \frac{4}{9} = \frac{13}{9}$$

calculation cont. on next page...

Solution #6 from previous page...

Now that the left side of the equation is a perfect square, we can solve the equation:

$$x^2 - \frac{2}{3}x + \frac{4}{9} = \frac{13}{9}$$

$$\left(x - \frac{2}{3}\right)^2 = \frac{13}{9}$$

$$\sqrt{\left(x - \frac{2}{3}\right)^2} = \sqrt{\frac{13}{9}}$$

$$x - \frac{2}{3} = \pm\frac{\sqrt{13}}{3}$$

Thus,

$$x - \frac{2}{3} = \frac{\sqrt{13}}{3} \qquad\qquad x - \frac{2}{3} = -\frac{\sqrt{13}}{3}$$

$$x = \frac{\sqrt{13}}{3} + \frac{2}{3} \qquad\qquad x = -\frac{\sqrt{13}}{3} + \frac{2}{3}$$

$$x = \frac{\sqrt{13} + 2}{3} \qquad\qquad x = -\frac{\sqrt{13} + 2}{3}$$

7. $2x^2 + 4x = 5$

First, we divide through by 2 so that the x^2 term has the required coefficient of 1:

$$2x^2 + 4x = 5$$

$$\frac{2}{2}x^2 + \frac{4}{2}x = \frac{5}{2}$$

$$x^2 + 2x = \frac{5}{2}$$

Next, we use the coefficient on x to find the term that must be added to both sides:

$$\left(\frac{2}{2}\right)^2 = (1)^2 = 1$$

Adding this term to both sides of the equation, we get:

$$x^2 + 2x + 1 = \frac{5}{2} + 1$$

$$x^2 + 2x + 1 = \frac{5}{2} + \frac{2}{2}$$

$$x^2 + 2x + 1 = \frac{7}{2}$$

calculation cont. on next page...

Solution #7 from previous page...

Now that the left side of the equation is a perfect square, we can solve the equation:

$$x^2 + 2x + 1 = \frac{7}{2}$$

$$(x+1)^2 = \frac{7}{2}$$

$$\sqrt{(x+1)^2} = \sqrt{\frac{7}{2}}$$

$$x + 1 = \pm \frac{\sqrt{7}}{\sqrt{2}}$$

Rationalizing the denominator on the right side:

$$x + 1 = \pm \frac{\sqrt{7}}{\sqrt{2}}$$

$$x + 1 = \pm \frac{\sqrt{7}}{\sqrt{2}} \cdot \frac{\sqrt{2}}{\sqrt{2}}$$

$$x + 1 = \pm \frac{\sqrt{14}}{2}$$

Thus,

$$x + 1 = \frac{\sqrt{14}}{2} \qquad\qquad x + 1 = -\frac{\sqrt{14}}{2}$$

$$x = \frac{\sqrt{14}}{2} - 1 \qquad\qquad x = -\frac{\sqrt{14}}{2} - 1$$

$$x = \frac{\sqrt{14}}{2} - \frac{2}{2} \qquad\qquad x = -\frac{\sqrt{14}}{2} - \frac{2}{2}$$

$$x = \frac{\sqrt{14} - 2}{2} \qquad\qquad x = -\frac{\sqrt{14} - 2}{2}$$

8. $x^2 + \dfrac{1}{3}x = \dfrac{1}{2}$

We begin by using the coefficient on x to find the term that must be added to both sides:

$$\left(\frac{\frac{1}{3}}{2} \right)^2 = \left(\frac{\frac{1}{3}}{\frac{2}{1}} \right)^2 = \left(\frac{1}{3} \cdot \frac{1}{2} \right)^2 = \left(\frac{1}{6} \right)^2 = \frac{1}{36}$$

calculation cont. on next page...

Solution #8 from previous page...

Adding this term to both sides, we get:

$$x^2 + \frac{1}{3}x = \frac{1}{2}$$

$$x^2 + \frac{1}{3}x + \frac{1}{36} = \frac{1}{2} + \frac{1}{36}$$

$$x^2 + \frac{1}{3}x + \frac{1}{36} = \frac{18}{36} + \frac{1}{36}$$

$$x^2 + \frac{1}{3}x + \frac{1}{36} = \frac{19}{36}$$

Now that the left side of the equation is a perfect square, we can solve the equation:

$$x^2 + \frac{1}{3}x + \frac{1}{36} = \frac{19}{36}$$

$$\left(x + \frac{1}{6}\right)^2 = \frac{19}{36}$$

$$\sqrt{\left(x + \frac{1}{6}\right)^2} = \sqrt{\frac{19}{36}}$$

$$x + \frac{1}{6} = \pm \frac{\sqrt{19}}{6}$$

Thus,

$$x + \frac{1}{6} = \frac{\sqrt{19}}{6} \qquad\qquad x + \frac{1}{6} = -\frac{\sqrt{19}}{6}$$

$$x = \frac{\sqrt{19}}{6} - \frac{1}{6} \qquad\qquad x = -\frac{\sqrt{19}}{6} - \frac{1}{6}$$

$$x = \frac{\sqrt{19} - 1}{6} \qquad\qquad x = -\frac{\sqrt{19} - 1}{6}$$

9. $3x^2\,2x - 5 = 0$

First, we add 5 to both sides to put the equation into the correct form to solve by completing the square:

$$3x^2 + 2x - 5 = 0$$

$$3x^2 + 2x - 5 + 5 = 0 + 5$$

$$3x^2 + 2x = 5$$

Next, we divide through by 3 so that the x^2 term has the required coefficient of 1:

$$3x^2 + 2x = 5$$

$$\frac{3}{3}x^2 + \frac{2}{3}x = \frac{5}{3}$$

$$x^2 + \frac{2}{3}x = \frac{5}{3}$$

calculation cont. on next page...

Notes

Solution #9 from previous page...

Using the coefficient on x to find the term that must be added to both sides:

$$\left(\frac{\frac{2}{3}}{2}\right)^2 = \left(\frac{\frac{2}{3}}{\frac{2}{1}}\right)^2 = \left(\frac{2}{3}\cdot\frac{1}{2}\right)^2 = \left(\frac{1}{3}\right)^2 = \frac{1}{9}$$

Adding this term to both sides of the equation, we get:

$$x^2 + \frac{2}{3}x = \frac{5}{3}$$

$$x^2 + \frac{2}{3}x + \frac{1}{9} = \frac{5}{3} + \frac{1}{9}$$

$$x^2 + \frac{2}{3}x + \frac{1}{9} = \frac{15}{9} + \frac{1}{9}$$

$$x^2 + \frac{2}{3}x + \frac{1}{9} = \frac{16}{9}$$

Now that the left side of the equation is a perfect square, we can solve the equation:

$$x^2 + \frac{2}{3}x + \frac{1}{9} = \frac{16}{9}$$

$$\left(x + \frac{1}{3}\right)^2 = \frac{16}{9}$$

$$\sqrt{\left(x + \frac{1}{3}\right)^2} = \sqrt{\frac{16}{9}}$$

$$x + \frac{1}{3} = \pm\frac{4}{3}$$

Thus,

$$x + \frac{1}{3} = \frac{4}{3} \qquad\qquad x + \frac{1}{3} = -\frac{4}{3}$$

$$x = \frac{4}{3} - \frac{1}{3} \qquad\qquad x = -\frac{4}{3} - \frac{1}{3}$$

$$x = \frac{3}{3} \qquad\qquad\qquad x = -\frac{5}{3}$$

$$x = 1$$

10. $4x^2 + \sqrt{3}x - 2 = 3$

First, we add 2 to both sides to put the equation into the correct form to solve by completing the square:

$$4x^2 + \sqrt{3}x - 2 = 3$$

$$4x^2 + \sqrt{3}x - 2 + 2 = 3 + 2$$

$$4x^2 + \sqrt{3}x = 5$$

calculation cont. on next page...

Solution #10 from previous page...

Next, we divide through by 4 so that the x^2 term has the required coefficient of 1:

$$4x^2 + \sqrt{3}\,x = 5$$

$$\frac{4}{4}x^2 + \frac{\sqrt{3}}{4}x = \frac{5}{4}$$

$$x^2 + \frac{\sqrt{3}}{4}x = \frac{5}{4}$$

Now using the coefficient on x to find the term that must be added to both sides:

$$\left(\frac{\frac{\sqrt{3}}{4}}{2}\right)^2 = \left(\frac{\frac{\sqrt{3}}{4}}{\frac{2}{1}}\right)^2 = \left(\frac{\sqrt{3}}{4}\cdot\frac{1}{2}\right)^2 = \left(\frac{\sqrt{3}}{8}\right)^2 = \frac{3}{64}$$

Adding this term to both sides of the equation, we get:

$$x^2 + \frac{\sqrt{3}}{4}x + \frac{3}{64} = \frac{5}{4} + \frac{3}{64}$$

$$x^2 + \frac{\sqrt{3}}{4}x + \frac{3}{64} = \frac{80}{64} + \frac{3}{64}$$

$$x^2 + \frac{\sqrt{3}}{4}x + \frac{3}{64} = \frac{83}{64}$$

Now that the left side of the equation is a perfect square, we can solve the equation:

$$x^2 + \frac{\sqrt{3}}{4}x + \frac{3}{64} = \frac{83}{64}$$

$$\left(x + \frac{\sqrt{3}}{8}\right)^2 = \frac{83}{64}$$

$$\sqrt{\left(x + \frac{\sqrt{3}}{8}\right)^2} = \sqrt{\frac{83}{64}}$$

$$x + \frac{\sqrt{3}}{8} = \pm\frac{\sqrt{83}}{8}$$

Thus,

$$x + \frac{\sqrt{3}}{8} = \frac{\sqrt{83}}{8}$$

$$x = \frac{\sqrt{83}}{8} - \frac{\sqrt{3}}{8}$$

$$x = \frac{\sqrt{83} - \sqrt{3}}{8}$$

$$x + \frac{\sqrt{3}}{8} = -\frac{\sqrt{83}}{8}$$

$$x = -\frac{\sqrt{83}}{8} - \frac{\sqrt{3}}{8}$$

$$x = -\frac{\sqrt{83} - \sqrt{3}}{8}$$

QUADRATIC EQUATIONS III: THE QUADRATIC FORMULA

12

General Form of a Quadratic Equation

$$ax^2 + bx + c = 0$$

The Discriminant

$$b^2 - 4ac$$

If $b^2 - 4ac \geq 0$ for an equation the solutions to the equation will be real.

If $b^2 - 4ac \leq 0$ for an equation the solutions to the equation will be complex (i.e. involve $i = \sqrt{-1}$).

The Quadratic Formula

$$x = \frac{-b \pm \sqrt{b^2 - 4ac}}{2a}$$

For each of the following quadratic equations, calculate the discriminant and use it to determine whether the solutions to the equation are real or complex.

1. $3x^2 + 4 - 7 = 0$

2. $x^2 + 5x = 6$

3. $4x^2 + 2x + 9 = 0$

4. $x^2 = 3 - 10x$

5. $3.5x^2 + 4.2x + 6.5 = 0$

Use the quadratic formula to solve the following quadratic equations that have real solutions.

6. $x^2 + 7x + 10 = 0$

7. $x^2 - x - 6 = 0$

8. $3x^2 + 9x = 5$

9. $6x^2 = 3x + 10$

10. $4.6x^2 + 9.3x - 5.2 = 0$

Use the quadratic formula to solve the following quadratic equations that have complex solutions.

11. $x^2 + 2x + 26 = 0$

12. $2x^2 + 2x + 1 = 0$

13. $3x^2 + 4x + 2 = 0$

14. $4x^2 = -3x - 10$

15. $3.7x^2 + 2.3x + 9.7 = 0$

Notes

Answer Key

1. The solutions will be real.

2. The solutions will be real.

3. The solutions will be complex.

4. The solutions will be real.

5. The solutions will be complex.

6. $x_1 = -2$

   $x_2 = -5$

7. $x_1 = 3$

   $x_2 = -2$

8. $x_1 = \dfrac{-9 + \sqrt{141}}{6}$

   $x_2 = \dfrac{-9 - \sqrt{141}}{6}$

9. $x_1 = \dfrac{3 + \sqrt{249}}{12}$

   $x_2 = \dfrac{3 - \sqrt{249}}{12}$

10. $x_1 = 0.5$

    $x_2 = -2.5$

11. $x_1 = -1 + 5i$

    $x_2 = -1 - 5i$

12. $x_1 = -\dfrac{1}{2} + \dfrac{1}{2} i$

    $x_2 = -\dfrac{1}{2} - \dfrac{1}{2} i$

13. $x_1 = \dfrac{-2}{3} + \dfrac{\sqrt{2}}{3} i$

    $x_2 = \dfrac{-2}{3} - \dfrac{\sqrt{2}}{3} i$

14. $x_1 = \dfrac{-3}{8} + \dfrac{\sqrt{151}}{8} i$

    $x_2 = \dfrac{-3}{8} - \dfrac{\sqrt{151}}{8} i$

15. $x_1 = -0.3 + 1.6i$

    $x_2 = -0.3 - 1.6i$

Solutions

1. $3x^2 + 4 - 7 = 0$

   $a = 3, b = 4, c = -7$

   $b^2 - 4ac = 4^2 - 4(3)(-7)$

   $\qquad = 16 + 84$ Since $100 \geq 0$, the solutions will be real.

   $\qquad = 100 \geq 0$

2. $x^2 + 5x = 6$

   $x^2 + 5x - 6 = 6 - 6$

   $x^2 + 5x - 6 = 0$

   $a = 1, b = 5, c = -6$

   $b^2 - 4ac = 5^2 - 4(1)(-6)$

   $\qquad = 25 + 24$ Since $49 \geq 0$, the solutions will be real.

   $\qquad = 49 \geq 0$

3. $4x^2 + 2x + 9 = 0$

   $a = 4, b = 2, c = 9$

   $b^2 - 4ac = 2^2 - 4(4)(9)$

   $\qquad = 4 - 144$ Since $-140 < 0$, the solutions will be complex.

   $\qquad = -140 < 0$

4. $x^2 = 3 - 10x$

   $x^2 + 10x = 3 - 10x + 10x$

   $x^2 + 10x = 3$

   $x^2 + 10x - 3 = 3 - 3$

   $x^2 + 10x - 3 = 0$

   $a = 1, b = 10, c = -3$

   $b^2 - 4ac = 10^2 - 4(1)(-3)$

   $\qquad = 100 + 12$ Since $112 \geq 0$, the solutions will be real.

   $\qquad = 112 \geq 0$

Notes

5. $3.5x^2 + 4.2x + 6.5 = 0$

$a = 3.5, b = 4.2, c = 6.5$

$$b^2 - 4ac = 4.2^2 - 4(3.5)(6.5)$$
$$= 17.6 - 91$$
$$= -73.4 < 0$$

Since $-73.4 < 0$, the solutions will be complex.

6. $x^2 + 7x + 10 = 0$

$a = 1, b = 7, c = 10$

$$x = \frac{-b \pm \sqrt{b^2 - 4ac}}{2a}$$

$$x = \frac{-7 \pm \sqrt{7^2 - 4(1)(10)}}{2(1)}$$

$$x = \frac{-7 \pm \sqrt{49 - 40}}{2}$$

$$x = \frac{-7 \pm \sqrt{9}}{2}$$

$$x = \frac{-7 \pm 3}{2}$$

$$x_1 = \frac{-7 + 3}{2} = \frac{-4}{2} = -2$$

$$x_2 = \frac{-7 - 3}{2} = \frac{-10}{2} = -5$$

7. $x^2 - x - 6 = 0$

$a = 1, b = -1, c = -6$

$$x = \frac{-b \pm \sqrt{b^2 - 4ac}}{2a}$$

$$x = \frac{-(-1) \pm \sqrt{(-1)^2 - 4(1)(-6)}}{2(1)}$$

$$x = \frac{1 \pm \sqrt{1 + 24}}{2}$$

calculation cont. on next page...

Solution #7 from previous page...

$$x = \frac{1 \pm \sqrt{25}}{2}$$

$$x = \frac{1 \pm 5}{2}$$

$$x_1 = \frac{1+5}{2} = \frac{6}{2} = 3$$

$$x_2 = \frac{1-5}{2} = \frac{-4}{2} = -2$$

8. $3x^2 + 9x = 5$

$3x^2 + 9x - 5 = 5 - 5$

$3x^2 + 9x - 5 = 0$

$a = 3, b = 9, c = -5$

$$x = \frac{-b \pm \sqrt{b^2 - 4ac}}{2a}$$

$$x = \frac{-9 \pm \sqrt{9^2 - 4(3)(-5)}}{2(3)}$$

$$x = \frac{-9 \pm \sqrt{81 + 60}}{6}$$

$$x = \frac{-9 \pm \sqrt{141}}{6}$$

$$x_1 = \frac{-9 + \sqrt{141}}{6}$$

$$x_2 = \frac{-9 - \sqrt{141}}{6}$$

9. $6x^2 = 3x + 10$

$6x^2 - 3x = 3x + 10 - 3x$

$6x^2 - 3x = 10$

$6x^2 - 3x - 10 = 10 - 10$

$6x^2 - 3x - 10 = 0$

$a = 6, b = -3, c = -10$

$$x = \frac{-b \pm \sqrt{b^2 - 4ac}}{2a}$$

$$x = \frac{-(-3) \pm \sqrt{(-3)^2 - 4(6)(-10)}}{2(6)}$$

$$x = \frac{3 \pm \sqrt{9 + 240}}{12}$$

$$x = \frac{3 \pm \sqrt{249}}{12}$$

$$x_1 = \frac{3 + \sqrt{249}}{12}$$

$$x_2 = \frac{3 - \sqrt{249}}{12}$$

10. $4.6x^2 + 9.3x - 5.2 = 0$

$a = 4.6, b = 9.3, c = -5.2$

$$x = \frac{-b \pm \sqrt{b^2 - 4ac}}{2a}$$

$$x = \frac{-9.3 \pm \sqrt{(9.3)^2 - 4(4.6)(-5.2)}}{2(4.6)}$$

$$x = \frac{-9.3 \pm \sqrt{86.5 + 95.7}}{2(4.6)}$$

$$x = \frac{-9.3 + \sqrt{182.2}}{9.2} \cong \frac{-9.3 \pm 13.5}{9.2}$$

$$x_1 = \frac{-9.3 + 13.5}{9.2} = 0.5$$

$$x_2 = \frac{-9.3 - 13.5}{9.2} = -2.5$$

11. $x^2 + 2x + 26 = 0$

$a = 1, b = 2, c = 26$

$$x = \frac{-b \pm \sqrt{b^2 - 4ac}}{2a}$$

$$x = \frac{-2 \pm \sqrt{2^2 - 4(1)(26)}}{2(1)}$$

$$x = \frac{-2 \pm \sqrt{4 - 104}}{2}$$

$$x = \frac{-2 \pm \sqrt{-100}}{2}$$

$$x = \frac{-2 \pm 10i}{2} = \frac{-2 \pm 2(5i)}{2} = \frac{-2}{2} \pm \frac{2(5i)}{2} = -1 \pm 5i$$

$x_1 = -1 + 5i$

$x_2 = -1 - 5i$

12. $2x^2 + 2x + 1 = 0$

$a = 2, b = 2, c = 1$

$$x = \frac{-b \pm \sqrt{b^2 - 4ac}}{2a}$$

$$x = \frac{-2 \pm \sqrt{2^2 - 4(2)(1)}}{2(2)}$$

$$x = \frac{-2 \pm \sqrt{4 - 8}}{4}$$

$$x = \frac{-2 \pm \sqrt{-4}}{4}$$

$$x = \frac{-2 \pm 2i}{4} = \frac{-2}{4} \pm \frac{2i}{4} = -\frac{1}{2} \pm \frac{1}{2}i$$

$x_1 = -\frac{1}{2} + \frac{1}{2}i$

$x_2 = -\frac{1}{2} - \frac{1}{2}i$

13. $3x^2 + 4x + 2 = 0$

$a = 3, b = 4, c = 2$

$$x = \frac{-b \pm \sqrt{b^2 - 4ac}}{2a}$$

$$x = \frac{-4 \pm \sqrt{4^2 - 4(3)(2)}}{2(3)}$$

$$x = \frac{-4 \pm \sqrt{16 - 24}}{6}$$

$$x = \frac{-4 \pm \sqrt{-8}}{6} = \frac{-4 \pm 2\sqrt{-2}}{6} = \frac{-2(2) \pm 2\sqrt{-2}}{2(3)} = \frac{-2 \pm \sqrt{-2}}{3}$$

$$x = \frac{-2 \pm i\sqrt{2}}{3} = \frac{-2}{3} \pm \frac{\sqrt{2}}{3}i$$

$$x_1 = \frac{-2}{3} + \frac{\sqrt{2}}{3}i$$

$$x_2 = \frac{-2}{3} - \frac{\sqrt{2}}{3}i$$

14. $4x^2 = -3x - 10$

$4x^2 + 3x = -3x - 10 + 3x$

$4x^2 + 3x = -10$

$4x^2 + 3x + 10 = -10 + 10$

$4x^2 + 3x + 10 = 0$

$a = 4, b = 3, c = 10$

$$x = \frac{-b \pm \sqrt{b^2 - 4ac}}{2a}$$

$$x = \frac{-3 \pm \sqrt{3^2 - 4(4)(10)}}{2(4)}$$

$$x = \frac{-3 \pm \sqrt{9 - 160}}{8}$$

$$x = \frac{-3 \pm \sqrt{-151}}{8} = \frac{-3 \pm i\sqrt{151}}{8} = \frac{-3}{8} \pm \frac{\sqrt{151}}{8}i$$

calculation cont. on next page...

Solution #14 from previous page...

$$x_1 = \frac{-3}{8} + \frac{\sqrt{151}}{8} i$$

$$x_2 = \frac{-3}{8} - \frac{\sqrt{151}}{8} i$$

15. $3.7x^2 + 2.3x + 9.7 = 0$

$a = 3.7, b = 2.3, c = 9.7$

$$x = \frac{-b \pm \sqrt{b^2 - 4ac}}{2a}$$

$$x = \frac{-2.3 \pm \sqrt{2.3^2 - 4(3.7)(9.7)}}{2(3.7)}$$

$$x = \frac{-2.3 \pm \sqrt{5.3 - 143.7}}{7.4}$$

$$x = \frac{-2.3 \pm \sqrt{-138.4}}{7.4} \cong \frac{-2.3 \pm 11.7i}{7.4}$$

$$x_1 = \frac{-2.3 + 11.7i}{7.4} = \frac{-2.3}{7.4} + \frac{11.7}{7.4} i = -0.3 + 1.6i$$

$$x_2 = \frac{-2.3 - 11.7i}{7.4} = \frac{-2.3}{7.4} - \frac{11.7}{7.4} i = -0.3 - 1.6i$$

QUADRATIC EQUATIONS IV: FACTORING

Solve the following quadratic equations by factoring.

1. $x^2 + 7x + 12 = 0$

2. $x^2 - x - 6 = 0$

3. $x^2 - 7x + 10 = 0$

4. $x^2 + 3x - 10 = 0$

5. $x^2 + 5x = 0$

6. $x^2 - 4 = 0$

7. $2x^2 - 14x + 12 = 0$

8. $x^2 = 3x + 18$

9. $3x^2 = 9x + 30$

10. $4x^2 - 36 = 0$

11. $x^3 - 16x = 0$

12. $1 + \dfrac{4}{x} + \dfrac{4}{x^2} = 0$

13. $\dfrac{1}{x^4} - \dfrac{1}{x^2} = 0$

14. $3x^3 + 18x^2 + 27x = 0$

15. $x^4 - 1 = 0$

Answer Key

1. $x = -3$ and $x = -4$

2. $x = 3$ and $x = -2$

3. $x = 2$ and $x = 5$

4. $x = -5$ and $x = 2$

5. $x = 0$ and $x = -5$

6. $x = -2$ and $x = 2$

7. $x = 1$ and $x = 6$

8. $x = 6$ and $x = -3$

9. $x = 5$ and $x = -2$

10. $x = -3$ and $x = 3$

11. $x = 0$, $x = -4$, and $x = 4$

12. $x = -2$ and $x = -2$

13. $x = -1$ and $x = 1$

14. $x = 0$, $x = -3$, and $x = -3$

15. $x = -1$, $x = 1$, and $x = \pm i$

Solutions

1. $x^2 + 7x + 12 = 0$

   $(x+3)(x+4) = 0$

$x + 3 = 0$	$x + 4 = 0$
$x + 3 - 3 = 0 - 3$	$x + 4 - 4 = 0 - 4$
$x = -3$	$x = -4$

2. $x^2 - x - 6 = 0$

   $(x-3)(x+2) = 0$

$x - 3 = 0$	$x + 2 = 0$
$x - 3 + 3 = 0 + 3$	$x + 2 - 2 = 0 - 2$
$x = 3$	$x = -2$

3. $x^2 - 7x + 10 = 0$

   $(x-2)(x-5) = 0$

$x - 2 = 0$	$x - 5 = 0$
$x - 2 + 2 = 0 + 2$	$x - 5 + 5 = 0 + 5$
$x = 2$	$x = 5$

4. $x^2 + 3x - 10 = 0$

   $(x+5)(x-2) = 0$

$x + 5 = 0$	$x - 2 = 0$
$x + 5 - 5 = 0 - 5$	$x - 2 + 2 = 0 + 2$
$x = -5$	$x = 2$

5. $x^2 + 5x = 0$

   $x(x+5) = 0$

$x = 0$	$x + 5 = 0$
	$x + 5 - 5 = 0 - 5$
	$x = -5$

6. $x^2 - 4 = 0$

$(x+2)(x-2) = 0$

$x + 2 = 0$ | $x - 2 = 0$

$x + 2 - 2 = 0 - 2$ | $x - 2 + 2 = 0 + 2$

$x = -2$ | $x = 2$

7. $2x^2 - 14x + 12 = 0$

$2(x^2 - 7x + 6) = 0$

$\dfrac{2(x^2 - 7x + 6)}{2} = \dfrac{0}{2}$

$x^2 - 7x + 6 = 0$

$(x-1)(x-6) = 0$

$x - 1 = 0$ | $x - 6 = 0$

$x - 1 + 1 = 0 + 1$ | $x - 6 + 6 = 0 + 6$

$x = 1$ | $x = 6$

8. $x^2 = 3x + 18$

$x^2 - 3x = 3x + 18 - 3x$

$x^2 - 3x = 18$

$x^2 - 3x - 18 = 18 - 18$

$x^2 - 3x - 18 = 0$

$(x-6)(x+3) = 0$

$x - 6 = 0$ | $x + 3 = 0$

$x - 6 + 6 = 0 + 6$ | $x + 3 - 3 = 0 - 3$

$x = 6$ | $x = -3$

9. $3x^2 = 9x + 30$

$3x^2 - 9x = 9x + 30 - 9x$

$3x^2 - 9x = 30$

$3x^2 - 9x - 30 = 30 - 30$

$3x^2 - 9x - 30 = 0$

$3(x^2 - 3x - 10) = 0$

calculation cont. on next page...

Solution #9 from previous page...

$$\frac{3\left(x^2 - 3x - 10\right)}{3} = \frac{0}{3}$$

$$x^2 - 3x - 10 = 0$$

$$(x - 5)(x + 2) = 0$$

$x - 5 = 0$	$x + 2 = 0$
$x - 5 + 5 = 0 + 5$	$x + 2 - 2 = 0 - 2$
$x = 5$	$x = -2$

10. $4x^2 - 36 = 0$

$$4\left(x^2 - 9\right) = 0$$

$$\frac{4\left(x^2 - 9\right)}{4} = \frac{0}{4}$$

$$x^2 - 9 = 0$$

$$(x + 3)(x - 3) = 0$$

$x + 3 = 0$	$x - 3 = 0$
$x + 3 - 3 = 0 - 3$	$x - 3 + 3 = 0 + 3$
$x = -3$	$x = 3$

11. $x^3 - 16x = 0$

$$x\left(x^2 - 16\right) = 0$$

$$x(x + 4)(x - 4) = 0$$

$x = 0$	$x + 4 = 0$	$x - 4 = 0$
	$x + 4 - 4 = 0 - 4$	$x - 4 + 4 = 0 + 4$
	$x = -4$	$x = 4$

12. $1 + \dfrac{4}{x} + \dfrac{4}{x^2} = 0$

$$x^2 \left(1 + \frac{4}{x} + \frac{4}{x^2}\right) = 0\left(x^2\right)$$

$$x^2 + 4x + 4 = 0$$

$$(x + 2)(x + 2) = 0$$

$x + 2 = 0$	$x + 2 = 0$
$x + 2 - 2 = 0 - 2$	$x + 2 - 2 = 0 - 2$
$x = -2$	$x = -2$

Notes

13. $\dfrac{1}{x^4} - \dfrac{1}{x^2} = 0$

$x^4 \left(\dfrac{1}{x^4} - \dfrac{1}{x^2} \right) = 0 \left(x^4 \right)$

$1 - x^2 = 0$

$(1 + x)(1 - x) = 0$

$1 + x = 0$	$1 - x = 0$
$1 + x - 1 = 0 - 1$	$1 - x + x = 0 + x$
$x = -1$	$1 = x$ or,
	$x = 1$

14. $3x^3 + 18x^2 + 27x = 0$

$3x\left(x^2 + 6x + 9 \right) = 0$

$\dfrac{3x\left(x^2 + 6x + 9 \right)}{3} = \dfrac{0}{3}$

$x\left(x^2 + 6x + 9 \right) = 0$

$x(x + 3)(x + 3) = 0$

$x = 0$	$x + 3 = 0$	$x + 3 = 0$
	$x + 3 - 3 = 0 - 3$	$x + 3 - 3 = 0 - 3$
	$x = -3$	$x = -3$

15. $x^4 - 1 = 0$

$\left(x^2 - 1 \right)\left(x^2 + 1 \right) = 0$

$(x + 1)(x - 1)\left(x^2 + 1 \right) = 0$

$x + 1 = 0$	$x - 1 = 0$	$x^2 + 1 = 0$
$x + 1 - 1 = 0 - 1$	$x - 1 + 1 = 0 + 1$	$x^2 = -1$
$x = -1$	$x = 1$	$x = \pm\sqrt{-1}$
		$x = \pm i$

EXPONENTIALS AND LOGARITHMS

Express each of the following exponential expressions in logarithmic form.

Notes

1. $4^2 = 16$

2. $3^4 = 81$

3. $2^x = 14$

4. $10^3 = 1000$

5. $5^3 = 125$

6. $x^b = c$

7. $e^x = 5$

8. $e^4 = x$

9. $10^{x+2} = 5$

10. $3^{2x-1} = 8$

Express each of the following logarithmic expressions in exponential form.

11. $\log_2 8 = 3$

12. $\log_4 16 = 2$

13. $\text{Log } 1000 = 3$

14. $\text{Ln } x = 5$

15. $\log_6 (3x + 5) = 2$

16. $\log_b x = p$

17. $\text{Ln } 1 = 0$

18. $\text{Log } (4x + 7) = 2$

19. $\log_x 3.75 = 2.63$

20. $\text{Ln } x = y + 3$

Solutions

1. $4^2 = 16 \implies \log_4 16 = 2$

2. $3^4 = 81 \implies \log_3 81 = 4$

3. $2^x = 14 \implies \log_2 14 = x$

4. $10^3 = 1000 \implies \log_{10} 1000 = 3 \implies \text{Log } 1000 = 3$

5. $5^3 = 125 \implies \log_5 125 = 3$

6. $x^b = c \implies \log_x c = b$

7. $e^x = 5 \implies \log_e 5 = x \implies \text{Ln } 5 = x$

8. $e^4 = x \implies \log_e x = 4 \implies \text{Ln } x = 4$

9. $10^{x+2} = 5 \implies \log_{10} 5 = x + 2 \implies \text{Log } 5 = x + 2$

10. $3^{2x-1} = 8 \implies \log_3 8 = 2x - 1$

11. $\log_2 8 = 3 \implies 2^3 = 8$

12. $\log_4 16 = 2 \implies 4^2 = 16$

13. $\text{Log } 1000 = 3 \implies \log_{10} 1000 = 3 \implies 10^3 = 1000$

14. $\text{Ln } x = 5 \implies \log_e x = 5 \implies e^5 = x$

15. $\log_6 (3x + 5) = 2 \implies 6^2 = 3x + 5$

16. $\log_b x = p \implies b^p = x$

17. $\text{Ln } 1 = 0 \implies \log_e 1 = 0 \implies e^0 = 1$

18. $\text{Log } (4x + 7) = 2 \implies \log_{10} (4x + 7) = 2 \implies 10^2 = 4x + 7$

19. $\log_x 3.75 = 2.63 \implies x^{2.63} = 3.75$

20. $\text{Ln } x = y + 3 \implies \log_e x = y + 3 \implies e^{y+3} = x$

PROPERTIES OF LOGARITHMS

Expand each of the following as far as possible using the properties of logarithms.

Notes

$$\text{Log } mn = \text{Log } m + \text{Log } n$$

$$\text{Log } \frac{m}{n} = \text{Log } m - \text{Log } n$$

$$\text{Log } m^n = n \text{ Log } m$$

1. $\text{Log } ab$

2. $\text{Log } \dfrac{a}{b}$

3. $\text{Log } xyz$

4. $\text{Log } x^2$

5. $\text{Log } x^2 y^3$

6. $\text{Log } (xy)^3$

7. $\text{Log } \left(\dfrac{x}{yz} \right)$

8. $\text{Log } \dfrac{x^2}{y^4}$

9. $\text{Ln } xy^5$

10. $\log_3 \dfrac{x^2}{y}$

11. $\text{Log } \sqrt{x}$

12. $\log_4 \dfrac{\sqrt{y}}{x}$

13. $\text{Ln } \sqrt{x+1}$

14. $\text{Ln } \dfrac{\sqrt{x}}{\sqrt{y}}$

15. $\text{Log } \dfrac{a^2 x^3}{\sqrt[3]{y-1}}$

Combine each of the following as far as possible using the properties of logarithms.

16. $\text{Log } x + \text{Log } y$

17. $\text{Log } x - \text{Log } y$

18. $3 \text{ Log } x$

19. $\dfrac{1}{2} \text{Log } y$

20. $2 \text{ Log } x + 5 \text{ Log } y$

21. $3 \text{ Log } x - 7 \text{ Log } y$

22. $\text{Log } x + \text{Log } y + \text{Log } w$

23. $\text{Log } x - \text{Log } y - 2 \text{ Log } z$

24. $4 \text{ Log } x - 4 \text{ Log } y$

25. $3 \text{ Ln } x$

26. $5 \text{ Ln } x + \dfrac{1}{2} \text{Ln } y$

27. $\log_6 x + 7 \log_6 y - \dfrac{1}{4} \log_6 z$

28. $\text{Log } (x+1) + \text{Log } 10$

29. $\text{Ln } e + \text{Ln } e^2$

30. $\text{Log } (x^2 - 4) - \text{Log } (x - 2)$

Answer Key

1. $\text{Log } ab = \text{Log } a + \text{Log } b$

2. $\text{Log } \dfrac{a}{b} = \text{Log } a - \text{Log } b$

3. $\text{Log } xyz = \text{Log } x + \text{Log } y + \text{Log } z$

4. $\text{Log } x^2 = 2 \text{ Log } x$

5. $\text{Log } x^2 y^3 = 2 \text{ Log } x + 3 \text{ Log } y$

6. $\text{Log } (xy)^3 = 3 \text{ Log } x + 3 \text{ Log } y$

7. $\text{Log } \left(\dfrac{x}{yz} \right) = \text{Log } x - \text{Log } y - \text{Log } z$

8. $\text{Log } \dfrac{x^2}{y^4} = 2 \text{ Log } x - 4 \text{ Log } y$

9. $\text{Ln } xy^5 = \text{Ln } x + 5 \text{ Ln } y$

10. $\log_3 \dfrac{x^2}{y} = 2 \log_3 x - \log_3 y$

11. $\text{Log } \sqrt{x} = \dfrac{1}{2} \text{ Log } x$

12. $\log_4 \dfrac{\sqrt{y}}{x} = \dfrac{1}{2} \log_4 y - \log_4 x$

13. $\text{Ln } \sqrt{x+1} = \dfrac{1}{2} \text{ Ln } (x+1)$

14. $\text{Ln } \dfrac{\sqrt{x}}{\sqrt{y}} = \dfrac{1}{2} \text{ Ln } x - \dfrac{1}{2} \text{ Ln } y$

15. $\text{Log } \dfrac{a^2 x^3}{\sqrt[3]{y-1}} = 2 \text{ Log } a + 3 \text{ Log } x - \dfrac{1}{3} \text{ Log } (y-1)$

16. $\text{Log } x + \text{Log } y = \text{Log } xy$

17. $\text{Log } x - \text{Log } y = \text{Log } \dfrac{x}{y}$

18. $3 \text{ Log } x = \text{Log } x^3$

19. $\dfrac{1}{2} \text{ Log } y = \text{Log } \sqrt{y}$

20. $2 \text{ Log } x + 5 \text{ Log } y = \text{Log } x^2 + \text{Log } y^5 = \text{Log } x^2 y^5$

21. $3 \text{ Log } x - 7 \text{ Log } y = \text{Log } \dfrac{x^3}{y^7}$

22. $\text{Log } x + \text{Log } y + \text{Log } w = \text{Log } xyw$

23. $\text{Log } x - \text{Log } y - 2 \text{ Log } z = \text{Log } \dfrac{x}{yz^2}$

24. $4 \text{ Log } x - 4 \text{ Log } y = \text{Log } \left(\dfrac{x}{y} \right)^4$

25. $3 \text{ Ln } x = \text{Ln } x^3$

26. $5 \text{ Ln } x + \dfrac{1}{2} \text{ Ln } y = \text{Ln } x^5 \sqrt{y}$

27. $\log_6 x + 7 \log_6 y - \dfrac{1}{4} \log_6 z = \log_6 \dfrac{xy^7}{\sqrt[4]{z}}$

28. $\text{Log } (x+1) + \text{Log } 10 = \text{Log } (x+1) + 1$

29. $\text{Ln } e + \text{Ln } e^2 = 3$

30. $\text{Log } (x^2 - 4) - \text{Log } (x-2) = \text{Log } (x+2)$

Solutions

1. $\text{Log } ab = \text{Log } a + \text{Log } b$

2. $\text{Log } \dfrac{a}{b} = \text{Log } a - \text{Log } b$

3. $\text{Log } xyz = \text{Log } x + \text{Log } y + \text{Log } z$

4. $\text{Log } x^2 = 2\,\text{Log } x$

5. $\text{Log } x^2 y^3 = \text{Log } x^2 + \text{Log } y^3 = 2\,\text{Log } x + 3\,\text{Log } y$

6. $\text{Log }(xy)^3 = 3\,\text{Log } xy = 3\,\text{Log } x + 3\,\text{Log } y$

7. $\text{Log }\left(\dfrac{x}{yz}\right) = \text{Log } x - \text{Log } yz = \text{Log } x - \text{Log } y - \text{Log } z$

8. $\text{Log } \dfrac{x^2}{y^4} = \text{Log } x^2 - \text{Log } y^4 = 2\,\text{Log } x - 4\,\text{Log } y$

9. $\text{Ln } xy^5 = \text{Ln } x + \text{Ln } y^5 = \text{Ln } x + 5\,\text{Ln } y$

10. $\log_3 \dfrac{x^2}{y} = \log_3 x^2 - \log_3 y = 2\log_3 x - \log_3 y$

11. $\text{Log }\sqrt{x} = \text{Log } x^{\frac{1}{2}} = \dfrac{1}{2}\,\text{Log } x$

12. $\log_4 \dfrac{\sqrt{y}}{x} = \log_4 \sqrt{y} - \log_4 x = \log_4 y^{\frac{1}{2}} - \log_4 x = \dfrac{1}{2}\log_4 y - \log_4 x$

13. $\text{Ln }\sqrt{x+1} = \text{Ln }(x+1)^{\frac{1}{2}} = \dfrac{1}{2}\,\text{Ln }(x+1)$

14. $\text{Ln }\dfrac{\sqrt{x}}{\sqrt{y}} = \text{Ln }\sqrt{x} - \text{Ln }\sqrt{y} = \text{Ln } x^{\frac{1}{2}} - \text{Ln } y^{\frac{1}{2}} = \dfrac{1}{2}\,\text{Ln } x - \dfrac{1}{2}\,\text{Ln } y$

15. $\text{Log }\dfrac{a^2 x^3}{\sqrt[3]{y-1}} = \text{Log } a^2 + \text{Log } x^3 - \text{Log }\sqrt[3]{y-1} = \text{Log } a^2 + \text{Log } x^3 - \text{Log }(y-1)^{\frac{1}{3}}$

$$= 2\,\text{Log } a + 3\,\text{Log } x - \dfrac{1}{3}\,\text{Log }(y-1)$$

16. $\text{Log } x + \text{Log } y = \text{Log } xy$

17. $\text{Log } x - \text{Log } y = \text{Log }\dfrac{x}{y}$

18. $3\,\text{Log } x = \text{Log } x^3$

19. $\dfrac{1}{2}\,\text{Log } y = \text{Log } y^{\frac{1}{2}} = \text{Log }\sqrt{y}$

20. $2\,\text{Log } x + 5\,\text{Log } y = \text{Log } x^2 + \text{Log } y^5 = \text{Log } x^2 y^5$

21. $3 \operatorname{Log} x - 7 \operatorname{Log} y = \operatorname{Log} x^3 - \operatorname{Log} y^7 = \operatorname{Log} \dfrac{x^3}{y^7}$

22. $\operatorname{Log} x + \operatorname{Log} y + \operatorname{Log} w = \operatorname{Log} xyw$

23. $\operatorname{Log} x - \operatorname{Log} y - 2 \operatorname{Log} z = \operatorname{Log} x - \operatorname{Log} y - \operatorname{Log} z^2 = \operatorname{Log} \dfrac{x}{yz^2}$

24. $4 \operatorname{Log} x - 4 \operatorname{Log} y = \operatorname{Log} x^4 - \operatorname{Log} y^4 = \operatorname{Log} \dfrac{x^4}{y^4} = \operatorname{Log} \left(\dfrac{x}{y} \right)^4$

25. $3 \operatorname{Ln} x = \operatorname{Ln} x^3$

26. $5 \operatorname{Ln} x + \dfrac{1}{2} \operatorname{Ln} y = \operatorname{Ln} x^5 + \operatorname{Ln} y^{\frac{1}{2}} = \operatorname{Ln} x^5 + \operatorname{Ln} \sqrt{y} = \operatorname{Ln} x^5 \sqrt{y}$

27. $\log_6 x + 7 \log_6 y - \dfrac{1}{4} \log_6 z = \log_6 x + \log_6 y^7 - \log_6 z^{\frac{1}{4}}$

$$= \log_6 x + \log_6 y^7 - \log_6 \sqrt[4]{z}$$

$$= \log_6 \dfrac{xy^7}{\sqrt[4]{z}}$$

28. $\operatorname{Log} (x+1) + \operatorname{Log} 10 = \operatorname{Log} (x+1) + 1$

29. $\operatorname{Ln} e + \operatorname{Ln} e^2 = \operatorname{Ln} e + 2 \operatorname{Ln} e = 1 + 2(1) = 3$

30. $\operatorname{Log} (x^2 - 4) - \operatorname{Log} (x-2) = \operatorname{Log} \left(\dfrac{x^2 - 4}{x - 2} \right) = \operatorname{Log} \left[\dfrac{(x+2)(x-2)}{(x-2)} \right] = \operatorname{Log} (x+2)$

THE EQUATION OF A CIRCLE

Write the standard form of the equation of each of the following circles given the radius r and the center (h, k).

Notes

1. $r = 1;$ $(h, k) = (1, -2)$

2. $r = 3;$ $(h, k) = (0, 0)$

3. $r = \dfrac{1}{2};$ $(h, k) = (-1, -1)$

4. $r = 2;$ $(h, k) = (-4, 3)$

5. $r = \dfrac{1}{4};$ $(h, k) = \left(\dfrac{1}{2}, \dfrac{1}{3}\right)$

Find the radius r and the center (h, k) of each of the following circles.

6. $x^2 + y^2 = 9$

7. $(x - 3)^2 + (y - 2)^2 = 16$

8. $3(x - 1)^2 + 3y^2 = 75$

9. $x^2 + \left(y - \dfrac{1}{3}\right)^2 = 10$

10. $(x + 5)^2 + (y - 6)^2 = 1$

Solutions

1. $(x-h)^2 + (y-k)^2 = r^2$

   $(x-1)^2 + [y-(-2)]^2 = 1^2$

   $(x-1)^2 + (y+2)^2 = 1$

2. $(x-h)^2 + (y-k)^2 = r^2$

   $(x-0)^2 + (y-o)^2 = 3^2$

   $x^2 + y^2 = 9$

3. $(x-h)^2 + (y-k)^2 = r^2$

   $[x-(-1)]^2 + [y-(-1)]^2 = \left(\dfrac{1}{2}\right)^2$

   $(x+1)^2 + (y+1)^2 = \dfrac{1}{4}$

4. $(x-h)^2 + (y-k)^2 = r^2$

   $[x-(-4)]^2 + (y-3)^2 = 2^2$

   $(x+4)^2 + (y-3)^2 = 4$

5. $(x-h)^2 + (y-k)^2 = r^2$

   $\left(x-\dfrac{1}{2}\right)^2 + \left(y-\dfrac{1}{3}\right)^2 = \left(\dfrac{1}{4}\right)^2$

   $\left(x-\dfrac{1}{2}\right)^2 + \left(y-\dfrac{1}{3}\right)^2 = \dfrac{1}{16}$

6. $x^2 + y^2 = 9$

   $(h, k) = (0, 0)$

   $r = \sqrt{9} = 3$

7. $(x-3)^2 + (y-2)^2 = 16$

   $(h, k) = (3, 2)$

   $r = \sqrt{16} = 4$

8. $3(x-1)^2 + 3y^2 = 75$

   $\dfrac{3(x-1)^2}{3} + \dfrac{3y^2}{3} = \dfrac{75}{3}$

   $(x-1)^2 + y^2 = 25$

   $(h, k) = (1, 0)$

   $r = \sqrt{25} = 5$

9. $x^2 + \left(y-\dfrac{1}{3}\right)^2 = 10$

   $(h, k) = \left(0, \dfrac{1}{3}\right)$

   $r = \sqrt{10}$

10. $(x+5)^2 + (y-6)^2 = 1$

    $(h, k) = (-5, 6)$

    $r = \sqrt{1} = 1$

THE AREA AND VOLUME OF GEOMETRIC FIGURES

Find the area of each of the following:

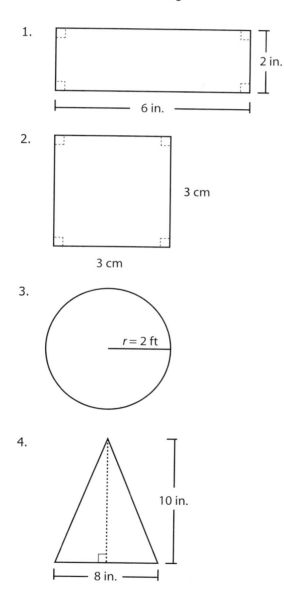

1.

    2 in.

    6 in.

2.

    3 cm

    3 cm

3.

    $r = 2$ ft

4.

    10 in.

    8 in.

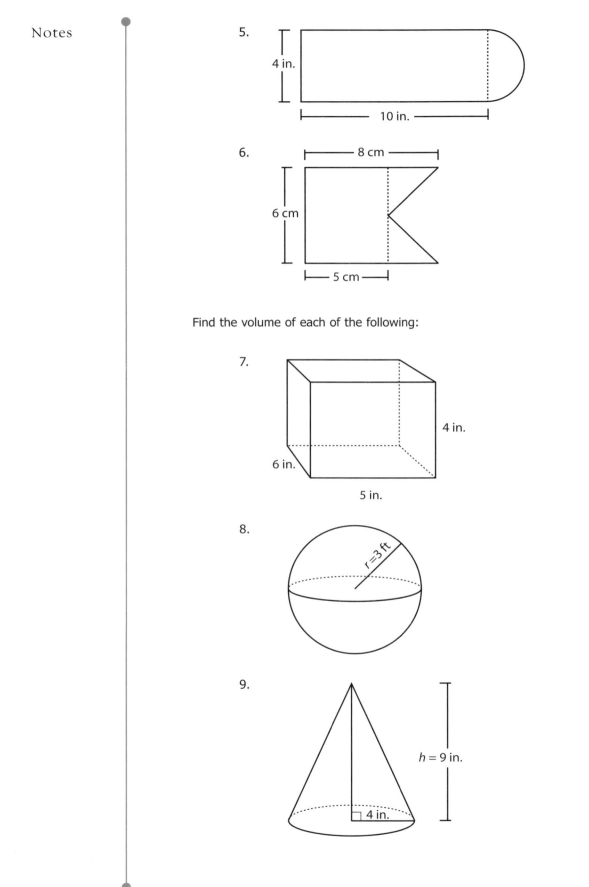

5.

4 in.

10 in.

6.

8 cm

6 cm

5 cm

Find the volume of each of the following:

7.

4 in.

6 in.

5 in.

8.

r = 3 ft

9.

h = 9 in.

4 in.

10.

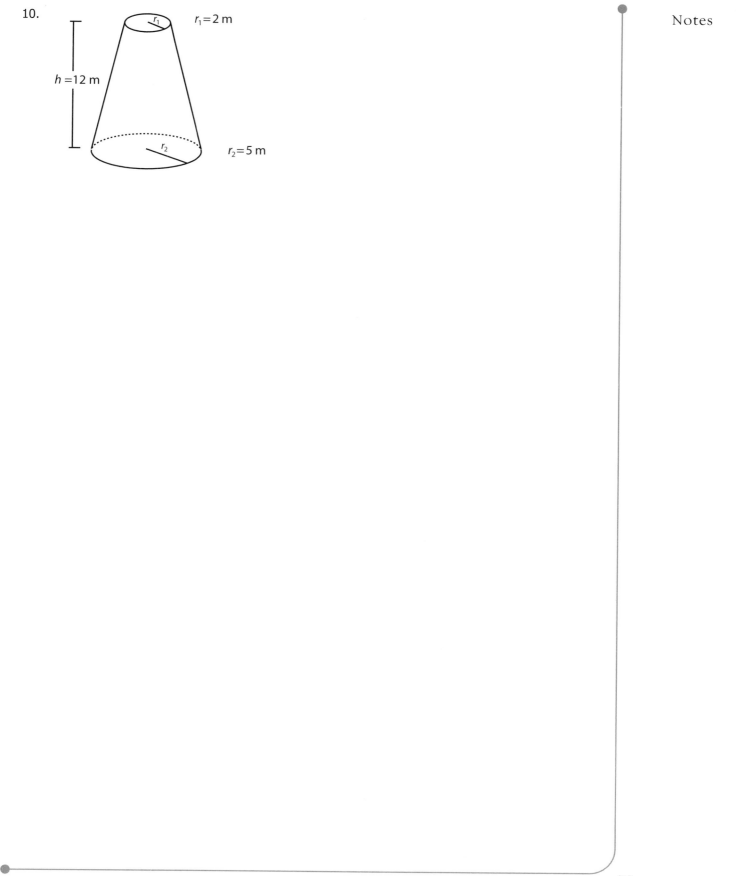

$r_1 = 2\,m$

$h = 12\,m$

$r_2 = 5\,m$

Answer Key

1. $A_{\text{Rectangle}} = 12\,\text{in.}^2$

2. $A_{\text{Square}} = 9\,\text{cm}^2$

3. $A_{\text{Circle}} = 12.56\,\text{ft}^2$

4. $A_{\text{Triangle}} = 40\,\text{in.}^2$

5. $A_{\text{Figure}} = A_{\text{Rectangle}} + A_{\frac{1}{2}\text{Circle}} = 46.28\,\text{in}^2$

6. $A_{\text{Figure}} = A_{\text{Rectangle}} - A_{\text{Triangle}} = 39\,\text{cm}^2$

7. $V_{\text{Cube}} = 120\,\text{in.}^3$

8. $V_{\text{Sphere}} = 113.1\,\text{ft}^3$

9. $V_{\text{Cone}} = 150.8\,\text{in.}^3$

10. $V_{\text{Frustrum}} = 490.1\,\text{m}^3$

Solutions

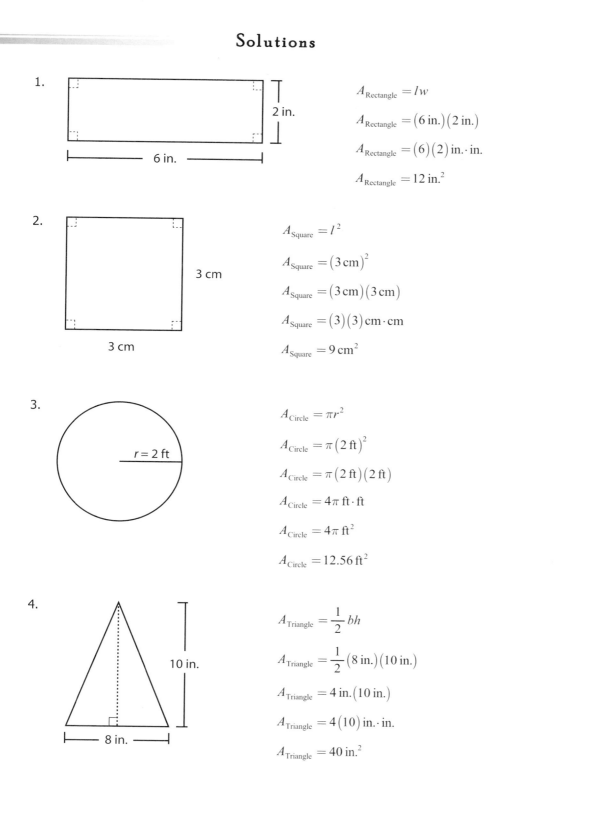

1.

$$A_{\text{Rectangle}} = lw$$

$$A_{\text{Rectangle}} = (6\,\text{in.})(2\,\text{in.})$$

$$A_{\text{Rectangle}} = (6)(2)\,\text{in.}\cdot\text{in.}$$

$$A_{\text{Rectangle}} = 12\,\text{in.}^2$$

2.

$$A_{\text{Square}} = l^2$$

$$A_{\text{Square}} = (3\,\text{cm})^2$$

$$A_{\text{Square}} = (3\,\text{cm})(3\,\text{cm})$$

$$A_{\text{Square}} = (3)(3)\,\text{cm}\cdot\text{cm}$$

$$A_{\text{Square}} = 9\,\text{cm}^2$$

3.

$$A_{\text{Circle}} = \pi r^2$$

$$A_{\text{Circle}} = \pi(2\,\text{ft})^2$$

$$A_{\text{Circle}} = \pi(2\,\text{ft})(2\,\text{ft})$$

$$A_{\text{Circle}} = 4\pi\,\text{ft}\cdot\text{ft}$$

$$A_{\text{Circle}} = 4\pi\,\text{ft}^2$$

$$A_{\text{Circle}} = 12.56\,\text{ft}^2$$

4.

$$A_{\text{Triangle}} = \frac{1}{2}bh$$

$$A_{\text{Triangle}} = \frac{1}{2}(8\,\text{in.})(10\,\text{in.})$$

$$A_{\text{Triangle}} = 4\,\text{in.}(10\,\text{in.})$$

$$A_{\text{Triangle}} = 4(10)\,\text{in.}\cdot\text{in.}$$

$$A_{\text{Triangle}} = 40\,\text{in.}^2$$

5.

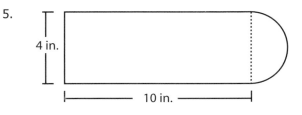

We begin by finding the area of the rectangular portion of the figure:

$$A_{\text{Rectangle}} = lw = (10 \text{ in.})(4 \text{ in.}) = 10(4) \text{ in.} \cdot \text{in.} = 40 \text{ in}^2$$

Next, since the remainder of the figure is 1/2 of a circle of radius 2 in., we calculate this area and add it to the area of the rectangle.

Area of 1/2 of the circle:

$$A_{\frac{1}{2}\text{Circle}} = \frac{1}{2}\left(\pi r^2\right)$$

$$A_{\frac{1}{2}\text{Circle}} = \frac{1}{2}\pi\left(2 \text{ in.}\right)^2$$

$$A_{\frac{1}{2}\text{Circle}} = \frac{1}{2}\pi\left(2 \text{ in.}\right)\left(2 \text{ in.}\right) = 2\pi \text{ in.}^2 = 6.28 \text{ in.}^2$$

Total area of the figure $= A_{\text{Rectangle}} + A_{\frac{1}{2}\text{Circle}} = 40 \text{ in}^2 + 6.28 \text{ in}^2 = 46.28 \text{ in}^2$

6.

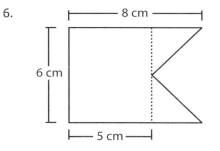

The area of the figure can be found by calculating the area of a rectangle of length 8 cm and width 6 cm and subtracting the area of the missing trianglar section.

$$A_{\text{Rectangle}} = (8 \text{ cm})(6 \text{ cm}) = 8(6) \text{ cm} \cdot \text{cm} = 48 \text{ cm}^2$$

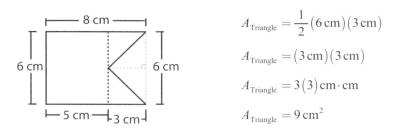

$$A_{\text{Triangle}} = \frac{1}{2}(6 \text{ cm})(3 \text{ cm})$$

$$A_{\text{Triangle}} = (3 \text{ cm})(3 \text{ cm})$$

$$A_{\text{Triangle}} = 3(3) \text{ cm} \cdot \text{cm}$$

$$A_{\text{Triangle}} = 9 \text{ cm}^2$$

Total area of the figure $= A_{\text{Rectangle}} - A_{\text{Triangle}} = 48 \text{ cm}^2 - 9 \text{ cm}^2 = 39 \text{ cm}^2$

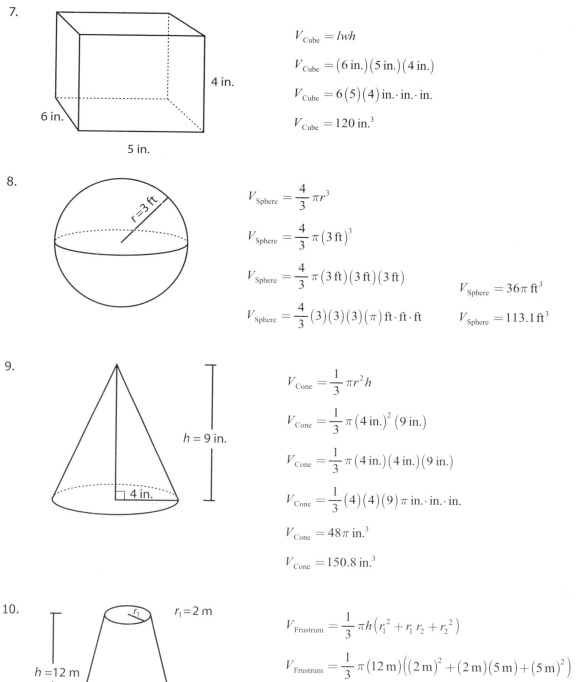

7.

$$V_{Cube} = lwh$$

$$V_{Cube} = (6\,\text{in.})(5\,\text{in.})(4\,\text{in.})$$

$$V_{Cube} = 6(5)(4)\,\text{in.}\cdot\text{in.}\cdot\text{in.}$$

$$V_{Cube} = 120\,\text{in.}^3$$

4 in.

6 in.

5 in.

8.

$r = 3\,\text{ft}$

$$V_{Sphere} = \frac{4}{3}\pi r^3$$

$$V_{Sphere} = \frac{4}{3}\pi(3\,\text{ft})^3$$

$$V_{Sphere} = \frac{4}{3}\pi(3\,\text{ft})(3\,\text{ft})(3\,\text{ft})$$

$$V_{Sphere} = \frac{4}{3}(3)(3)(3)(\pi)\,\text{ft}\cdot\text{ft}\cdot\text{ft}$$

$$V_{Sphere} = 36\pi\,\text{ft}^3$$

$$V_{Sphere} = 113.1\,\text{ft}^3$$

9.

$h = 9\,\text{in.}$

4 in.

$$V_{Cone} = \frac{1}{3}\pi r^2 h$$

$$V_{Cone} = \frac{1}{3}\pi(4\,\text{in.})^2(9\,\text{in.})$$

$$V_{Cone} = \frac{1}{3}\pi(4\,\text{in.})(4\,\text{in.})(9\,\text{in.})$$

$$V_{Cone} = \frac{1}{3}(4)(4)(9)\pi\,\text{in.}\cdot\text{in.}\cdot\text{in.}$$

$$V_{Cone} = 48\pi\,\text{in.}^3$$

$$V_{Cone} = 150.8\,\text{in.}^3$$

10.

r_1 $r_1 = 2\,\text{m}$

$h = 12\,\text{m}$

r_2 $r_2 = 5\,\text{m}$

$$V_{Frustrum} = \frac{1}{3}\pi h\left(r_1^2 + r_1 r_2 + r_2^2\right)$$

$$V_{Frustrum} = \frac{1}{3}\pi(12\,\text{m})\left((2\,\text{m})^2 + (2\,\text{m})(5\,\text{m}) + (5\,\text{m})^2\right)$$

$$V_{Frustrum} = \frac{1}{3}\pi(12\,\text{m})(4\,\text{m}^2 + 10\,\text{m}^2 + 25\,\text{m}^2)$$

$$V_{Frustrum} = \frac{1}{3}\pi(12\,\text{m})(39\,\text{m}^2)$$

$$V_{Frustrum} = 4\pi\,\text{m}(39\,\text{m}^2)$$

$$V_{Frustrum} = 490.1\,\text{m}^3$$

Notes

ADDITION, SUBTRACTION, MULTIPLICATION, AND DIVISION OF COMPLEX NUMBERS

18

Perform each of the indicated operations.

Notes

1. $(2+3i)+(5+6i)$

2. $(3+7i)+(2+i)$

3. $(4+5i)+(-3-2i)$

4. $(2+4i)-(5+3i)$

5. $(6+2i)-(4-i)$

6. $(7-3i)-(-2+4i)$

7. $3(2+6i)$

8. $-2(1+3i)$

9. $4i(2+5i)$

10. $2i(3-i)$

11. $-4i(2+i)$

12. $(3+4i)(2+5i)$

13. $(5+2i)(3+i)$

14. $(6-i)(2+4i)$

15. $(2-i)(3-i)$

16. $3i(2+i)(4-i)$

17. $\dfrac{2+5i}{3+4i}$

18. $\dfrac{3+2i}{1-i}$

19. $\dfrac{1+2i}{-3+i}$

20. $\dfrac{2+5i}{8+2i}$

Answer Key

1. $(2+3i)+(5+6i)=7+9i$

2. $(3+7i)+(2+i)=5+8i$

3. $(4+5i)+(-3-2i)=1+3i$

4. $(2+4i)-(5+3i)=-3+i$

5. $(6+2i)-(4-i)=2+3i$

6. $(7-3i)-(-2+4i)=9-7i$

7. $3(2+6i)=6+18i$

8. $-2(1+3i)=-2-6i$

9. $4i(2+5i)=-20+8i$

10. $2i(3-i)=2+6i$

11. $-4i(2+i)=4+8i$

12. $(3+4i)(2+5i)=-14+23i$

13. $(5+2i)(3+i)=13+11i$

14. $(6-i)(2+4i)=16+22i$

15. $(2-i)(3-i)=5-5i$

16. $3i(2+i)(4-i)=-6+27i$

17. $\dfrac{2+5i}{3+4i}=\dfrac{26}{25}+\dfrac{7}{25}i$

18. $\dfrac{3+2i}{1-i}=\dfrac{1}{2}+\dfrac{5}{2}i$

19. $\dfrac{1+2i}{-3+i}=-\dfrac{1}{10}-\dfrac{7}{10}i$

20. $\dfrac{2+5i}{8+2i}=\dfrac{13}{34}+\dfrac{9}{17}i$

Solutions

1. $(2+3i)+(5+6i)=2+3i+5+6i$

$$=7+9i$$

2. $(3+7i)+(2+i)=3+7i+2+i$

$$=5+8i$$

3. $(4+5i)+(-3-2i)=4+5i-3-2i$

$$=1+3i$$

4. $(2+4i)-(5+3i)=2+4i-5-3i$

$$=-3+i$$

5. $(6+2i)-(4-i)=6+2i-4+i$

$$=2+3i$$

6. $(7-3i)-(-2+4i)=7-3i+2-4i$

$$=9-7i$$

7. $3(2+6i)=3(2)+3(6i)$

$$=6+18i$$

8. $-2(1+3i)=-2(1)+(-2)(3i)$

$$=-2-6i$$

9. $4i(2+5i)=4i(2)+4i(5i)$

$$=8i+20i^2$$

$$=8i+20(-1)$$

$$=8i-20$$

$$=-20+8i$$

10. $2i(3-i)=2i(3)+2i(-i)$

$$=6i-2i^2$$

$$=6i-2(-1)$$

$$=6i+2$$

$$=2+6i$$

11. $-4i(2+i) = -4i(2) + (-4i)(i)$

$$= -8i - 4i^2$$

$$= 8i - 4(-1)$$

$$= 8i + 4$$

$$= 4 + 8i$$

12. $(3+4i)(2+5i) = 3(2) + 3(5i) + 4i(2) + 4i(5i)$

$$= 6 + 15i + 8i + 20i^2$$

$$= 6 + 23i + 20(-1)$$

$$= 6 + 23i - 20$$

$$= -14 + 23i$$

13. $(5+2i)(3+i) = 5(3) + 5(i) + 2i(3) + 2i(i)$

$$= 15 + 5i + 6i + 2i^2$$

$$= 15 + 11i + 2(-1)$$

$$= 15 + 11i - 2$$

$$= 13 + 11i$$

14. $(6-i)(2+4i) = 6(2) + 6(4i) + (-i)(2) + (-i)(4i)$

$$= 12 + 24i - 2i - 4i^2$$

$$= 12 + 22i - 4(-1)$$

$$= 12 + 22i + 4$$

$$= 16 + 22i$$

15. $(2-i)(3-i) = 2(3) + 2(-i) + (-i)(3) + (-i)(-i)$

$$= 6 - 2i - 3i + i^2$$

$$= 6 - 5i - 1$$

$$= 5 - 5i$$

16. $3i(2+i)(4-i) = [3i(2)+3i(i)](4-i)$

$$= (6i+3i^2)(4-i)$$

$$= [6i+3(-1)](4-i)$$

$$= (6i-3)(4-i)$$

$$= 6i(4)+6i(-i)+(-3)(4)+(-3)(-i)$$

$$= 24i-6i^2-12+3i$$

$$= -12+27i-6(-1)$$

$$= -12+27i+6$$

$$= -6+27i$$

17. $\dfrac{2+5i}{3+4i} = \dfrac{2+5i}{3+4i} \cdot \dfrac{3-4i}{3-4i}$

$$= \frac{2(3)+2(-4i)+5i(3)+5i(-4i)}{3(3)+3(-4i)+4i(3)+4i(-4i)}$$

$$= \frac{6-8i+15i-20i^2}{9-16i^2}$$

$$= \frac{6+7i-20(-1)}{9-16(-1)}$$

$$= \frac{6+7i+20}{9+16}$$

$$= \frac{26+7i}{25}$$

$$= \frac{26}{25}+\frac{7}{25}i$$

18. $\dfrac{3+2i}{1-i} = \dfrac{3+2i}{1-i} \cdot \dfrac{1+i}{1+i}$

$$= \frac{3(1)+3(i)+2i(1)+2i(i)}{1(1)+1(i)+(-i)(1)+(-i)(i)}$$

$$= \frac{3+3i+2i+2i^2}{1-i^2}$$

$$= \frac{3+5i+2(-1)}{1-(-1)}$$

$$= \frac{3+5i-2}{1+1}$$

$$= \frac{1+5i}{2}$$

$$= \frac{1}{2}+\frac{5}{2}i$$

19. $\dfrac{1+2i}{-3+i} = \dfrac{1+2i}{-3+i} \cdot \dfrac{-3-i}{-3-i}$

$\quad = \dfrac{1(-3)+1(-i)+2i(-3)+2i(-i)}{(-3)(-3)+(-3)(-i)+i(-3)+i(-i)}$

$\quad = \dfrac{-3-i-6i-2i^2}{9-i^2}$

$\quad = \dfrac{-3-7i-2(-1)}{9-(-1)}$

$\quad = \dfrac{-3-7i+2}{9+1}$

$\quad = \dfrac{-1-7i}{10}$

$\quad = -\dfrac{1}{10} - \dfrac{7}{10}i$

20. $\dfrac{2+5i}{8+2i} = \dfrac{2+5i}{8+2i} \cdot \dfrac{8-2i}{8-2i}$

$\quad = \dfrac{2(8)+2(-2i)+5i(8)+5i(-2i)}{8(8)+8(-2i)+2i(8)+2i(-2i)}$

$\quad = \dfrac{16-4i+40i-10i^2}{64-4i^2}$

$\quad = \dfrac{16+36i-10(-1)}{64-4(-1)}$

$\quad = \dfrac{16+36i+10}{64+4}$

$\quad = \dfrac{26+36i}{68}$

$\quad = \dfrac{26}{68} + \dfrac{36}{68}i$

$\quad = \dfrac{13}{34} + \dfrac{9}{17}i$

THE SLOPE
OF A LINE

19

Find the slopes of the lines that pass through the following sets of points.

$$\text{slope} = m = \frac{y_2 - y_1}{x_2 - x_1}$$

1. $(2, 3), (4, 7)$

2. $(0, 1), (1, 2)$

3. $(-1, 2), (4, -4)$

4. $\left(\frac{1}{2}, -\frac{1}{2}\right), (2, 5)$

5. $(0.5, 0.7), (1.5, 2.8)$

6. $(2, 5), (3, 5)$

7. $(3, 5), (3, 8)$

8. $\left(2, -\frac{1}{5}\right), (0, 0)$

9. $(3, 8), (0, -5)$

10. $(2, 5), (5, 2)$

Find the slope of each of the following lines.

11. The line $y = 2x + 5$

12. The line $y = \frac{1}{3}x - 5$

13. The line $y = -4x + 3$

14. A line parallel to the line $y = 5x + 6$

15. A line parallel to the line $y = -7x + 1$

16. A line parallel to the line $y = \frac{1}{4}x + 2$

17. A line perpendicular to the line $y = \frac{2}{3}x + 4$

18. A line perpendicular to the line $y = -\frac{4}{5}x + 7$

19. A line perpendicular to the line $y = 3x + 9$

20. A line perpendicular to the line $y = -2x + 5$

Notes

Answer Key

1. $m = 2$

2. $m = 1$

3. $m = \dfrac{-6}{5}$

4. $m = \dfrac{11}{3}$

5. $m = 2.1$

6. $m = 0$

7. $m = \dfrac{3}{0}$

   Slope is undefined

8. $m = -\dfrac{1}{10}$

9. $m = \dfrac{13}{3}$

10. $m = -1$

11. slope $= 2$

12. slope $= \dfrac{1}{3}$

13. slope $= -4$

14. slope $= 5$

15. slope $= -7$

16. slope $= \dfrac{1}{4}$

17. slope $= -\dfrac{3}{2}$

18. slope $= \dfrac{5}{4}$

19. slope $= -\dfrac{1}{3}$

20. slope $= \dfrac{1}{2}$

Solutions

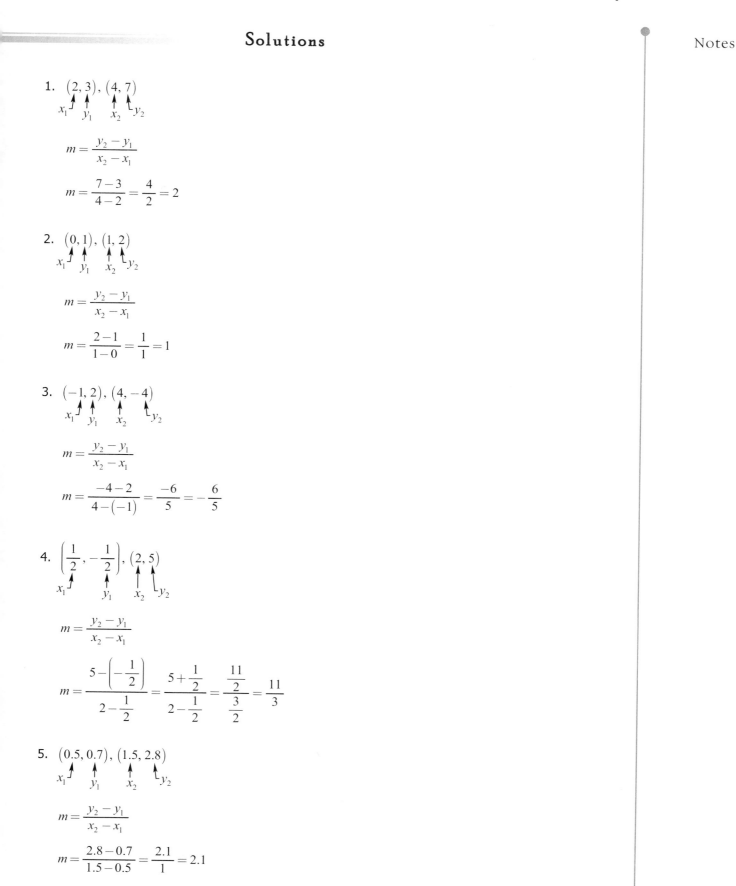

1. $(2, 3), (4, 7)$

   $x_1 \quad y_1 \quad x_2 \quad y_2$

   $m = \dfrac{y_2 - y_1}{x_2 - x_1}$

   $m = \dfrac{7 - 3}{4 - 2} = \dfrac{4}{2} = 2$

2. $(0, 1), (1, 2)$

   $x_1 \quad y_1 \quad x_2 \quad y_2$

   $m = \dfrac{y_2 - y_1}{x_2 - x_1}$

   $m = \dfrac{2 - 1}{1 - 0} = \dfrac{1}{1} = 1$

3. $(-1, 2), (4, -4)$

   $x_1 \quad y_1 \quad x_2 \quad y_2$

   $m = \dfrac{y_2 - y_1}{x_2 - x_1}$

   $m = \dfrac{-4 - 2}{4 - (-1)} = \dfrac{-6}{5} = -\dfrac{6}{5}$

4. $\left(\dfrac{1}{2}, -\dfrac{1}{2}\right), (2, 5)$

   $x_1 \quad y_1 \quad x_2 \quad y_2$

   $m = \dfrac{y_2 - y_1}{x_2 - x_1}$

   $m = \dfrac{5 - \left(-\dfrac{1}{2}\right)}{2 - \dfrac{1}{2}} = \dfrac{5 + \dfrac{1}{2}}{2 - \dfrac{1}{2}} = \dfrac{\dfrac{11}{2}}{\dfrac{3}{2}} = \dfrac{11}{3}$

5. $(0.5, 0.7), (1.5, 2.8)$

   $x_1 \quad y_1 \quad x_2 \quad y_2$

   $m = \dfrac{y_2 - y_1}{x_2 - x_1}$

   $m = \dfrac{2.8 - 0.7}{1.5 - 0.5} = \dfrac{2.1}{1} = 2.1$

6. $(2, 5), (3, 5)$

$$x_1 \uparrow \uparrow y_1 \quad x_2 \uparrow \uparrow y_2$$

$$m = \frac{y_2 - y_1}{x_2 - x_1}$$

$$m = \frac{5-5}{3-2} = \frac{0}{1} = 0$$

7. $(3, 5), (3, 8)$

$$x_1 \uparrow \uparrow y_1 \quad x_2 \uparrow \uparrow y_2$$

$$m = \frac{y_2 - y_1}{x_2 - x_1}$$

$$m = \frac{8-5}{3-3} = \frac{3}{0}$$

Slope is undefined

8. $\left(2, -\frac{1}{5}\right), (0, 0)$

$$x_1 \uparrow \quad \uparrow y_1 \quad x_2 \uparrow \uparrow y_2$$

$$m = \frac{y_2 - y_1}{x_2 - x_1}$$

$$m = \frac{0 - \left(-\frac{1}{5}\right)}{0 - 2} = \frac{\frac{1}{5}}{-2} = \frac{1}{5}\left(-\frac{1}{2}\right) = -\frac{1}{10}$$

9. $(3, 8), (0, -5)$

$$x_1 \uparrow \uparrow y_1 \quad x_2 \uparrow \uparrow y_2$$

$$m = \frac{y_2 - y_1}{x_2 - x_1}$$

$$m = \frac{-5-8}{0-3} = \frac{-13}{-3} = \frac{13}{3}$$

10. $(2, 5), (5, 2)$

$$x_1 \uparrow \uparrow y_1 \quad x_2 \uparrow \uparrow y_2$$

$$m = \frac{y_2 - y_1}{x_2 - x_1}$$

$$m = \frac{2-5}{5-2} = \frac{-3}{3} = -1$$

DISTANCE
AND MIDPOINT

Find:
a) the distance between the following sets of points.
b) the coordinates of the midpoint between the two points.

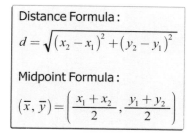

Distance Formula :

$$d = \sqrt{\left(x_2 - x_1\right)^2 + \left(y_2 - y_1\right)^2}$$

Midpoint Formula :

$$\left(\bar{x}, \bar{y}\right) = \left(\frac{x_1 + x_2}{2}, \frac{y_1 + y_2}{2}\right)$$

1. $(1, 2), (3, 6)$

2. $(0, 0), (2, 5)$

3. $(-1, -2), (3, 4)$

4. $(0, 2), (2, 0)$

5. $(-6, 5), (1, 1)$

6. $\left(\frac{1}{2}, 0\right), \left(\frac{2}{3}, \frac{1}{2}\right)$

7. $(-15, 13), (-13, 15)$

8. $(0.5, 2.1), (3.7, 4.2)$

9. $(a, b), (c, d)$

10. $(-1, -2), (-3, -5)$

Answer Key

1.
   a) $d = \sqrt{20}$

   b) $(\bar{x}, \bar{y}) = (2, 4)$

2.
   a) $d = \sqrt{29}$

   b) $(\bar{x}, \bar{y}) = \left(1, \dfrac{5}{2}\right)$

3.
   a) $d = \sqrt{52}$

   b) $(\bar{x}, \bar{y}) = (1, 1)$

4.
   a) $d = 2\sqrt{2}$

   b) $(\bar{x}, \bar{y}) = (1, 1)$

5.
   a) $d = \sqrt{65}$

   b) $(\bar{x}, \bar{y}) = \left(-\dfrac{5}{2}, 3\right)$

6.
   a) $d = \dfrac{\sqrt{10}}{6}$

   b) $(\bar{x}, \bar{y}) = \left(\dfrac{7}{12}, \dfrac{1}{4}\right)$

7.
   a) $d = 2\sqrt{2}$

   b) $(\bar{x}, \bar{y}) = (-14, 14)$

8.
   a) $d = 3.8$

   b) $(\bar{x}, \bar{y}) = (2.1, 3.15)$

9.
   a) $d = \sqrt{(c-a)^2 + (d-b)^2}$

   b) $(\bar{x}, \bar{y}) = \left(\dfrac{a+c}{2}, \dfrac{b+d}{2}\right)$

10.
   a) $d = \sqrt{13}$

   b) $(\bar{x}, \bar{y}) = (-2, -3.5)$

Solutions

1. $(1, 2), (3, 6)$
   $x_1 \quad y_1 \quad x_2 \quad y_2$

   a) **Distance:**

   $$d = \sqrt{(x_2 - x_1)^2 + (y_2 - y_1)^2}$$

   $$d = \sqrt{(3-1)^2 + (6-2)^2} = \sqrt{2^2 + 4^2} = \sqrt{4+16} = \sqrt{20}$$

   b) **Midpoint:**

   $$(\bar{x}, \bar{y}) = \left(\frac{x_1 + x_2}{2}, \frac{y_1 + y_2}{2} \right)$$

   $$(\bar{x}, \bar{y}) = \left(\frac{1+3}{2}, \frac{2+6}{2} \right)$$

   $$(\bar{x}, \bar{y}) = \left(\frac{4}{2}, \frac{8}{2} \right)$$

   $$(\bar{x}, \bar{y}) = (2, 4)$$

2. $(0, 0), (2, 5)$
   $x_1 \quad y_1 \quad x_2 \quad y_2$

   a) **Distance:**

   $$d = \sqrt{(x_2 - x_1)^2 + (y_2 - y_1)^2}$$

   $$d = \sqrt{(2-0)^2 + (5-0)^2} = \sqrt{2^2 + 5^2} = \sqrt{4+25} = \sqrt{29}$$

   b) **Midpoint:**

   $$(\bar{x}, \bar{y}) = \left(\frac{x_1 + x_2}{2}, \frac{y_1 + y_2}{2} \right)$$

   $$(\bar{x}, \bar{y}) = \left(\frac{0+2}{2}, \frac{0+5}{2} \right)$$

   $$(\bar{x}, \bar{y}) = \left(\frac{2}{2}, \frac{5}{2} \right)$$

   $$(\bar{x}, \bar{y}) = \left(1, \frac{5}{2} \right)$$

3. $(-1, -2), (3, 4)$

$x_1 \uparrow \quad \uparrow y_1 \quad \uparrow x_2 \quad \uparrow y_2$

a) **Distance:**

$$d = \sqrt{(x_2 - x_1)^2 + (y_2 - y_1)^2}$$

$$d = \sqrt{(3-(-1))^2 + (4-(-2))^2} = \sqrt{(3+1)^2 + (4+2)^2} = \sqrt{4^2 + 6^2} = \sqrt{16+36} = \sqrt{52}$$

b) **Midpoint:**

$$(\bar{x}, \bar{y}) = \left(\frac{x_1 + x_2}{2}, \frac{y_1 + y_2}{2} \right)$$

$$(\bar{x}, \bar{y}) = \left(\frac{-1+3}{2}, \frac{-2+4}{2} \right)$$

$$(\bar{x}, \bar{y}) = \left(\frac{2}{2}, \frac{2}{2} \right)$$

$$(\bar{x}, \bar{y}) = (1, 1)$$

4. $(0, 2), (2, 0)$

$x_1 \uparrow \quad \uparrow y_1 \quad \uparrow x_2 \quad \uparrow y_2$

a) **Distance:**

$$d = \sqrt{(x_2 - x_1)^2 + (y_2 - y_1)^2}$$

$$d = \sqrt{(2-0)^2 + (0-2)^2} = \sqrt{2^2 + (-2)^2} = \sqrt{4+4} = \sqrt{8} = 2\sqrt{2}$$

b) **Midpoint:**

$$(\bar{x}, \bar{y}) = \left(\frac{x_1 + x_2}{2}, \frac{y_1 + y_2}{2} \right)$$

$$(\bar{x}, \bar{y}) = \left(\frac{0+2}{2}, \frac{2+0}{2} \right)$$

$$(\bar{x}, \bar{y}) = \left(\frac{2}{2}, \frac{2}{2} \right)$$

$$(\bar{x}, \bar{y}) = (1, 1)$$

5. $(-6, 5), (1, 1)$

$\quad x_1 \quad y_1 \quad x_2 \quad y_2$

a) **Distance:**

$$d = \sqrt{(x_2 - x_1)^2 + (y_2 - y_1)^2}$$

$$d = \sqrt{(1 - (-6))^2 + (1 - 5)^2} = \sqrt{7^2 + (-4)^2} = \sqrt{49 + 16} = \sqrt{65}$$

b) **Midpoint:**

$$(\bar{x}, \bar{y}) = \left(\frac{x_1 + x_2}{2}, \frac{y_1 + y_2}{2} \right)$$

$$(\bar{x}, \bar{y}) = \left(\frac{-6 + 1}{2}, \frac{5 + 1}{2} \right)$$

$$(\bar{x}, \bar{y}) = \left(\frac{-5}{2}, \frac{6}{2} \right)$$

$$(\bar{x}, \bar{y}) = \left(-\frac{5}{2}, 3 \right)$$

6. $\left(\frac{1}{2}, 0 \right), \left(\frac{2}{3}, \frac{1}{2} \right)$

$\quad x_1 \quad y_1 \quad x_2 \quad y_2$

a) **Distance:**

$$d = \sqrt{(x_2 - x_1)^2 + (y_2 - y_1)^2}$$

$$d = \sqrt{\left(\frac{2}{3} - \frac{1}{2} \right)^2 + \left(\frac{1}{2} - 0 \right)^2}$$

$$d = \sqrt{\left(\frac{4}{6} - \frac{3}{6} \right)^2 + \left(\frac{1}{2} \right)^2}$$

$$d = \sqrt{\left(\frac{1}{6} \right)^2 + \left(\frac{1}{2} \right)^2}$$

$$d = \sqrt{\frac{1}{36} + \frac{1}{4}}$$

$$d = \sqrt{\frac{1}{36} + \frac{9}{36}}$$

$$d = \sqrt{\frac{10}{36}} = \frac{\sqrt{10}}{\sqrt{36}} = \frac{\sqrt{10}}{6}$$

Solution #6 cont. on next page...

Solution #6 from previous page...

b) **Midpoint:**

$$(\bar{x}, \bar{y}) = \left(\frac{x_1 + x_2}{2}, \frac{y_1 + y_2}{2} \right)$$

$$(\bar{x}, \bar{y}) = \left(\frac{\frac{1}{2} + \frac{2}{3}}{2}, \frac{0 + \frac{1}{2}}{2} \right)$$

$$(\bar{x}, \bar{y}) = \left(\frac{\frac{3}{6} + \frac{4}{6}}{2}, \frac{\frac{1}{2}}{2} \right)$$

$$(\bar{x}, \bar{y}) = \left(\frac{\frac{7}{6}}{2}, \frac{1}{4} \right)$$

$$(\bar{x}, \bar{y}) = \left(\frac{7}{12}, \frac{1}{4} \right)$$

7. $(-15, 13), (-13, 15)$

   $x_1 \quad y_1 \quad x_2 \quad y_2$

a) **Distance:**

$$d = \sqrt{(x_2 - x_1)^2 + (y_2 - y_1)^2}$$

$$d = \sqrt{(-13 - (-15))^2 + (15 - 13)^2} = \sqrt{(2)^2 + (2)^2} = \sqrt{8} = 2\sqrt{2}$$

b) **Midpoint:**

$$(\bar{x}, \bar{y}) = \left(\frac{x_1 + x_2}{2}, \frac{y_1 + y_2}{2} \right)$$

$$(\bar{x}, \bar{y}) = \left(\frac{-15 + (-13)}{2}, \frac{13 + 15}{2} \right)$$

$$(\bar{x}, \bar{y}) = \left(\frac{-28}{2}, \frac{28}{2} \right)$$

$$(\bar{x}, \bar{y}) = (-14, 14)$$

8. $(0.5, 2.1), (3.7, 4.2)$

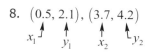

a) **Distance:**

$$d = \sqrt{(x_2 - x_1)^2 - (y_2 - y_1)^2}$$

$$d = \sqrt{(3.7 - 0.5)^2 + (4.2 - 2.1)^2}$$

$$d = \sqrt{3.2^2 + 2.1^2}$$

$$d = \sqrt{10.24 + 4.41}$$

$$d = \sqrt{14.65} = 3.8$$

b) **Midpoint:**

$$(\bar{x}, \bar{y}) = \left(\frac{x_1 + x_2}{2}, \frac{y_1 + y_2}{2} \right)$$

$$(\bar{x}, \bar{y}) = \left(\frac{0.5 + 3.7}{2}, \frac{2.1 + 4.2}{2} \right)$$

$$(\bar{x}, \bar{y}) = \left(\frac{4.2}{2}, \frac{6.3}{2} \right)$$

$$(\bar{x}, \bar{y}) = (2.1, 3.15)$$

9. $(a, b), (c, d)$

a) **Distance:**

$$d = \sqrt{(x_2 - x_1)^2 - (y_2 - y_1)^2}$$

$$d = \sqrt{(c - a)^2 + (d - b)^2}$$

b) **Midpoint:**

$$(\bar{x}, \bar{y}) = \left(\frac{x_1 + x_2}{2}, \frac{y_1 + y_2}{2} \right)$$

$$(\bar{x}, \bar{y}) = \left(\frac{a + c}{2}, \frac{b + d}{2} \right)$$

10. $(-1, -2), (-3, -5)$

$x_1 \uparrow \quad \uparrow y_1 \quad \uparrow x_2 \quad \uparrow y_2$

a) **Distance:**

$$d = \sqrt{(x_2 - x_1)^2 - (y_2 - y_1)^2}$$

$$d = \sqrt{(-3 - (-1))^2 + (-5 - (-2))^2}$$

$$d = \sqrt{(-3 + 1)^2 + (-5 + 2)^2}$$

$$d = \sqrt{(-2)^2 + (-3)^2}$$

$$d = \sqrt{4 + 9} = \sqrt{13}$$

b) **Midpoint:**

$$(\bar{x}, \bar{y}) = \left(\frac{x_1 + x_2}{2}, \frac{y_1 + y_2}{2} \right)$$

$$(\bar{x}, \bar{y}) = \left(\frac{-1 + (-3)}{2}, \frac{-2 + (-5)}{2} \right)$$

$$(\bar{x}, \bar{y}) = \left(\frac{-1 - 3}{2}, \frac{-2 - 5}{2} \right)$$

$$(\bar{x}, \bar{y}) = \left(\frac{-4}{2}, \frac{-7}{2} \right)$$

$$(\bar{x}, \bar{y}) = (-2, -3.5)$$

FUNCTIONS I: DETERMINING IF AN EQUATION IS A FUNCTION

21

Determine if the following are functions.

Notes

1. $y = 3x + 1$

2. $y = -x^2$

3. $x + y = 4$

4. $y^2 = x$

5. $y = x^3$

6. $y = \sqrt{x+1}$

7. $y^3 = x$

8. $2y - 4x = 1$

9. $xy = 2$

10. $y^4 - x = 2$

11. $y = \sqrt[5]{x}$

12. $y = \sin x$

13. $\sin y = x$

14. $x^2 + y^2 = 25$

15. $y = 3$

Solutions

1. $y = 3x + 1$

   Yes - Each value of x is associated with only one value of y.

2. $y = -x^2$

   Yes - Each value of x is associated with only one value of y.

3. $x + y = 4$

   $y = 4 - x$

   Yes - Each value of x is associated with only one value of y.

4. $y^2 = x$

   $y = \pm\sqrt{x}$

   No. Because of the $\pm$ that arises from taking the square root, each value of x is associated with two values of y.

5. $y = x^3$

   Yes - Each value of x is associated with only one value of y.

6. $y = \sqrt{x+1}$

   Yes - Each value of x is associated with only one value of y. Notice that we were specifically given the positive square root. This is not the same situation as problem #4 in which we had to solve for y generating a positive and negative square root.

7. $y^3 = x$

   $y = \sqrt[3]{x}$

   Yes - Each value of x is associated with only one value of y.

8. $2y - 4x = 1$

   $2y = 4x + 1$

   $y = 2x + \dfrac{1}{2}$

   Yes - Each value of x is associated with only one value of y.

9. $xy = 2$

   $y = \dfrac{2}{x}$

   Yes - Each value of x is associated with only one value of y.

10. $y^4 - x = 2$

$$y^4 = x + 2$$

$$y = \pm\sqrt[4]{x + 2}$$

No. Because of the $\pm$ that arises from taking the 4th root, each value of x is associated with two values of y.

11. $y = \sqrt[5]{x}$

Yes - Each value of x is associated with only one value of y.

12. $y = \sin x$

Yes - Each value of x is associated with only one value of y.

13. $\sin y = x$

$$y = \sin^{-1}(x)$$

No - Each value of x is actually associated with an infinite number of y's.

14. $x^2 + y^2 = 25$

$$y^2 = 25 - x^2$$

$$y = \pm\sqrt{25 - x^2}$$

No. Because of the $\pm$ that arises from taking the square root, each value of x is associated with two values of y.

15. $y = 3$

Yes - Each value of x is associated with a single value of y, in this case 3.

22

FUNCTIONS II:
DETERMINING IF A GRAPH
DEFINES A FUNCTION

Use the vertical line test to decide which of the following are functions.

1.

2.

3.

4.

5.

6.

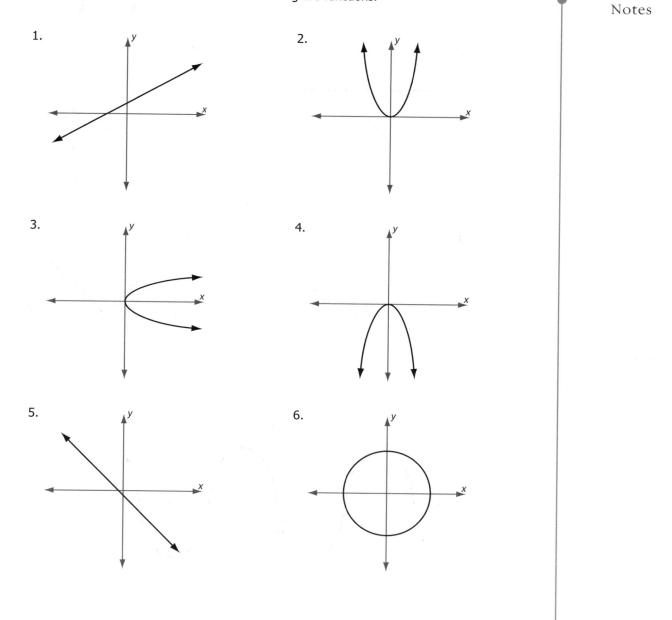

Notes

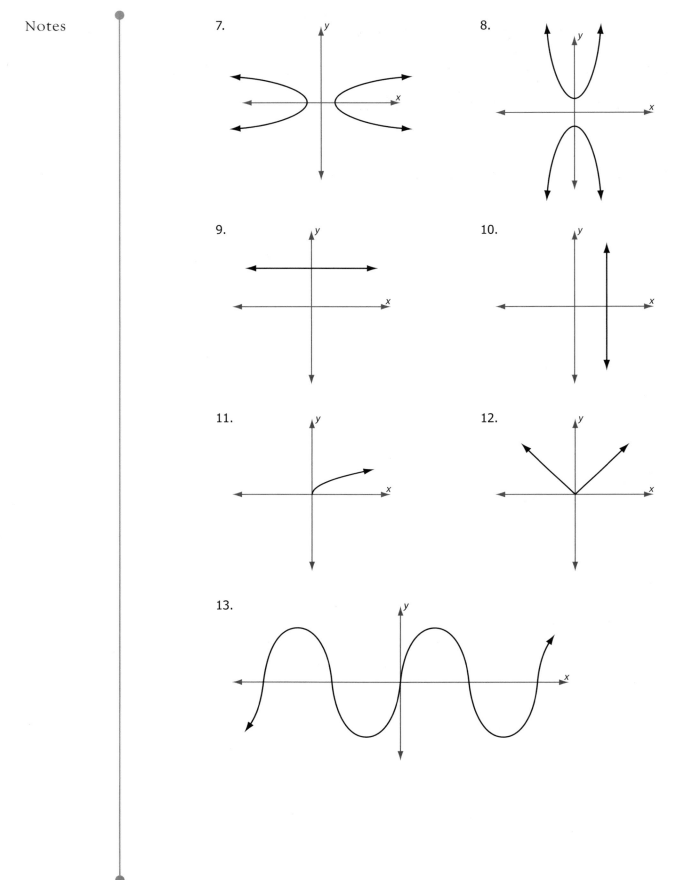

7.

8.

9.

10.

11.

12.

13.

14.

15.

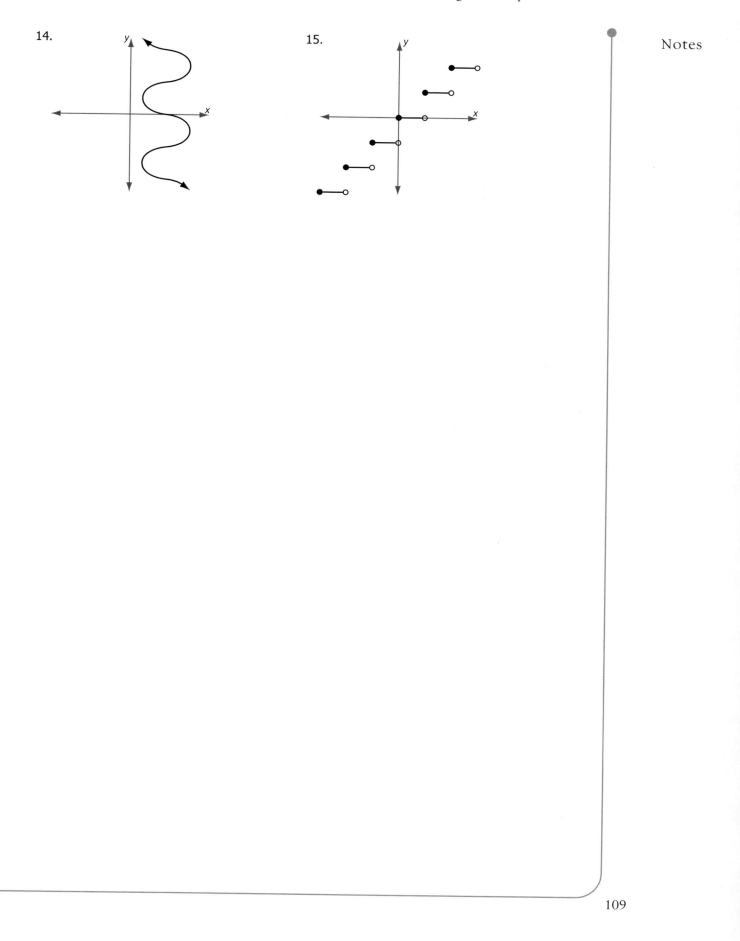

Solutions

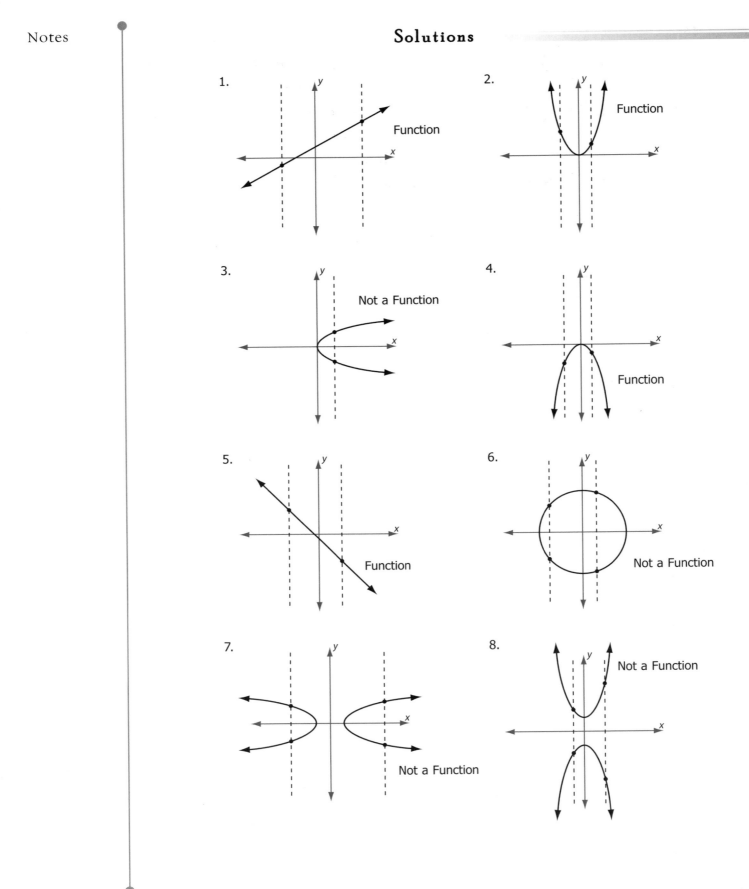

1. Function

2. Function

3. Not a Function

4. Function

5. Function

6. Not a Function

7. Not a Function

8. Not a Function

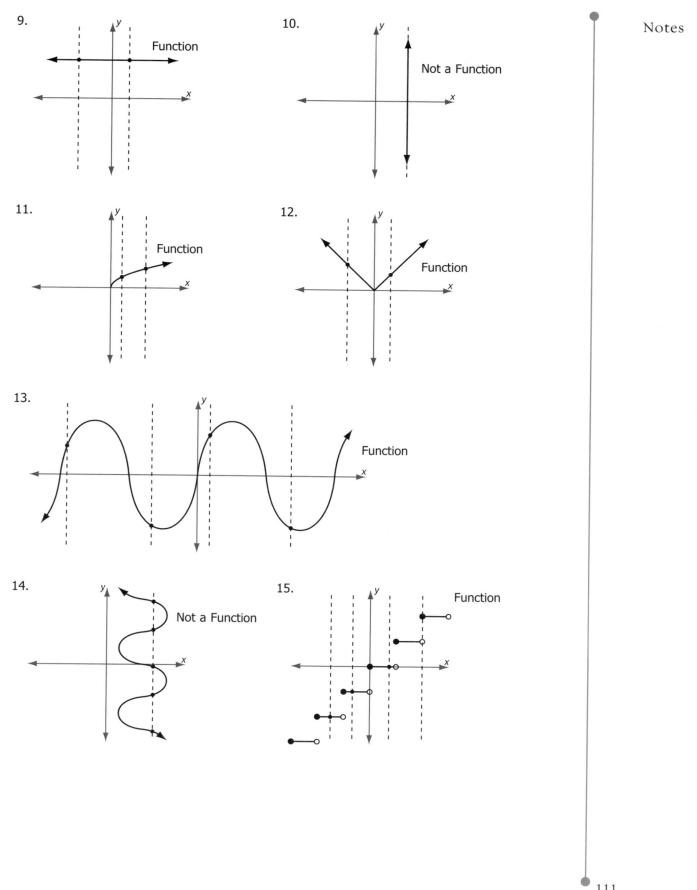

9. Function

10. Not a Function

11. Function

12. Function

13. Function

14. Not a Function

15. Function

23

FUNCTIONS III:
EVALUATING FUNCTIONS AND
COMPOSITIONS OF FUNCTIONS

Evaluating Functions

For each of the following functions find:

a) $f(0)$, b) $f(-1)$, c) $f(x+1)$

1. $f(x) = 2x + 3$

2. $f(x) = x^2$

3. $f(x) = \dfrac{1}{x+2}$

4. $f(x) = 4x^2 + 3x$

5. $f(x) = x^3$

Composing Functions

For each of the following functions find:

a) $f \circ g(x)$, b) $g \circ f(x)$, c) $f \circ g(1)$

6. $f(x) = x^2 + 3$ $\qquad\qquad$ $g(x) = 4x - 1$

7. $f(x) = 4 - 6x$ $\qquad\qquad$ $g(x) = \dfrac{1}{x}$

8. $f(x) = x^3$ $\qquad\qquad$ $g(x) = x + 1$

9. $f(x) = \sqrt{x+3}$ $\qquad\qquad$ $g(x) = x - 4$

10. $f(x) = 4x^2 + 3x$ $\qquad\qquad$ $g(x) = -x$

Answer Key

1.

a) $f(0) = 3$

b) $f(-1) = 1$

c) $f(x+1) = 2x+5$

2.

a) $f(0) = 0$

b) $f(-1) = 1$

c) $f(x+1) = x^2 + 2x + 1$

3.

a) $f(0) = \dfrac{1}{2}$

b) $f(-1) = 1$

c) $f(x+1) = \dfrac{1}{x+3}$

4.

a) $f(0) = 0$

b) $f(-1) = 1$

c) $f(x+1) = 4x^2 + 11x + 7$

5.

a) $f(0) = 0$

b) $f(-1) = -1$

c) $f(x+1) = x^3 + 3x^2 + 3x + 1$

6.

a) $f \circ g(x) = 16x^2 - 8x + 4$

b) $g \circ f(x) = 4x^2 + 11$

c) $f \circ g(1) = 12$

7.

a) $f \circ g(x) = 4 - \dfrac{6}{x}$

b) $g \circ f(x) = \dfrac{1}{4 - 6x}$

c) $f \circ g(1) = -2$

8.

a) $f \circ g(x) = x^3 + 3x^2 + 3x + 1$

b) $g \circ f(x) = x^3 + 1$

c) $f \circ g(1) = 8$

9.

a) $f \circ g(x) = \sqrt{x-1}$

b) $g \circ f(x) = \sqrt{x+3} - 4$

c) $f \circ g(1) = 0$

10.

a) $f \circ g(x) = 4x^2 - 3x$

b) $g \circ f(x) = -4x^2 - 3x$

c) $f \circ g(1) = 1$

Solutions

1.

a) $f(0) = 2(0) + 3$

$f(0) = 3$

b) $f(-1) = 2(-1) + 3$

$f(-1) = -2 + 3$

$f(-1) = 1$

c) $f(x+1) = 2(2+1) + 3$

$f(x+1) = 2x + 2 + 3$

$f(x+1) = 2x + 5$

2.

a) $f(0) = (0)^2$

$f(0) = 0$

b) $f(-1) = (-1)^2$

$f(-1) = 1$

c) $f(x+1) = (x+1)^2$

$f(x+1) = x^2 + 2x + 1$

3.

a) $f(0) = \dfrac{1}{0+2}$

$f(0) = \dfrac{1}{2}$

b) $f(-1) = \dfrac{1}{-1+2}$

$f(-1) = \dfrac{1}{1}$

$f(-1) = 1$

c) $f(x+1) = \dfrac{1}{(x+1)+2}$

$f(x+1) = \dfrac{1}{x+3}$

4.

a) $f(0) = 4(0)^2 + 3(0)$

$f(0) = 0$

b) $f(-1) = 4(-1)^2 + 3(-1)$

$f(-1) = 4(1) - 3$

$f(-1) = 1$

c) $f(x+1) = 4(x+1)^2 + 3(x+1)$

$f(x+1) = 4(x^2 + 2x + 1) + 3x + 3$

$f(x+1) = 4x^2 + 8x + 4 + 3x + 3$

$f(x+1) = 4x^2 + 11x + 7$

5.

a) $f(0) = (0)^3$

$f(0) = 0$

b) $f(-1) = (-1)^3$

$f(-1) = -1$

c) $f(x+1) = (x+1)^3$

$f(x+1) = (x+1)(x+1)(x+1)$

$f(x+1) = (x^2 + 2x + 1)(x+1)$

$f(x+1) = x^3 + 3x^2 + 3x + 1$

6.

a) Replacing x in the function $f(x)$ with the entire $g(x)$ function we get :

$$f \circ g(x) = (4x - 1)^2 + 3$$

$$f \circ g(x) = \left[16x^2 - 8x + 1\right] + 3$$

$$f \circ g(x) = 16x^2 - 8x + 4$$

b) Replacing x in the function $g(x)$ with the entire $f(x)$ function we get :

$$g \circ f(x) = 4(x^2 + 3) - 1$$

$$g \circ f(x) = 4x^2 + 12 - 1$$

$$g \circ f(x) = 4x^2 + 11$$

c) Evaluating at $x = 1$ the result for $f \circ g(x)$ (found in problem 6a) we get :

$$f \circ g(1) = 16(1)^2 - 8(1) + 4$$

$$f \circ g(1) = 16 - 8 + 4$$

$$f \circ g(1) = 12$$

7.

a) Replacing x in the function $f(x)$ with the entire $g(x)$ function we get :

$$f \circ g(x) = 4 - 6\left(\frac{1}{x}\right)$$

$$f \circ g(x) = 4 - \frac{6}{x}$$

b) Replacing x in the function $g(x)$ with the entire $f(x)$ function we get :

$$g \circ f(x) = \frac{1}{4 - 6x}$$

c) Evaluating at $x = 1$ the result for $f \circ g(x)$ (found in problem 7a) we get :

$$f \circ g(1) = 4 - \frac{6}{1}$$

$$f \circ g(1) = 4 - 6$$

$$f \circ g(1) = -2$$

8.

a) Replacing x in the function $f(x)$ with the entire $g(x)$ function we get :

$$f \circ g(x) = (x + 1)^3$$

$$f \circ g(x) = (x + 1)(x + 1)(x + 1)$$

$$f \circ g(x) = (x^2 + 2x + 1)(x + 1)$$

$$f \circ g(x) = x^3 + 3x^2 + 3x + 1$$

calculation cont. on next page...

Solution #8 from previous page...

b) Replacing x in the function $g(x)$ with the entire $f(x)$ function we get :

$$g \circ f(x) = x^3 + 1$$

c) Evaluating at $x = 1$ the result for $f \circ g(x)$ (found in problem 8a) we get :

$$f \circ g(1) = (1+1)^3$$

$$f \circ g(1) = (2)^3$$

$$f \circ g(1) = 8$$

9.

a) Replacing x in the function $f(x)$ with the entire $g(x)$ function we get :

$$f \circ g(x) = \sqrt{(x-4)+3}$$

$$f \circ g(x) = \sqrt{x-1}$$

b) Replacing x in the function $g(x)$ with the entire $f(x)$ function we get :

$$g \circ f(x) = \sqrt{x+3} - 4$$

c) Evaluating at $x = 1$ the result for $f \circ g(x)$ (found in problem 9a) we get :

$$f \circ g(1) = \sqrt{1-1}$$

$$f \circ g(1) = \sqrt{0}$$

$$f \circ g(1) = 0$$

10.

a) Replacing x in the function $f(x)$ with the entire $g(x)$ function we get :

$$f \circ g(x) = 4(-x)^2 + 3(-x)$$

$$f \circ g(x) = 4x^2 - 3x$$

b) Replacing x in the function $g(x)$ with the entire $f(x)$ function we get :

$$g \circ f(x) = -(4x^2 + 3x)$$

$$g \circ f(x) = -4x^2 - 3x$$

c) Evaluating at $x = 1$ the result for $f \circ g(x)$ (found in problem 10a) we get :

$$f \circ g(1) = 4(1)^2 - 3(1)$$

$$f \circ g(1) = 4 - 3$$

$$f \circ g(1) = 1$$

CONVERTING BETWEEN
DEGREES AND RADIANS

Convert the following from degrees to radians.

1. 0°

2. 30°

3. 45°

4. 90°

5. 180°

6. 225°

7. 270°

8. 360°

9. −45°

10. 42.6°

Convert the following from radians to degrees.

11. $\dfrac{\pi}{6}$ Rad

12. $\dfrac{\pi}{4}$ Rad

13. $\dfrac{\pi}{2}$ Rad

14. $\dfrac{2\pi}{3}$ Rad

15. π Rad

16. $\dfrac{7\pi}{6}$ Rad

17. $\dfrac{3\pi}{2}$ Rad

18. 6 Rad

19. −4.3 Rad

20. 2.9 Rad

Answer Key

1. $0° = 0\,\text{Rad}$

2. $30° = \dfrac{\pi}{6}\,\text{Rad}$

3. $45° = \dfrac{\pi}{4}\,\text{Rad}$

4. $90° = \dfrac{\pi}{2}\,\text{Rad}$

5. $180° = \pi\,\text{Rad}$

6. $225° = \dfrac{5\pi}{4}\,\text{Rad}$

7. $270° = \dfrac{3\pi}{2}\,\text{Rad}$

8. $360° = 2\pi\,\text{Rad}$

9. $-45° = -\dfrac{\pi}{4}\,\text{Rad}$

10. $42.6° = 0.74\,\text{Rad}$

11. $\dfrac{\pi}{6}\,\text{Rad} = 30°$

12. $\dfrac{\pi}{4}\,\text{Rad} = 45°$

13. $\dfrac{\pi}{2}\,\text{Rad} = 90°$

14. $\dfrac{2\pi}{3}\,\text{Rad} = 120°$

15. $\pi\,\text{Rad} = 180°$

16. $\dfrac{7\pi}{6}\,\text{Rad} = 210°$

17. $\dfrac{3\pi}{2}\,\text{Rad} = 270°$

18. $6\,\text{Rad} = 343.8°$

19. $-4.3\,\text{Rad} = -246.4°$

20. $2.9\,\text{Rad} = 166.2°$

Solutions

1. $0° \cdot \dfrac{\pi \, \text{Rad}}{180°} = 0 \, \text{Rad}$

2. $30° \cdot \dfrac{\pi \, \text{Rad}}{180°} = 30° \cdot \dfrac{\pi \, \text{Rad}}{30(6)°} = \dfrac{\pi}{6} \, \text{Rad}$

3. $45° \cdot \dfrac{\pi \, \text{Rad}}{180°} = 45° \cdot \dfrac{\pi \, \text{Rad}}{45(4)°} = \dfrac{\pi}{4} \, \text{Rad}$

4. $90° \cdot \dfrac{\pi \, \text{Rad}}{180°} = 90° \cdot \dfrac{\pi \, \text{Rad}}{90(2)°} = \dfrac{\pi}{2} \, \text{Rad}$

5. $180° \cdot \dfrac{\pi \, \text{Rad}}{180°} = \pi \, \text{Rad}$

6. $225° \cdot \dfrac{\pi \, \text{Rad}}{180°} = 5(45)° \cdot \dfrac{\pi \, \text{Rad}}{4(45)°} = \dfrac{5\pi}{4} \, \text{Rad}$

7. $270° \cdot \dfrac{\pi \, \text{Rad}}{180°} = 3(90)° \cdot \dfrac{\pi \, \text{Rad}}{2(90)°} = \dfrac{3\pi}{2} \, \text{Rad}$

8. $360° \cdot \dfrac{\pi \, \text{Rad}}{180°} = 2(180)° \cdot \dfrac{\pi \, \text{Rad}}{180°} = 2\pi \, \text{Rad}$

9. $-45° \cdot \dfrac{\pi \, \text{Rad}}{180°} = -45° \dfrac{\pi \, \text{Rad}}{4(45)°} = -\dfrac{\pi}{4} \, \text{Rad}$

10. $42.6° \cdot \dfrac{\pi \, \text{Rad}}{180°} = \dfrac{42.6(\pi) \, \text{Rad}}{180} = \dfrac{133.83 \, \text{Rad}}{180} = 0.74 \, \text{Rad}$

11. $\dfrac{\pi}{6} \, \text{Rad} \cdot \dfrac{180°}{\pi \, \text{Rad}} = \dfrac{180°}{6} = 30°$

12. $\dfrac{\pi}{4} \, \text{Rad} \cdot \dfrac{180°}{\pi \, \text{Rad}} = \dfrac{180°}{4} = 45°$

13. $\dfrac{\pi}{2} \, \text{Rad} \cdot \dfrac{180°}{\pi \, \text{Rad}} = \dfrac{180°}{2} = 90°$

14. $\dfrac{2\pi}{3} \, \text{Rad} \cdot \dfrac{180°}{\pi \, \text{Rad}} = \dfrac{2(180)°}{3} = \dfrac{2(3)(60)°}{3} = 120°$

15. $\pi \, \text{Rad} \cdot \dfrac{180°}{\pi \, \text{Rad}} = 180°$

16. $\dfrac{7\pi}{6} \, \text{Rad} \cdot \dfrac{180°}{\pi \, \text{Rad}} = \dfrac{7(180)°}{6} = \dfrac{7(6)(30)°}{6} = 210°$

17. $\dfrac{3\pi}{2} \, \text{Rad} \cdot \dfrac{180°}{\pi \, \text{Rad}} = \dfrac{3(180)°}{2} = \dfrac{3(2)(90)°}{2} = 270°$

18. $6\,\text{Rad} \cdot \dfrac{180°}{\pi\,\text{Rad}} = \dfrac{6\,(180)°}{\pi} = \dfrac{1080°}{\pi} = 343.8°$

19. $-4.3\,\text{Rad} \cdot \dfrac{180°}{\pi\,\text{Rad}} = \dfrac{-4.3\,(180)°}{\pi} = \dfrac{-774.0°}{\pi} = -246.4°$

20. $2.9\,\text{Rad} \cdot \dfrac{180°}{\pi\,\text{Rad}} = \dfrac{2.9\,(180)°}{\pi} = \dfrac{522°}{\pi} = 166.2°$

RIGHT TRIANGLES I:
THE PYTHAGOREAN THEOREM

25

For each of these triangles, find the missing side using the Pythagorean Theorem.

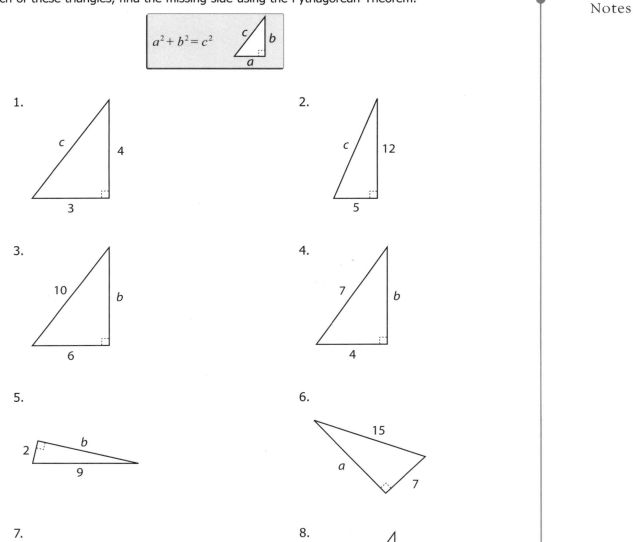

$a^2 + b^2 = c^2$

1.

2.

3.

4.

5.

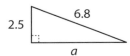

6.

7.

8.

Answer Key

1. $c = 5$
2. $c = 13$
3. $b = 8$
4. $b = 5.74$
5. $b = 8.77$
6. $a = 13.27$
7. $a = 6.32$
8. $b = 1.41$

Solutions

1.

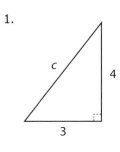

$$a^2 + b^2 = c^2$$
$$3^2 + 4^2 = c^2$$
$$9 + 16 = c^2$$
$$25 = c^2$$
$$\sqrt{25} = c^2$$
$$5 = c$$

2.

$$a^2 + b^2 = c^2$$
$$5^2 + 12^2 = c^2$$
$$25 + 144 = c^2$$
$$169 = c^2$$
$$\sqrt{169} = \sqrt{c^2}$$
$$13 = c$$

3.

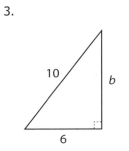

$$a^2 + b^2 = c^2$$
$$6^2 + b^2 = 10^2$$
$$36 + b^2 = 100$$
$$b^2 = 64$$
$$\sqrt{b^2} = \sqrt{64}$$
$$b = 8$$

4.

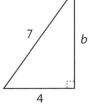

$$a^2 + b^2 = c^2$$
$$4^2 + b^2 = 7^2$$
$$16 + b^2 = 49$$
$$b^2 = 33$$
$$\sqrt{b^2} = \sqrt{33}$$
$$b = 5.74$$

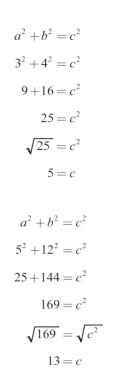

Notes

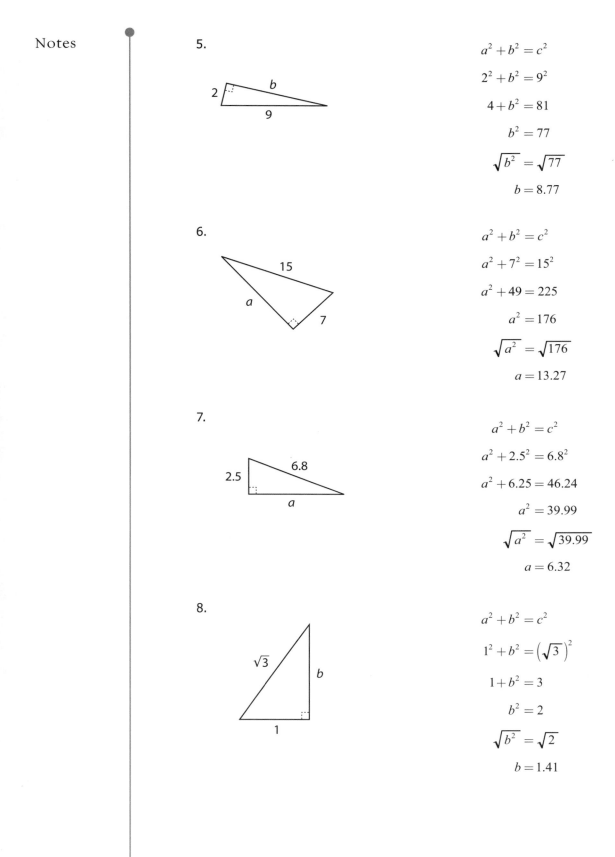

5.

$$a^2 + b^2 = c^2$$
$$2^2 + b^2 = 9^2$$
$$4 + b^2 = 81$$
$$b^2 = 77$$
$$\sqrt{b^2} = \sqrt{77}$$
$$b = 8.77$$

6.

$$a^2 + b^2 = c^2$$
$$a^2 + 7^2 = 15^2$$
$$a^2 + 49 = 225$$
$$a^2 = 176$$
$$\sqrt{a^2} = \sqrt{176}$$
$$a = 13.27$$

7.

$$a^2 + b^2 = c^2$$
$$a^2 + 2.5^2 = 6.8^2$$
$$a^2 + 6.25 = 46.24$$
$$a^2 = 39.99$$
$$\sqrt{a^2} = \sqrt{39.99}$$
$$a = 6.32$$

8.

$$a^2 + b^2 = c^2$$
$$1^2 + b^2 = \left(\sqrt{3}\right)^2$$
$$1 + b^2 = 3$$
$$b^2 = 2$$
$$\sqrt{b^2} = \sqrt{2}$$
$$b = 1.41$$

26

RIGHT TRIANGLES II: THE SIX TRIGONOMETRIC FUNCTIONS

Find the six trigonometric functions $\sin\theta$, $\cos\theta$, $\tan\theta$, $\sec\theta$, $\csc\theta$, and $\cot\theta$ for each of the following right triangles.

$$\sin\theta = \frac{opp}{hyp} \qquad \sec\theta = \frac{hyp}{adj}$$

$$\cos\theta = \frac{adj}{hyp} \qquad \csc\theta = \frac{hyp}{opp}$$

$$\tan\theta = \frac{opp}{adj} \qquad \cot\theta = \frac{adj}{opp}$$

1.

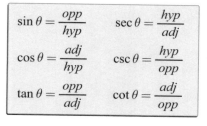

2.

3.

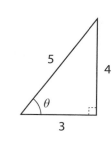

4.

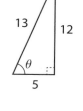

5.

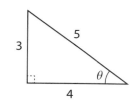

6.

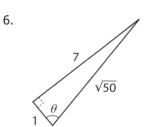

7.

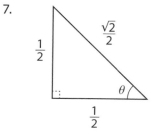

8.

Notes

Answer Key

1. $\sin\theta = \dfrac{4}{5}$ $\qquad$ $\sec\theta = \dfrac{5}{3}$

   $\cos\theta = \dfrac{3}{5}$ $\qquad$ $\csc\theta = \dfrac{5}{4}$

   $\tan\theta = \dfrac{4}{3}$ $\qquad$ $\cot\theta = \dfrac{3}{4}$

2. $\sin\theta = \dfrac{12}{13}$ $\qquad$ $\sec\theta = \dfrac{13}{5}$

   $\cos\theta = \dfrac{5}{13}$ $\qquad$ $\csc\theta = \dfrac{13}{12}$

   $\tan\theta = \dfrac{12}{5}$ $\qquad$ $\cot\theta = \dfrac{5}{12}$

3. $\sin\theta = \dfrac{3}{5}$ $\qquad$ $\sec\theta = \dfrac{5}{4}$

   $\cos\theta = \dfrac{4}{5}$ $\qquad$ $\csc\theta = \dfrac{5}{3}$

   $\tan\theta = \dfrac{3}{4}$ $\qquad$ $\cot\theta = \dfrac{4}{3}$

4. $\sin\theta = \dfrac{\sqrt{2}}{2}$ $\qquad$ $\sec\theta = \sqrt{2}$

   $\cos\theta = \dfrac{\sqrt{2}}{2}$ $\qquad$ $\csc\theta = \sqrt{2}$

   $\tan\theta = 1$ $\qquad$ $\cot\theta = 1$

5. $\sin\theta = \dfrac{5\sqrt{29}}{29}$ $\qquad$ $\sec\theta = \dfrac{\sqrt{29}}{2}$

   $\cos\theta = \dfrac{2\sqrt{29}}{29}$ $\qquad$ $\csc\theta = \dfrac{\sqrt{29}}{5}$

   $\tan\theta = \dfrac{5}{2}$ $\qquad$ $\cot\theta = \dfrac{2}{5}$

6. $\sin\theta = \dfrac{7\sqrt{50}}{50}$ $\qquad$ $\sec\theta = \sqrt{50}$

   $\cos\theta = \dfrac{\sqrt{50}}{50}$ $\qquad$ $\csc\theta = \dfrac{\sqrt{50}}{7}$

   $\tan\theta = 7$ $\qquad$ $\cot\theta = \dfrac{1}{7}$

7. $\sin\theta = \dfrac{\sqrt{2}}{2}$ $\qquad$ $\sec\theta = \sqrt{2}$

   $\cos\theta = \dfrac{\sqrt{2}}{2}$ $\qquad$ $\csc\theta = \sqrt{2}$

   $\tan\theta = 1$ $\qquad$ $\cot\theta = 1$

8. $\sin\theta = 0.44$ $\qquad$ $\sec\theta = \dfrac{2.7}{x}$

   $\cos\theta = \dfrac{x}{2.7}$ $\qquad$ $\csc\theta = 2.25$

   $\tan\theta = \dfrac{1.2}{x}$ $\qquad$ $\cot\theta = \dfrac{x}{1.2}$

Solutions

1.

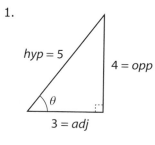

$$\sin\theta = \frac{opp}{hyp} = \frac{4}{5} \qquad \sec\theta = \frac{hyp}{adj} = \frac{5}{3}$$

$$\cos\theta = \frac{adj}{hyp} = \frac{3}{5} \qquad \csc\theta = \frac{hyp}{opp} = \frac{5}{4}$$

$$\tan\theta = \frac{opp}{adj} = \frac{4}{3} \qquad \cot\theta = \frac{adj}{opp} = \frac{3}{4}$$

2.

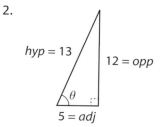

$$\sin\theta = \frac{opp}{hyp} = \frac{12}{13} \qquad \sec\theta = \frac{hyp}{adj} = \frac{13}{5}$$

$$\cos\theta = \frac{adj}{hyp} = \frac{5}{13} \qquad \csc\theta = \frac{hyp}{opp} = \frac{13}{12}$$

$$\tan\theta = \frac{opp}{adj} = \frac{12}{5} \qquad \cot\theta = \frac{adj}{opp} = \frac{5}{12}$$

3.

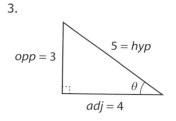

$$\sin\theta = \frac{opp}{hyp} = \frac{3}{5} \qquad \sec\theta = \frac{hyp}{adj} = \frac{5}{4}$$

$$\cos\theta = \frac{adj}{hyp} = \frac{4}{5} \qquad \csc\theta = \frac{hyp}{opp} = \frac{5}{3}$$

$$\tan\theta = \frac{opp}{adj} = \frac{3}{4} \qquad \cot\theta = \frac{adj}{opp} = \frac{4}{3}$$

4.

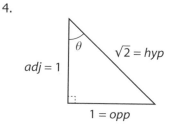

$$\sin\theta = \frac{opp}{hyp} = \frac{1}{\sqrt{2}} = \frac{\sqrt{2}}{2} \qquad \sec\theta = \frac{hyp}{adj} = \frac{\sqrt{2}}{1} = \sqrt{2}$$

$$\cos\theta = \frac{adj}{hyp} = \frac{1}{\sqrt{2}} = \frac{\sqrt{2}}{2} \qquad \csc\theta = \frac{hyp}{opp} = \frac{\sqrt{2}}{1} = \sqrt{2}$$

$$\tan\theta = \frac{opp}{adj} = \frac{1}{1} = 1 \qquad \cot\theta = \frac{adj}{opp} = \frac{1}{1} = 1$$

5.

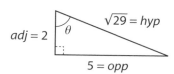

$$\sin\theta = \frac{opp}{hyp} = \frac{5}{\sqrt{29}} = \frac{5\sqrt{29}}{29} \qquad \sec\theta = \frac{hyp}{adj} = \frac{\sqrt{29}}{2}$$

$$\cos\theta = \frac{adj}{hyp} = \frac{2}{\sqrt{29}} = \frac{2\sqrt{29}}{29} \qquad \csc\theta = \frac{hyp}{opp} = \frac{\sqrt{29}}{5}$$

$$\tan\theta = \frac{opp}{adj} = \frac{5}{2} \qquad \cot\theta = \frac{adj}{opp} = \frac{2}{5}$$

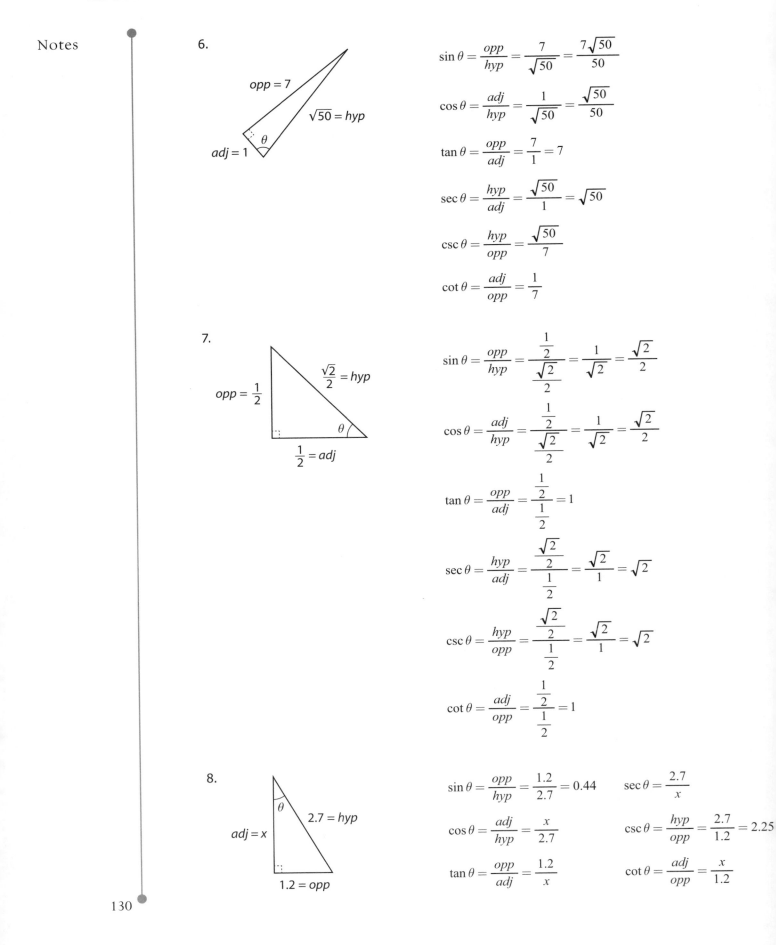

6.

$$\sin \theta = \frac{opp}{hyp} = \frac{7}{\sqrt{50}} = \frac{7\sqrt{50}}{50}$$

$$\cos \theta = \frac{adj}{hyp} = \frac{1}{\sqrt{50}} = \frac{\sqrt{50}}{50}$$

$$\tan \theta = \frac{opp}{adj} = \frac{7}{1} = 7$$

$$\sec \theta = \frac{hyp}{adj} = \frac{\sqrt{50}}{1} = \sqrt{50}$$

$$\csc \theta = \frac{hyp}{opp} = \frac{\sqrt{50}}{7}$$

$$\cot \theta = \frac{adj}{opp} = \frac{1}{7}$$

7.

$$\sin \theta = \frac{opp}{hyp} = \frac{\frac{1}{2}}{\frac{\sqrt{2}}{2}} = \frac{1}{\sqrt{2}} = \frac{\sqrt{2}}{2}$$

$$\cos \theta = \frac{adj}{hyp} = \frac{\frac{1}{2}}{\frac{\sqrt{2}}{2}} = \frac{1}{\sqrt{2}} = \frac{\sqrt{2}}{2}$$

$$\tan \theta = \frac{opp}{adj} = \frac{\frac{1}{2}}{\frac{1}{2}} = 1$$

$$\sec \theta = \frac{hyp}{adj} = \frac{\frac{\sqrt{2}}{2}}{\frac{1}{2}} = \frac{\sqrt{2}}{1} = \sqrt{2}$$

$$\csc \theta = \frac{hyp}{opp} = \frac{\frac{\sqrt{2}}{2}}{\frac{1}{2}} = \frac{\sqrt{2}}{1} = \sqrt{2}$$

$$\cot \theta = \frac{adj}{opp} = \frac{\frac{1}{2}}{\frac{1}{2}} = 1$$

8.

$$\sin \theta = \frac{opp}{hyp} = \frac{1.2}{2.7} = 0.44 \qquad \sec \theta = \frac{2.7}{x}$$

$$\cos \theta = \frac{adj}{hyp} = \frac{x}{2.7} \qquad \csc \theta = \frac{hyp}{opp} = \frac{2.7}{1.2} = 2.25$$

$$\tan \theta = \frac{opp}{adj} = \frac{1.2}{x} \qquad \cot \theta = \frac{adj}{opp} = \frac{x}{1.2}$$

27

RIGHT TRIANGLES III: SOLVING A RIGHT TRIANGLE

Find the missing side, x, of each of the following right triangles.

1.

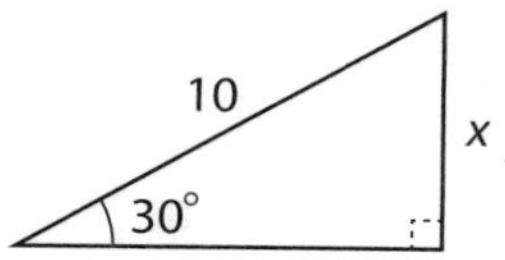

10
x
30°

2.

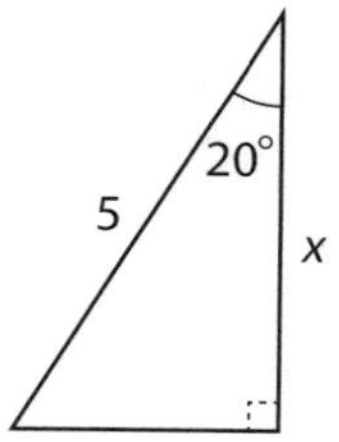

5
20°
x

3.

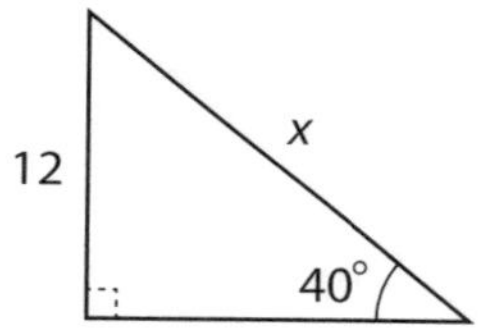

12
x
40°

4.

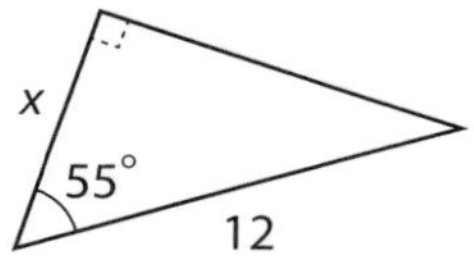

x
55°
12

5.

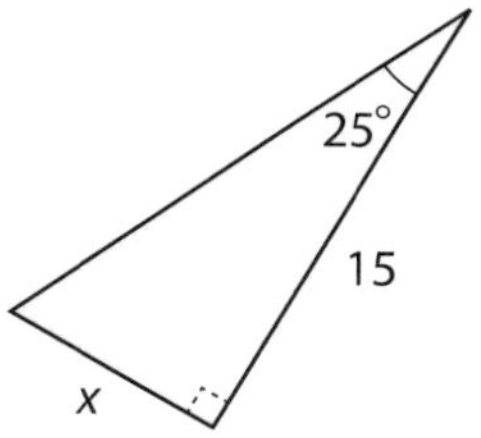

25°
15
x

6.

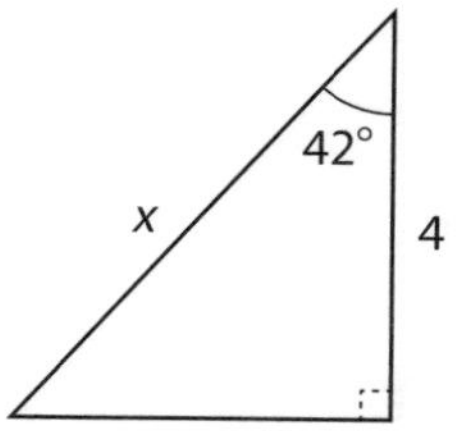

42°
x
4

7.

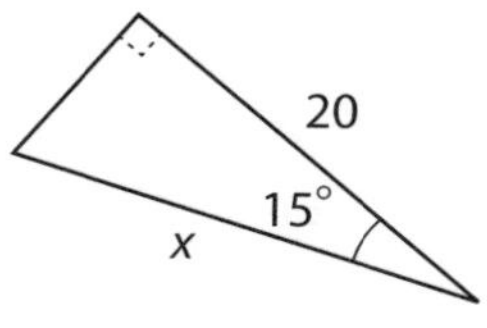

20
15°
x

8.

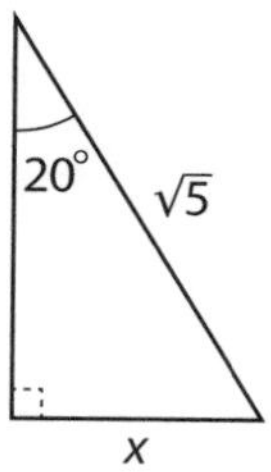

20°
$\sqrt{5}$
x

Answer Key

1. $x = 5$
2. $x = 4.7$
3. $x = 18.66$
4. $x = 6.876$
5. $x = 6.99$
6. $x = 5.384$
7. $x = 20.704$
8. $x = 0.76$

Solutions

1.

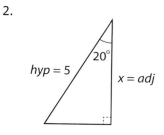

$$\sin \theta = \frac{opp}{hyp}$$

$$\sin 30° = \frac{x}{10}$$

$$10 \sin 30° = x$$

$$10(0.5) = x$$

$$5 = x$$

2.

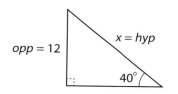

$$\cos \theta = \frac{adj}{hyp}$$

$$\cos 20° = \frac{x}{5}$$

$$5 \cos 20° = x$$

$$5(0.94) = x$$

$$4.7 = x$$

3.

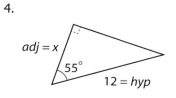

$$\sin \theta = \frac{opp}{hyp}$$

$$\sin 40° = \frac{12}{x}$$

$$x \sin 40° = 12$$

$$x = \frac{12}{\sin 40°}$$

$$x = \frac{12}{0.643}$$

$$x = 18.66$$

4.

$$\cos \theta = \frac{adj}{hyp}$$

$$\cos 55° = \frac{x}{12}$$

$$12 \cos 55° = x$$

$$12(0.573) = x$$

$$6.876 = x$$

Notes

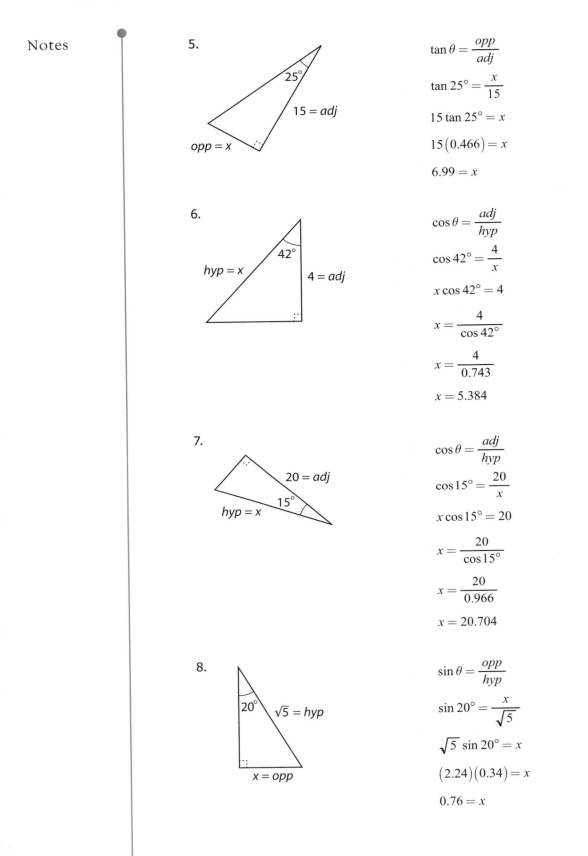

5.

25°

15 = adj

opp = x

$$\tan \theta = \frac{opp}{adj}$$

$$\tan 25° = \frac{x}{15}$$

$$15 \tan 25° = x$$

$$15(0.466) = x$$

$$6.99 = x$$

6.

42°

hyp = x

4 = adj

$$\cos \theta = \frac{adj}{hyp}$$

$$\cos 42° = \frac{4}{x}$$

$$x \cos 42° = 4$$

$$x = \frac{4}{\cos 42°}$$

$$x = \frac{4}{0.743}$$

$$x = 5.384$$

7.

20 = adj

15°

hyp = x

$$\cos \theta = \frac{adj}{hyp}$$

$$\cos 15° = \frac{20}{x}$$

$$x \cos 15° = 20$$

$$x = \frac{20}{\cos 15°}$$

$$x = \frac{20}{0.966}$$

$$x = 20.704$$

8.

20°

$\sqrt{5}$ = hyp

x = opp

$$\sin \theta = \frac{opp}{hyp}$$

$$\sin 20° = \frac{x}{\sqrt{5}}$$

$$\sqrt{5} \sin 20° = x$$

$$(2.24)(0.34) = x$$

$$0.76 = x$$

Inverse Trigonometric Functions I: Introduction to Inverse Trigonometric Functions

Find θ in each of the following using the appropriate inverse trigonometric function.

1. $\sin \theta = 0.5$

2. $\cos \theta = 1$

3. $\tan \theta = 1$

4. $\sin \theta = 0$

5. $\cos \theta = -1$

6. $\tan \theta = 0$

7. $\sin \theta = 0.643$

8. $\cos \theta = 0.866$

9. $\tan \theta = 2.4$

10. $\cos \theta = 0.95$

11. $\sin \theta = -1$

12. $\sin \theta = 0.75$

13. $\tan \theta = -1$

14. $\cos \theta = -0.5$

15. $\sin \theta = 0.45$

16 $\cos \theta = 0.5$

17. $\tan \theta = 1.4$

18. $\tan \theta = -1.4$

19. $\sin \theta = 0.03$

20. $\cos \theta = -0.05$

Notes

Answer Key

1. $\theta = 30°$
2. $\theta = 0°$
3. $\theta = 45°$
4. $\theta = 0°$
5. $\theta = 180°$
6. $\theta = 0°$
7. $\theta = 40°$
8. $\theta = 30°$
9. $\theta = 67.38°$
10. $\theta = 18.19°$
11. $\theta = 270°$
12. $\theta = 48.59°$
13. $\theta = 135°$
14. $\theta = 120°$
15. $\theta = 26.74°$
16. $\theta = 60°$
17. $\theta = 54.46°$
18. $\theta = 305.54°$
19. $\theta = 1.72°$
20. $\theta = 92.87°$

Solutions

1. $\sin\theta = 0.5$

   $\sin^{-1}(\sin\theta) = \sin^{-1}(0.5)$

   $\theta = 30°$

2. $\cos\theta = 1$

   $\cos^{-1}(\cos\theta) = \cos^{-1}(1)$

   $\theta = 0°$

3. $\tan\theta = 1$

   $\tan^{-1}(\tan\theta) = \tan^{-1}(1)$

   $\theta = 45°$

4. $\sin\theta = 0$

   $\sin^{-1}(\sin\theta) = \sin^{-1}(0)$

   $\theta = 0°$

5. $\cos\theta = -1$

   $\cos^{-1}(\cos\theta) = \cos^{-1}(-1)$

   $\theta = 180$

6. $\tan\theta = 0$

   $\tan^{-1}(\tan\theta) = \tan^{-1}(0)$

   $\theta = 0°$

7. $\sin\theta = 0.643$

   $\sin^{-1}(\sin\theta) = \sin^{-1}(0.643)$

   $\theta = 40°$

8. $\cos\theta = 0.866$

   $\cos^{-1}(\cos\theta) = \cos^{-1}(0.866)$

   $\theta = 30°$

9. $\tan\theta = 2.4$

   $\tan^{-1}(\tan\theta) = \tan^{-1}(2.4)$

   $\theta = 67.38°$

10. $\cos\theta = 0.95$

    $\cos^{-1}(\cos\theta) = \cos^{-1}(0.95)$

    $\theta = 18.19°$

11. $\sin\theta = -1$

    $\sin^{-1}(\sin\theta) = \sin^{-1}(-1)$

    $\theta = 270°$

12. $\sin\theta = 0.75$

    $\sin^{-1}(\sin\theta) = \sin^{-1}(0.75)$

    $\theta = 48.59°$

13. $\tan\theta = -1$

    $\tan^{-1}(\tan\theta)\tan^{-1}(-1)$

    $\theta = 135°$

14. $\cos\theta = -0.5$

    $\cos^{-1}(\cos\theta) = \cos^{-1}(-0.5)$

    $\theta = 120°$

15. $\sin\theta = 0.45$

    $\sin^{-1}(\sin\theta) = \sin^{-1}(0.45)$

    $\theta = 26.74°$

16. $\cos\theta = 0.5$

    $\cos^{-1}(\cos\theta) = \cos^{-1}(0.5)$

    $\theta = 60°$

17. $\tan\theta = 1.4$

    $\tan^{-1}(\tan\theta) = \tan^{-1}(1.4)$

    $\theta = 54.46°$

18. $\tan\theta = -1.4$

    $\tan^{-1}(\tan\theta) = \tan^{-1}(-1.4)$

    $\theta = 305.54°$

19. $\sin\theta = 0.03$

    $\sin^{-1}(\sin\theta) = \sin^{-1}(0.03)$

    $\theta = 1.72°$

20. $\cos\theta = -0.05$

    $\cos^{-1}(\cos\theta) = \cos^{-1}(-0.05)$

    $\theta = 92.87°$

29

INVERSE TRIGONOMETRIC FUNCTIONS II: RIGHT TRIANGLES AND INVERSE TRIGONOMETRIC FUNCTIONS

Find θ in each of the following right triangles.

Notes

1.
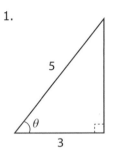

2.
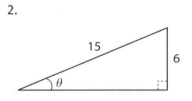

3.
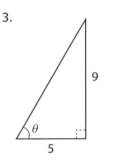

4.
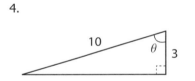

5.
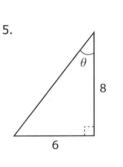

Notes

Answer Key

1. $\theta = 53.1°$
2. $\theta = 23.6°$
3. $\theta = 60.9°$
4. $\theta = 72.5°$
5. $\theta = 36.9°$

Solutions

1.

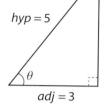

$$\cos\theta = \frac{3}{5}$$

$$\cos\theta = 0.6$$

$$\cos^{-1}(\cos\theta) = \cos^{-1}(0.6)$$

$$\theta = 53.1°$$

2.

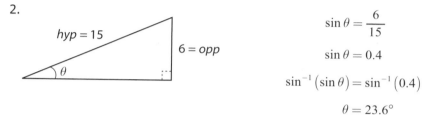

$$\sin\theta = \frac{6}{15}$$

$$\sin\theta = 0.4$$

$$\sin^{-1}(\sin\theta) = \sin^{-1}(0.4)$$

$$\theta = 23.6°$$

3.

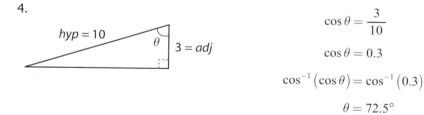

$$\tan\theta = \frac{9}{5}$$

$$\tan\theta = 1.8$$

$$\tan^{-1}(\tan\theta) = \tan^{-1}(1.8)$$

$$\theta = 60.9°$$

4.

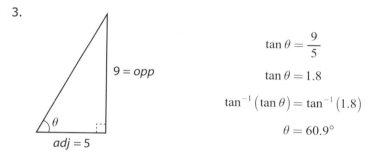

$$\cos\theta = \frac{3}{10}$$

$$\cos\theta = 0.3$$

$$\cos^{-1}(\cos\theta) = \cos^{-1}(0.3)$$

$$\theta = 72.5°$$

5.

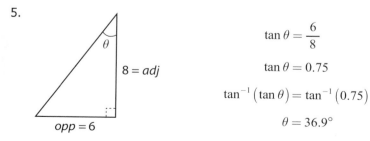

$$\tan\theta = \frac{6}{8}$$

$$\tan\theta = 0.75$$

$$\tan^{-1}(\tan\theta) = \tan^{-1}(0.75)$$

$$\theta = 36.9°$$

TRIGONOMETRIC IDENTITIES

30

Verify each of the following trigonometric identities.

1. $\sin x \sec x = \tan x$

2. $\csc x \cos x = \cot x$

3. $\dfrac{\tan x \cot x}{\csc x} = \sin x$

4. $\sin^2 x \left(1 + \cot^2 x\right) = 1$

5. $\sec x \csc x \tan x = \sec^2 x$

6. $\dfrac{\cot^2 x}{\csc x} + \sin x = \csc x$

7. $\tan x + \dfrac{\cos x}{1 + \sin x} = \sec x$

8. $\dfrac{\cos x}{\sec x} + \dfrac{\sin x}{\csc x} = 1$

9. $\csc^2 x \sec x - \csc x \cot x = \sec x$

10. $\dfrac{1 - \sin x}{\cos x} + \dfrac{\cos x}{1 - \sin x} = 2\sec x$

Solutions

1. $\sin x \sec = \tan x$

$\sin x \left(\dfrac{1}{\cos x} \right) = \tan x$

$\dfrac{\sin x}{\cos x} = \tan x$

$\tan x = \tan x$ ✓

2. $\csc x \cos x = \cot x$

$\left(\dfrac{1}{\sin x} \right) \cos x = \cot x$

$\dfrac{\cos x}{\sin x} = \cot x$

$\cot x = \cot x$ ✓

3. $\dfrac{\tan x \cot x}{\csc x} = \sin x$

$\dfrac{\left(\dfrac{\sin x}{\cos x} \right) \left(\dfrac{\cos x}{\sin x} \right)}{\dfrac{1}{\sin x}} = \sin x$

$\dfrac{1}{\dfrac{1}{\sin x}} = \sin x$

$\sin x = \sin x$ ✓

4. $\sin^2 x \left(1 + \cot^2 x \right) = 1$

$\sin^2 x + \sin^2 x \, \cot^2 x = 1$

$\sin^2 x + \sin^2 x \left(\dfrac{\cos^2 x}{\sin^2 x} \right) = 1$

$\sin^2 x + \cos^2 x = 1$

$1 = 1$ ✓

5. $\sec x \csc x \tan x = \sec^2 x$

$\left(\dfrac{1}{\cos x} \right) \left(\dfrac{1}{\sin x} \right) \left(\dfrac{\sin x}{\cos x} \right) = \sec^2 x$

$\dfrac{1}{\cos^2 x} = \sec^2 x$

$\sec^2 x = \sec^2 x$ ✓

6. $\dfrac{\cot^2 x}{\csc x} + \sin x = \csc x$

$\dfrac{\dfrac{\cos^2 x}{\sin^2 x}}{\dfrac{1}{\sin x}} + \sin x = \csc x$

$\dfrac{\sin x \cos^2 x}{\sin^2 x} + \sin x = \csc x$

$\dfrac{\cos^2 x}{\sin x} + \sin x = \csc x$

$\dfrac{\cos^2 x}{\sin x} + \dfrac{\sin^2 x}{\sin x} = \csc x$

$\dfrac{\cos^2 x + \sin^2 x}{\sin x} = \csc x$

$\dfrac{1}{\sin x} = \csc x$

$\csc x = \csc x$ ✓

7. $\tan x + \dfrac{\cos x}{1 + \sin x} = \sec x$

$\dfrac{\sin x}{\cos x} + \dfrac{\cos x}{1 + \sin x} = \sec x$

$\dfrac{\sin x \left(1 + \sin x \right) + \cos x \left(\cos x \right)}{\cos x \left(1 + \sin x \right)} = \sec x$

$\dfrac{\sin x + \sin^2 x + \cos^2 x}{\cos x \left(1 + \sin x \right)} = \sec x$

$\dfrac{\sin x + 1}{\cos x \left(1 + \sin x \right)} = \sec x$

$\dfrac{1}{\cos x} = \sec x$

$\sec x = \sec x$ ✓

8. $\dfrac{\cos x}{\sec x} + \dfrac{\sin x}{\csc x} = 1$

$\dfrac{\cos x}{\dfrac{1}{\cos x}} + \dfrac{\sin x}{\dfrac{1}{\sin x}} = 1$

$\cos^2 x + \sin^2 x = 1$

$1 = 1$ ✓

9. $\csc^2 x \sec x - \csc x \cot x = \sec x$

$$\frac{1}{\sin^2 x}\left(\frac{1}{\cos x}\right) - \frac{1}{\sin x}\left(\frac{\cos x}{\sin x}\right) = \sec x$$

$$\frac{1}{\sin^2 x \cos x} - \frac{\cos x}{\sin^2 x} = \sec x$$

$$\frac{1}{\sin^2 x \cos x} - \frac{\cos x \cos x}{\sin^2 x \cos x} = \sec x$$

$$\frac{1}{\sin^2 x \cos x} - \frac{\cos^2 x}{\sin^2 x \cos x} = \sec x$$

$$\frac{1 - \cos^2 x}{\sin^2 x \cos x} = \sec x$$

$$\frac{\sin^2 x}{\sin^2 x \cos x} = \sec x$$

$$\frac{1}{\cos x} = \sec x$$

$$\sec x = \sec x \quad \checkmark$$

10. $\dfrac{1 - \sin x}{\cos x} + \dfrac{\cos x}{1 - \sin x} = 2\sec x$

$$\frac{(1 - \sin x)(1 - \sin x)}{\cos x (1 - \sin x)} + \frac{\cos x \cos x}{(1 - \sin x)\cos x} = 2\sec x$$

$$\frac{1 - 2\sin x + \sin^2 x}{\cos x (1 - \sin x)} + \frac{\cos^2 x}{\cos x (1 - \sin x)} = 2\sec x$$

$$\frac{1 - 2\sin x + \sin^2 x + \cos^2 x}{\cos x (1 - \sin x)} = 2\sec x$$

$$\frac{1 - 2\sin x + 1}{\cos x (1 - \sin x)} = 2\sec x$$

$$\frac{2 - 2\sin x}{\cos x (1 - \sin x)} = 2\sec x$$

$$\frac{2(1 - \sin x)}{\cos x (1 - \sin x)} = 2\sec x$$

$$\frac{2}{\cos x} = 2\sec x$$

$$2\left(\frac{1}{\cos x}\right) = 2\sec x$$

$$2\sec x = 2\sec x \quad \checkmark$$

ADDITION AND SUBTRACTION OF VECTORS

31

Find $\mathbf{v}+\mathbf{w}$ and $\mathbf{v}-\mathbf{w}$ for each of the following two-dimensional vectors.

1. $\mathbf{v} = 2\mathbf{i}+3\mathbf{j}$ $\mathbf{w} = 4\mathbf{i}+6\mathbf{j}$

2. $\mathbf{v} = 5\mathbf{i}-2\mathbf{j}$ $\mathbf{w} = 3\mathbf{i}-9\mathbf{j}$

3. $\mathbf{v} = 2\mathbf{i}$ $\mathbf{w} = 4\mathbf{i}+8\mathbf{j}$

4. $\mathbf{v} = -5\mathbf{j}$ $\mathbf{w} = 6\mathbf{i}$

5. $\mathbf{v} = 6.4\mathbf{i}+3.7\mathbf{j}$ $\mathbf{w} = 2.1\mathbf{i}-1.5\mathbf{j}$

For each of the following two-dimensional vectors, find:

a) $2\mathbf{v}+3\mathbf{w}$

b) $-6\mathbf{v}+4\mathbf{w}$

6. $\mathbf{v} = 2\mathbf{i}+\mathbf{j}$ $\mathbf{w} = \mathbf{i}+3\mathbf{j}$

7. $\mathbf{v} = \mathbf{i}-\mathbf{j}$ $\mathbf{w} = 2\mathbf{j}$

8. $\mathbf{v} = 5\mathbf{i}$ $\mathbf{w} = 2\mathbf{i}+\mathbf{j}$

9. $\mathbf{v} = 2.1\mathbf{i}+3.2\mathbf{j}$ $\mathbf{w} = 1.2\mathbf{i}-1.4\mathbf{j}$

10. $\mathbf{v} = -1.6\mathbf{i}-0.4\mathbf{j}$ $\mathbf{w} = 2.4\mathbf{i}+3.1\mathbf{j}$

Find $\mathbf{v}+\mathbf{w}$ and $\mathbf{v}-\mathbf{w}$ for each of the following three-dimensional vectors.

11. $\mathbf{v} = 2\mathbf{i}+3\mathbf{j}+5\mathbf{k}$ $\mathbf{w} = 4\mathbf{i}+2\mathbf{j}+6\mathbf{k}$

12. $\mathbf{v} = \mathbf{i}-\mathbf{j}+\mathbf{k}$ $\mathbf{w} = 2\mathbf{i}-3\mathbf{j}-\mathbf{k}$

13. $\mathbf{v} = 2\mathbf{j}+4\mathbf{k}$ $\mathbf{w} = 3\mathbf{i}+5\mathbf{j}$

14. $\mathbf{v} = 6\mathbf{i}+2\mathbf{k}$ $\mathbf{w} = -\mathbf{j}-\mathbf{k}$

15. $\mathbf{v} = 1.2\mathbf{i}+1.7\mathbf{j}-2.3\mathbf{k}$ $\mathbf{w} = 2.4\mathbf{i}+3.2\mathbf{j}+4.3\mathbf{k}$

Notes

Answer Key

1. $v + w = 6i + 9j$
   $v - w = -2i - 3j$

2. $v + w = 8i - 11j$
   $v - w = 2i + 7j$

3. $v + w = 6i + 8j$
   $v - w = -2i - 8j$

4. $v + w = 6i - 5j$
   $v - w = -6i - 5j$

5. $v + w = 8.5i + 2.2j$
   $v - w = 4.3i + 5.2j$

6.
   a) $2v + 3w = 7i + 11j$
   b) $-6v + 4w = -8i + 6j$

7.
   a) $2v + 3w = 2i + 4j$
   b) $-6v + 4w = -6i + 14j$

8.
   a) $2v + 3w = 16i + 3j$
   b) $-6v + 4w = -22i + 4j$

9.
   a) $2v + 3w = 7.8i + 2.2j$
   b) $-6v + 4w = -7.8i - 24.8j$

10.
   a) $2v + 3w = 4.0i + 8.5j$
   b) $-6v + 4w = 19.2i + 14.8j$

11. $v + w = 6i + 5j + 11k$
    $v - w = -2i + j - k$

12. $v + w = 3i - 4j$
    $v - w = -i + 2j + 2k$

13. $v + w = 3i + 7j + 4k$
    $v - w = -3i - 3j + 4k$

14. $v + w = 6i - j + k$
    $v - w = 6i + j + 3k$

15. $v + w = 3.6i + 4.9j + 2k$
    $v - w = -1.2i - 1.5j - 6.6k$

Solutions

1. $\mathbf{v} = 2\mathbf{i} + 3\mathbf{j}$ $\mathbf{w} = 4\mathbf{i} + 6\mathbf{j}$

   $\mathbf{v} + \mathbf{w} = (2+4)\mathbf{i} + (3+6)\mathbf{j}$

   $\mathbf{v} + \mathbf{w} = 6\mathbf{i} + 9\mathbf{j}$

   $\mathbf{v} - \mathbf{w} = (2-4)\mathbf{i} + (3-6)\mathbf{j}$

   $\mathbf{v} - \mathbf{w} = -2\mathbf{i} - 3\mathbf{j}$

2. $\mathbf{v} = 5\mathbf{i} - 2\mathbf{j}$ $\mathbf{w} = 3\mathbf{i} - 9\mathbf{j}$

   $\mathbf{v} + \mathbf{w} = (5+3)\mathbf{i} + (-2-9)\mathbf{j}$

   $\mathbf{v} + \mathbf{w} = 8\mathbf{i} - 11\mathbf{j}$

   $\mathbf{v} - \mathbf{w} = (5-3)\mathbf{i} + \left(-2-(-9)\right)\mathbf{j}$

   $\mathbf{v} - \mathbf{w} = 2\mathbf{i} + 7\mathbf{j}$

3. $\mathbf{v} = 2\mathbf{i}$ $\mathbf{w} = 4\mathbf{i} + 8\mathbf{j}$

   $\mathbf{v} + \mathbf{w} = (2+4)\mathbf{i} + (0+8)\mathbf{j}$

   $\mathbf{v} + \mathbf{w} = 6\mathbf{i} + 8\mathbf{j}$

   $\mathbf{v} - \mathbf{w} = (2-4)\mathbf{i} + (0-8)\mathbf{j}$

   $\mathbf{v} - \mathbf{w} = -2\mathbf{i} - 8\mathbf{j}$

4. $\mathbf{v} = -5\mathbf{j}$ $\mathbf{w} = 6\mathbf{i}$

   $\mathbf{v} + \mathbf{w} = (0+6)\mathbf{i} + (-5+0)\mathbf{j}$

   $\mathbf{v} + \mathbf{w} = 6\mathbf{i} - 5\mathbf{j}$

   $\mathbf{v} - \mathbf{w} = (0-6)\mathbf{i} + (-5-0)\mathbf{j}$

   $\mathbf{v} - \mathbf{w} = -6\mathbf{i} - 5\mathbf{j}$

5. $\mathbf{v} = 6.4\mathbf{i} + 3.7\mathbf{j}$ $\mathbf{w} = 2.1\mathbf{i} - 1.5\mathbf{j}$

   $\mathbf{v} + \mathbf{w} = (6.4+2.1)\mathbf{i} + (3.7-1.5)\mathbf{j}$

   $\mathbf{v} + \mathbf{w} = 8.5\mathbf{i} + 2.2\mathbf{j}$

   $\mathbf{v} - \mathbf{w} = (6.4-2.1)\mathbf{i} + \left(3.7-(-1.5)\right)\mathbf{j}$

   $\mathbf{v} - \mathbf{w} = 4.3\mathbf{i} + 5.2\mathbf{j}$

6. $\mathbf{v} = 2\mathbf{i} + \mathbf{j}$ $\mathbf{w} = \mathbf{i} + 3\mathbf{j}$

a) $2\mathbf{v} = 2(2\mathbf{i}) + 2(\mathbf{j}) = 4\mathbf{i} + 2\mathbf{j}$

$3\mathbf{w} = 3(\mathbf{i}) + 3(3\mathbf{j}) = 3\mathbf{i} + 9\mathbf{j}$

$2\mathbf{v} + 3\mathbf{w} = (4+3)\mathbf{i} + (2+9)\mathbf{j} = 7\mathbf{i} + 11\mathbf{j}$

b) $-6\mathbf{v} = -6(2\mathbf{i}) + (-6)(\mathbf{j}) = -12\mathbf{i} - 6\mathbf{j}$

$4\mathbf{w} = 4(\mathbf{i}) + 4(3\mathbf{j}) = 4\mathbf{i} + 12\mathbf{j}$

$-6\mathbf{v} + 4\mathbf{w} = (-12+4)\mathbf{i} + (-6+12)\mathbf{j} = -8\mathbf{i} + 6\mathbf{j}$

7. $\mathbf{v} = \mathbf{i} - \mathbf{j}$ $\mathbf{w} = 2\mathbf{j}$

a) $2\mathbf{v} = 2(\mathbf{i}) + 2(-\mathbf{j}) = 2\mathbf{i} - 2\mathbf{j}$

$3\mathbf{w} = 3(2\mathbf{j}) = 6\mathbf{j}$

$2\mathbf{v} + 3\mathbf{w} = (2+0)\mathbf{i} + (-2+6)\mathbf{j} = 2\mathbf{i} + 4\mathbf{j}$

b) $-6\mathbf{v} = -6(\mathbf{i}) + (-6)(-\mathbf{j}) = -6\mathbf{i} + 6\mathbf{j}$

$4\mathbf{w} = 4(2\mathbf{j}) = 8\mathbf{j}$

$-6\mathbf{v} + 4\mathbf{w} = (-6+0)\mathbf{i} + (6+8)\mathbf{j} = -6\mathbf{i} + 14\mathbf{j}$

8. $\mathbf{v} = 5\mathbf{i}$ $\mathbf{w} = 2\mathbf{i} + \mathbf{j}$

a) $2\mathbf{v} = 2(5\mathbf{i}) = 10\mathbf{i}$

$3\mathbf{w} = 3(2\mathbf{i}) + 3(\mathbf{j}) = 6\mathbf{i} + 3\mathbf{j}$

$2\mathbf{v} + 3\mathbf{w} = (10+6)\mathbf{i} + (0+3)\mathbf{j} = 16\mathbf{i} + 3\mathbf{j}$

b) $-6\mathbf{v} = -6(5\mathbf{i}) = -30\mathbf{i}$

$4\mathbf{w} = 4(2\mathbf{i}) + 4(\mathbf{j}) = 8\mathbf{i} + 4\mathbf{j}$

$-6\mathbf{v} + 4\mathbf{w} = (-30+8)\mathbf{i} + (0+4)\mathbf{j} = -22\mathbf{i} + 4\mathbf{j}$

9. $\mathbf{v} = 2.1\mathbf{i} + 3.2\mathbf{j}$ $\mathbf{w} = 1.2\mathbf{i} - 1.4\mathbf{j}$

a) $2\mathbf{v} = 2(2.1\mathbf{i}) + 2(3.2\mathbf{j}) = 4.2\mathbf{i} + 6.4\mathbf{j}$

$3\mathbf{w} = 3(1.2\mathbf{i}) + 3(-1.4\mathbf{j}) = 3.6\mathbf{i} - 4.2\mathbf{j}$

$2\mathbf{v} + 3\mathbf{w} = (4.2+3.6)\mathbf{i} + (6.4-4.2)\mathbf{j} = 7.8\mathbf{i} + 2.2\mathbf{j}$

calculation cont. on next page...

Solution #9 from previous page...

b) $-6\mathbf{v} = -6(2.1\mathbf{i}) + (-6)(3.2\mathbf{j}) = -12.6\mathbf{i} - 19.2\mathbf{j}$

$4\mathbf{w} = 4(1.2\mathbf{i}) + 4(-1.4\mathbf{j}) = 4.8\mathbf{i} - 5.6\mathbf{j}$

$-6\mathbf{v} + 4\mathbf{w} = (-12.6 + 4.8)\mathbf{i} + (-19.2 - 5.6)\mathbf{j} = -7.8\mathbf{i} - 24.8\mathbf{j}$

10. $\mathbf{v} = -1.6\mathbf{i} - 0.4\mathbf{j} \qquad \mathbf{w} = 2.4\mathbf{i} + 3.1\mathbf{j}$

a) $2\mathbf{v} = 2(-1.6\mathbf{i}) + 2(-0.4\mathbf{j}) = -3.2\mathbf{i} - 0.8\mathbf{j}$

$3\mathbf{w} = 3(2.4\mathbf{i}) + 3(3.1\mathbf{j}) = 7.2\mathbf{i} + 9.3\mathbf{j}$

$2\mathbf{v} + 3\mathbf{w} = (-3.2 + 7.2)\mathbf{i} + (-0.8 + 9.3)\mathbf{j} = 4.0\mathbf{i} + 8.5\mathbf{j}$

b) $-6\mathbf{v} = -6(-1.6\mathbf{i}) + (-6)(-0.4\mathbf{j}) = 9.6\mathbf{i} + 2.4\mathbf{j}$

$4\mathbf{w} = 4(2.4\mathbf{i}) + 4(3.1\mathbf{j}) = 9.6\mathbf{i} + 12.4\mathbf{j}$

$-6\mathbf{v} + 4\mathbf{w} = (9.6 + 9.6)\mathbf{i} + (2.4 + 12.4)\mathbf{j} = 19.2\mathbf{i} + 14.8\mathbf{j}$

11. $\mathbf{v} = 2\mathbf{i} + 3\mathbf{j} + 5\mathbf{k} \qquad \mathbf{w} = 4\mathbf{i} + 2\mathbf{j} + 6\mathbf{k}$

$\mathbf{v} + \mathbf{w} = (2 + 4)\mathbf{i} + (3 + 2)\mathbf{j} + (5 + 6)\mathbf{k} = 6\mathbf{i} + 5\mathbf{j} + 11\mathbf{k}$

$\mathbf{v} - \mathbf{w} = (2 - 4)\mathbf{i} + (3 - 2)\mathbf{j} + (5 - 6)\mathbf{k} = -2\mathbf{i} + \mathbf{j} - \mathbf{k}$

12. $\mathbf{v} = \mathbf{i} - \mathbf{j} + \mathbf{k} \qquad \mathbf{w} = 2\mathbf{i} - 3\mathbf{j} - \mathbf{k}$

$\mathbf{v} + \mathbf{w} = (1 + 2)\mathbf{i} + (-1 - 3)\mathbf{j} + (1 - 1)\mathbf{k} = 3\mathbf{i} - 4\mathbf{j}$

$\mathbf{v} - \mathbf{w} = (1 - 2)\mathbf{i} + (-1 - (-3))\mathbf{j} + (1 - (-1))\mathbf{k} = -\mathbf{i} + 2\mathbf{j} + 2\mathbf{k}$

13. $\mathbf{v} = 2\mathbf{j} + 4\mathbf{k} \qquad \mathbf{w} = 3\mathbf{i} + 5\mathbf{j}$

$\mathbf{v} + \mathbf{w} = (0 + 3)\mathbf{i} + (2 + 5)\mathbf{j} + (4 + 0)\mathbf{k} = 3\mathbf{i} + 7\mathbf{j} + 4\mathbf{k}$

$\mathbf{v} - \mathbf{w} = (0 - 3)\mathbf{i} + (2 - 5)\mathbf{j} + (4 - 0)\mathbf{k} = -3\mathbf{i} - 3\mathbf{j} + 4\mathbf{k}$

14. $\mathbf{v} = 6\mathbf{i} + 2\mathbf{k} \qquad \mathbf{w} = -\mathbf{j} - \mathbf{k}$

$\mathbf{v} + \mathbf{w} = (6 + 0)\mathbf{i} + (0 - 1)\mathbf{j} + (2 - 1)\mathbf{k} = 6\mathbf{i} - \mathbf{j} + \mathbf{k}$

$\mathbf{v} - \mathbf{w} = (6 - 0)\mathbf{i} + (0 - (-1))\mathbf{j} + (2 - (-1))\mathbf{k} = 6\mathbf{i} + \mathbf{j} + 3\mathbf{k}$

15. $\mathbf{v} = 1.2\mathbf{i} + 1.7\mathbf{j} - 2.3\mathbf{k} \qquad \mathbf{w} = 2.4\mathbf{i} + 3.2\mathbf{j} + 4.3\mathbf{k}$

$\mathbf{v} + \mathbf{w} = (1.2 + 2.4)\mathbf{i} + (1.7 + 3.2)\mathbf{j} + (-2.3 + 4.3)\mathbf{k} = 3.6\mathbf{i} + 4.9\mathbf{j} + 2\mathbf{k}$

$\mathbf{v} - \mathbf{w} = (1.2 - 2.4)\mathbf{i} + (1.7 - 3.2)\mathbf{j} + (-2.3 - 4.3)\mathbf{k} = -1.2\mathbf{i} - 1.5\mathbf{j} - 6.6\mathbf{k}$

FINDING THE MAGNITUDE OF A VECTOR

Find the magnitude of each of the following two-dimensional vectors.

$$\mathbf{v} = a\mathbf{i} + b\mathbf{j}$$

$$\|\mathbf{v}\| = \sqrt{a^2 + b^2}$$

Notes

1. $\mathbf{v} = 2\mathbf{i} + 3\mathbf{j}$

2. $\mathbf{v} = \mathbf{i} - \mathbf{j}$

3. $\mathbf{v} = 4\mathbf{i}$

4. $\mathbf{v} = -6\mathbf{j}$

5. $\mathbf{v} = \sqrt{2}\,\mathbf{i} + 3\mathbf{j}$

6. $\mathbf{v} = -\mathbf{i} - \sqrt{5}\,\mathbf{j}$

7. $\mathbf{v} = 1.2\mathbf{i} + 1.5\mathbf{j}$

8. $\mathbf{v} = \dfrac{1}{2}\mathbf{i} + \dfrac{1}{3}\mathbf{j}$

9. $\mathbf{v} = \sqrt{3}\,\mathbf{i} + \dfrac{1}{4}\mathbf{j}$

10. $\mathbf{v} = -0.6\mathbf{j}$

Find the magnitude of each of the following three-dimensional vectors.

$$\mathbf{v} = a\mathbf{i} + b\mathbf{j} + c\mathbf{k}$$

$$\|\mathbf{v}\| = \sqrt{a^2 + b^2 + c^2}$$

11. $\mathbf{v} = 2\mathbf{i} + 5\mathbf{j} + \mathbf{k}$

12. $\mathbf{v} = -3\mathbf{i} + 4\mathbf{k}$

13. $\mathbf{v} = 6\mathbf{i} - 5\mathbf{j} - \mathbf{k}$

14. $\mathbf{v} = \sqrt{2}\,\mathbf{i} + \mathbf{j} + \mathbf{k}$

15. $\mathbf{v} = 7\mathbf{i} - \sqrt{3}\,\mathbf{j} + 2\mathbf{k}$

16. $\mathbf{v} = \dfrac{1}{2}\mathbf{i} + \dfrac{1}{2}\mathbf{j} + \dfrac{1}{4}\mathbf{k}$

17. $\mathbf{v} = -\mathbf{k}$

18. $\mathbf{v} = 1.4\mathbf{i} - 0.6\mathbf{j} + 2.3\mathbf{k}$

19. $\mathbf{v} = \sqrt{3}\,\mathbf{i} - 1.2\mathbf{k}$

20. $\mathbf{v} = \dfrac{\sqrt{2}}{2}\mathbf{i} + \dfrac{\sqrt{3}}{2}\mathbf{j} + \dfrac{1}{2}\mathbf{k}$

Notes

Answer Key

1. $\|\mathbf{v}\| = \sqrt{13}$

2. $\|\mathbf{v}\| = \sqrt{2}$

3. $\|\mathbf{v}\| = 14$

4. $\|\mathbf{v}\| = 6$

5. $\|\mathbf{v}\| = \sqrt{11}$

6. $\|\mathbf{v}\| = \sqrt{6}$

7. $\|\mathbf{v}\| = 1.92$

8. $\|\mathbf{v}\| = \dfrac{\sqrt{13}}{6}$

9. $\|\mathbf{v}\| = \dfrac{7}{4}$

10. $\|\mathbf{v}\| = 0.6$

11. $\|\mathbf{v}\| = \sqrt{30}$

12. $\|\mathbf{v}\| = 5$

13. $\|\mathbf{v}\| = \sqrt{62}$

14. $\|\mathbf{v}\| = 2$

15. $\|\mathbf{v}\| = 2\sqrt{14}$

16. $\|\mathbf{v}\| = \dfrac{3}{4}$

17. $\|\mathbf{v}\| = 1$

18. $\|\mathbf{v}\| = 2.76$

19. $\|\mathbf{v}\| = 2.11$

20. $\|\mathbf{v}\| = \dfrac{\sqrt{6}}{2}$

Solutions

1. $\mathbf{v} = 2\mathbf{i} + 3\mathbf{j}$

$\|\mathbf{v}\| = \sqrt{2^2 + 3^2} = \sqrt{4+9} = \sqrt{13}$

2. $\mathbf{v} = \mathbf{i} - \mathbf{j}$

$\|\mathbf{v}\| = \sqrt{1^2 + (-1)^2} = \sqrt{1+1} = \sqrt{2}$

3. $\mathbf{v} = 4\mathbf{i}$

$\|\mathbf{v}\| = \sqrt{4^2 + 0^2} = \sqrt{16} = 4$

4. $\mathbf{v} = -6\mathbf{j}$

$\|\mathbf{v}\| = \sqrt{0^2 + (-6)^2} = \sqrt{36} = 6$

5. $\mathbf{v} = \sqrt{2}\,\mathbf{i} + 3\mathbf{j}$

$\|\mathbf{v}\| = \sqrt{\left(\sqrt{2}\right)^2 + 3^2} = \sqrt{2+9} = \sqrt{11}$

6. $\mathbf{v} = -\mathbf{i} - \sqrt{5}\,\mathbf{j}$

$\|\mathbf{v}\| = \sqrt{(-1)^2 + \left(-\sqrt{5}\right)^2} = \sqrt{1+5} = \sqrt{6}$

7. $\mathbf{v} = 1.2\mathbf{i} + 1.5\mathbf{j}$

$\|\mathbf{v}\| = \sqrt{1.2^2 + 1.5^2} = \sqrt{3.69} = 1.92$

8. $\mathbf{v} = \dfrac{1}{2}\mathbf{i} + \dfrac{1}{3}\mathbf{j}$

$\|\mathbf{v}\| = \sqrt{\left(\dfrac{1}{2}\right)^2 + \left(\dfrac{1}{3}\right)^2} = \sqrt{\dfrac{1}{4} + \dfrac{1}{9}} = \sqrt{\dfrac{9}{36} + \dfrac{4}{36}} = \sqrt{\dfrac{13}{36}} = \dfrac{\sqrt{13}}{6}$

9. $\mathbf{v} = \sqrt{3}\,\mathbf{i} + \dfrac{1}{4}\mathbf{j}$

$\|\mathbf{v}\| = \sqrt{\left(\sqrt{3}\right)^2 + \left(\dfrac{1}{4}\right)^2} = \sqrt{3 + \dfrac{1}{16}} = \sqrt{\dfrac{48}{16} + \dfrac{1}{16}} = \sqrt{\dfrac{49}{16}} = \dfrac{7}{4}$

10. $\mathbf{v} = -0.6\mathbf{j}$

$\|\mathbf{v}\| = \sqrt{0^2 + (-0.6)^2} = \sqrt{0.36} = 0.6$

11. $\mathbf{v} = 2\mathbf{i} + 5\mathbf{j} + \mathbf{k}$

$\|\mathbf{v}\| = \sqrt{2^2 + 5^2 + 1^2} = \sqrt{4+25+1} = \sqrt{30}$

12. $\mathbf{v} = -3\mathbf{i} + 4\mathbf{k}$

$\|\mathbf{v}\| = \sqrt{(-3)^2 + 0^2 + 4^2} = \sqrt{9+16} = \sqrt{25} = 5$

13. $\mathbf{v} = 6\mathbf{i} - 5\mathbf{j} - \mathbf{k}$

$$\|\mathbf{v}\| = \sqrt{6^2 + (-5)^2 + (-1)^2} = \sqrt{36 + 25 + 1} = \sqrt{62}$$

14. $\mathbf{v} = \sqrt{2}\,\mathbf{i} + \mathbf{j} + \mathbf{k}$

$$\|\mathbf{v}\| = \sqrt{\left(\sqrt{2}\right)^2 + 1^2 + 1^2} = \sqrt{2 + 2} = \sqrt{4} = 2$$

15. $\mathbf{v} = 7\mathbf{i} - \sqrt{3}\,\mathbf{j} + 2\mathbf{k}$

$$\|\mathbf{v}\| = \sqrt{7^2 + \left(-\sqrt{3}\right)^2 + 2^2} = \sqrt{49 + 3 + 4} = \sqrt{56} = 2\sqrt{14}$$

16. $\mathbf{v} = \dfrac{1}{2}\mathbf{i} + \dfrac{1}{2}\mathbf{j} + \dfrac{1}{4}\mathbf{k}$

$$\|\mathbf{v}\| = \sqrt{\left(\dfrac{1}{2}\right)^2 + \left(\dfrac{1}{2}\right)^2 + \left(\dfrac{1}{4}\right)^2} = \sqrt{\dfrac{1}{4} + \dfrac{1}{4} + \dfrac{1}{16}} = \sqrt{\dfrac{9}{16}} = \dfrac{3}{4}$$

17. $\mathbf{v} = -\mathbf{k}$

$$\|\mathbf{v}\| = \sqrt{0^2 + 0^2 + (-1)^2} = \sqrt{1} = 1$$

18. $\mathbf{v} = 1.4\mathbf{i} - 0.6\mathbf{j} + 2.3\mathbf{k}$

$$\|\mathbf{v}\| = \sqrt{1.4^2 + (-0.6)^2 + 2.3^2} = \sqrt{1.96 + 0.36 + 5.29} = \sqrt{7.61} = 2.76$$

19. $\mathbf{v} = \sqrt{3}\,\mathbf{i} - 1.2\mathbf{k}$

$$\|\mathbf{v}\| = \sqrt{\left(\sqrt{3}\right)^2 + (-1.2)^2} = \sqrt{3 + 1.44} = \sqrt{4.44} = 2.11$$

20. $\mathbf{v} = \dfrac{\sqrt{2}}{2}\mathbf{i} + \dfrac{\sqrt{3}}{2}\mathbf{j} + \dfrac{1}{2}\mathbf{k}$

$$\|\mathbf{v}\| = \sqrt{\left(\dfrac{\sqrt{2}}{2}\right)^2 + \left(\dfrac{\sqrt{3}}{2}\right)^2 + \left(\dfrac{1}{2}\right)^2} = \sqrt{\dfrac{2}{4} + \dfrac{3}{4} + \dfrac{1}{4}} = \sqrt{\dfrac{6}{4}} = \dfrac{\sqrt{6}}{2}$$

THE DOT PRODUCT OF TWO VECTORS

33

Find **u** • **v** for each of the following.

> Given two vectors
> $$\mathbf{u} = a_1\mathbf{i} + b_1\mathbf{j}$$
> $$\mathbf{v} = a_2\mathbf{i} + b_2\mathbf{j}$$
> the dot product, **u** • **v**, is found by
> $$\mathbf{u} \bullet \mathbf{v} = a_1 a_2 + b_1 b_2$$

1. $\mathbf{u} = 2\mathbf{i} + 4\mathbf{j}$ $\mathbf{v} = 3\mathbf{i} + 6\mathbf{j}$

2. $\mathbf{u} = -3\mathbf{i} + 2\mathbf{j}$ $\mathbf{v} = \mathbf{i} + 5\mathbf{j}$

3. $\mathbf{u} = 2.6\mathbf{i} + 3.7\mathbf{j}$ $\mathbf{v} = 5.1\mathbf{i} + 8.2\mathbf{j}$

4. $\mathbf{u} = 6\mathbf{i}$ $\mathbf{v} = 3\mathbf{i} + 2\mathbf{j}$

5. $\mathbf{u} = -4\mathbf{j}$ $\mathbf{v} = 5\mathbf{i}$

Find **A** • **B** for each of the following.

> Given two vectors **A** and **B** separated by an angle of θ :
>
> $$\mathbf{A} \bullet \mathbf{B} = \|\mathbf{A}\| \cdot \|\mathbf{B}\| \cos\theta$$

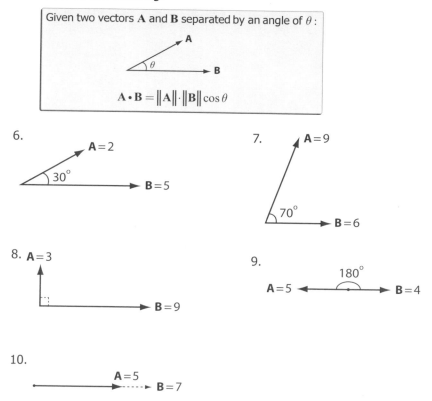

6. A=2, 30°, B=5

7. A=9, 70°, B=6

8. A=3, B=9

9. 180°, A=5, B=4

10. A=5, B=7

Notes

Answer Key

1. $\mathbf{u} \cdot \mathbf{v} = 30$

2. $\mathbf{u} \cdot \mathbf{v} = 7$

3. $\mathbf{u} \cdot \mathbf{v} = 43.6$

4. $\mathbf{u} \cdot \mathbf{v} = 18$

5. $\mathbf{u} \cdot \mathbf{v} = 0$

6. $\mathbf{A} \cdot \mathbf{B} = 8.66$

7. $\mathbf{A} \cdot \mathbf{B} = 18.47$

8. $\mathbf{A} \cdot \mathbf{B} = 0$

9. $\mathbf{A} \cdot \mathbf{B} = -20$

10. $\mathbf{A} \cdot \mathbf{B} = 35$

Solutions

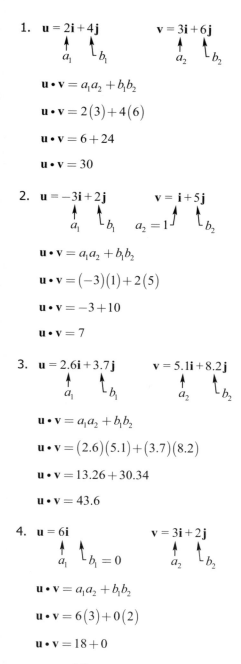

1. $\mathbf{u} = 2\mathbf{i} + 4\mathbf{j}$ $\mathbf{v} = 3\mathbf{i} + 6\mathbf{j}$

       a_1 b_1 a_2 b_2

$\mathbf{u} \cdot \mathbf{v} = a_1 a_2 + b_1 b_2$

$\mathbf{u} \cdot \mathbf{v} = 2(3) + 4(6)$

$\mathbf{u} \cdot \mathbf{v} = 6 + 24$

$\mathbf{u} \cdot \mathbf{v} = 30$

2. $\mathbf{u} = -3\mathbf{i} + 2\mathbf{j}$ $\mathbf{v} = \mathbf{i} + 5\mathbf{j}$

       a_1 b_1 $a_2 = 1$ b_2

$\mathbf{u} \cdot \mathbf{v} = a_1 a_2 + b_1 b_2$

$\mathbf{u} \cdot \mathbf{v} = (-3)(1) + 2(5)$

$\mathbf{u} \cdot \mathbf{v} = -3 + 10$

$\mathbf{u} \cdot \mathbf{v} = 7$

3. $\mathbf{u} = 2.6\mathbf{i} + 3.7\mathbf{j}$ $\mathbf{v} = 5.1\mathbf{i} + 8.2\mathbf{j}$

       a_1 b_1 a_2 b_2

$\mathbf{u} \cdot \mathbf{v} = a_1 a_2 + b_1 b_2$

$\mathbf{u} \cdot \mathbf{v} = (2.6)(5.1) + (3.7)(8.2)$

$\mathbf{u} \cdot \mathbf{v} = 13.26 + 30.34$

$\mathbf{u} \cdot \mathbf{v} = 43.6$

4. $\mathbf{u} = 6\mathbf{i}$ $\mathbf{v} = 3\mathbf{i} + 2\mathbf{j}$

       a_1 $b_1 = 0$ a_2 b_2

$\mathbf{u} \cdot \mathbf{v} = a_1 a_2 + b_1 b_2$

$\mathbf{u} \cdot \mathbf{v} = 6(3) + 0(2)$

$\mathbf{u} \cdot \mathbf{v} = 18 + 0$

$\mathbf{u} \cdot \mathbf{v} = 18$

5. $\mathbf{u} = -4\mathbf{j}$ $\mathbf{v} = 5\mathbf{i}$

   $a_1 = 0$ ↗ ↖ b_1 a_2 ↖ $b_2 = 0$

   $\mathbf{u} \cdot \mathbf{v} = a_1 a_2 + b_1 b_2$

   $\mathbf{u} \cdot \mathbf{v} = 0(5) + (-4)(0)$

   $\mathbf{u} \cdot \mathbf{v} = 0 + 0$

   $\mathbf{u} \cdot \mathbf{v} = 0$

6. $\mathbf{A} \cdot \mathbf{B} = \|\mathbf{A}\| \cdot \|\mathbf{B}\| \cos\theta$

   $\mathbf{A} \cdot \mathbf{B} = 2(5)\cos 30°$

   $\mathbf{A} \cdot \mathbf{B} = 10(0.866)$

   $\mathbf{A} \cdot \mathbf{B} = 8.66$

7. $\mathbf{A} \cdot \mathbf{B} = \|\mathbf{A}\| \cdot \|\mathbf{B}\| \cos\theta$

   $\mathbf{A} \cdot \mathbf{B} = 9(6)\cos 70°$

   $\mathbf{A} \cdot \mathbf{B} = 54(0.342)$

   $\mathbf{A} \cdot \mathbf{B} = 18.47$

8. $\mathbf{A} \cdot \mathbf{B} = \|\mathbf{A}\| \cdot \|\mathbf{B}\| \cos\theta$

   $\mathbf{A} \cdot \mathbf{B} = 3(9)\cos 90°$

   $\mathbf{A} \cdot \mathbf{B} = 27(0)$

   $\mathbf{A} \cdot \mathbf{B} = 0$

9. $\mathbf{A} \cdot \mathbf{B} = \|\mathbf{A}\| \cdot \|\mathbf{B}\| \cos\theta$

   $\mathbf{A} \cdot \mathbf{B} = 4(5)\cos 180°$

   $\mathbf{A} \cdot \mathbf{B} = 20(-1)$

   $\mathbf{A} \cdot \mathbf{B} = -20$

10. Since the vectors lie along one another, $\theta = 0°$.

   Thus,

   $\mathbf{A} \cdot \mathbf{B} = \|\mathbf{A}\| \cdot \|\mathbf{B}\| \cos\theta$

   $\mathbf{A} \cdot \mathbf{B} = 5(7)\cos 0°$

   $\mathbf{A} \cdot \mathbf{B} = 35(1)$

   $\mathbf{A} \cdot \mathbf{B} = 35$

GRAPHING FUNCTIONS I: SIMPLE FUNCTIONS

34

Graph the following functions by plotting points.

1. $f(x) = x + 2$

2. $f(x) = 3x - 1$

3. $f(x) = x^2$

4. $f(x) = x^2 - 1$

5. $f(x) = (x+1)^2$

6. $f(x) = x^3$

7. $f(x) = x^3 + 2$

8. $f(x) = \sqrt{x}$

9. $f(x) = \dfrac{1}{x}$

10. $f(x) = |x|$

11. $f(x) = |x| - 3$

12. $f(x) = \sqrt{x+2}$

13. $f(x) = 3$

14. $f(x) = [\![x]\!]$

15. $f(x) = (x-1)^2 + 3$

16. $f(x) = -x^2$

17. $f(x) = -x^3$

18. $f(x) = |x| + 1$

19. $f(x) = -|x| + 4$

20. $f(x) = -(x+2)^2 - 4$

Solutions

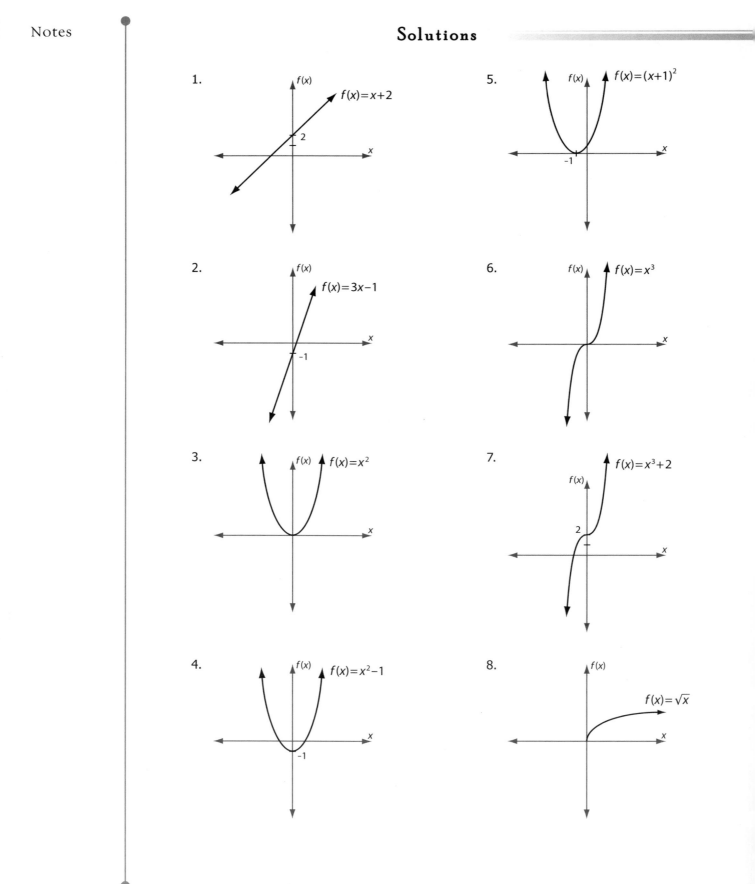

1. $f(x)=x+2$

2. $f(x)=3x-1$

3. $f(x)=x^2$

4. $f(x)=x^2-1$

5. $f(x)=(x+1)^2$

6. $f(x)=x^3$

7. $f(x)=x^3+2$

8. $f(x)=\sqrt{x}$

9.

$$f(x) = \frac{1}{x}$$

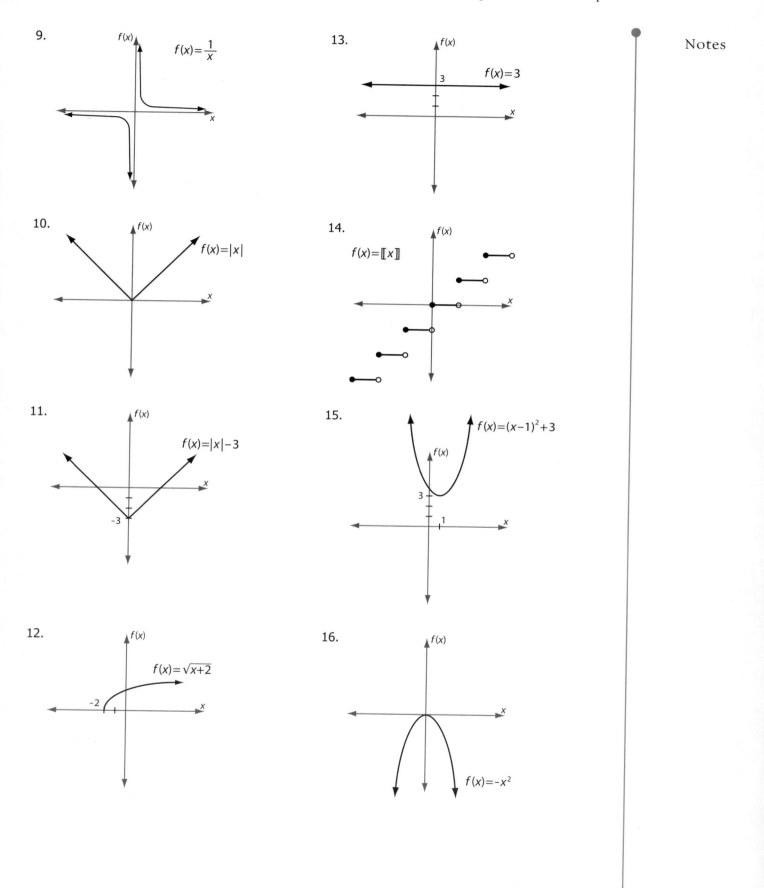

13.

$$f(x) = 3$$

3

Notes

10.

$$f(x) = |x|$$

14.

$$f(x) = [\![x]\!]$$

11.

$$f(x) = |x| - 3$$

-3

15.

$$f(x) = (x-1)^2 + 3$$

3

1

12.

$$f(x) = \sqrt{x+2}$$

-2

16.

$$f(x) = -x^2$$

17.

$f(x) = -x^3$

18.

$f(x) = |x| + 1$

19.

$f(x) = -|x| + 4$

20.

$f(x) = -(x+2)^2 - 4$

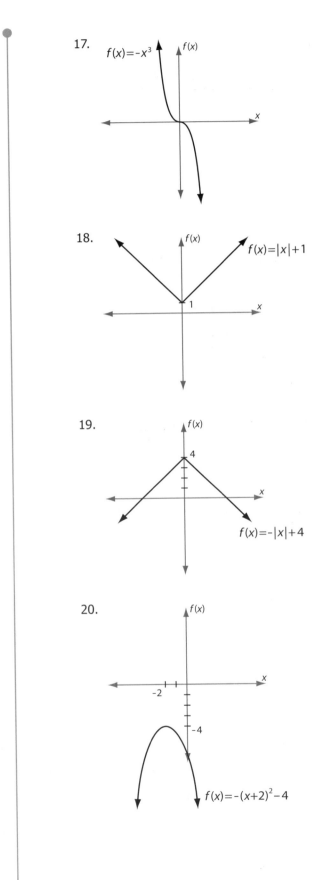

GRAPHING FUNCTIONS II: TRIGONOMETRIC FUNCTIONS

35

Graph the following trigonometric functions by plotting points.

1. $y = \sin x$

2. $y = \cos x$

3. $y = \tan x$

4. $y = 2 \sin x$

5. $y = \cos 4x$

6. $y = 2 \tan x$

7. $y = \sin x + 3$

8. $y = \cot x$

9. $y = \sec x$

10. $y = \csc x$

Solutions

1. $y = \sin x$

x	y
0°	0
15°	0.259
30°	0.5
45°	0.707
60°	0.866
75°	0.966
90°	1.0
105°	0.966
120°	0.866
135°	0.707
150°	0.5
165°	0.259
180°	0
195°	-0.259
210°	-0.5
225°	-0.707
240°	-0.866
255°	-0.966
270°	-1.0
285°	-0.966
300°	-0.866
315°	-0.707
330°	-0.5
345°	-0.259
360°	0

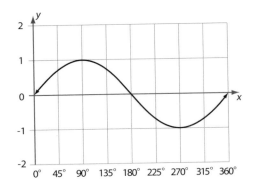

2. $y = \cos x$

x	y
0°	1.0
15°	0.966
30°	0.866
45°	0.707
60°	0.5
75°	0.259
90°	0
105°	-0.259
120°	-0.5
135°	-0.707
150°	-0.866
165°	-0.966
180°	-1.0
195°	-0.966
210°	-0.866
225°	-0.707
240°	-0.5
255°	-0.259
270°	0
285°	0.259
300°	0.5
315°	0.707
330°	0.866
345°	0.966
360°	1.0

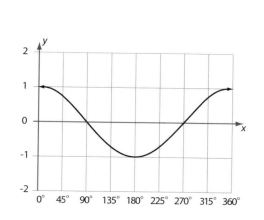

Notes

3. $y = \tan x$

x	y
$0°$	0
$15°$	0.268
$30°$	0.577
$45°$	1.0
$60°$	1.732
$75°$	3.732
$90°$	undefined
$105°$	-3.732
$120°$	-1.732
$135°$	-1.0
$150°$	-0.577
$165°$	-0.268
$180°$	0
$195°$	0.268
$210°$	0.577
$225°$	1.0
$240°$	1.732
$255°$	3.732
$270°$	undefined
$285°$	-3.732
$300°$	-1.732
$315°$	-1.0
$330°$	-0.577
$345°$	-0.268
$360°$	0

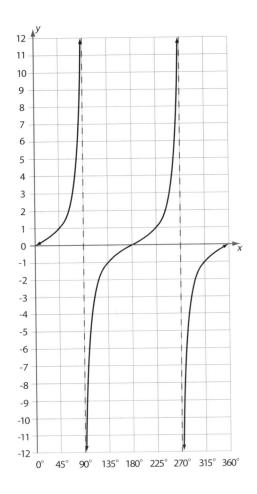

4. $y = 2\sin x$

x	y
0°	0
15°	0.512
30°	1.0
45°	1.414
60°	1.732
75°	1.932
90°	2.0
105°	1.932
120°	1.732
135°	1.414
150°	1.0
165°	0.512
180°	0
195°	-0.512
210°	-1.0
225°	-1.414
240°	-1.732
255°	-1.932
270°	-2.0
285°	-1.932
300°	-1.732
315°	-1.414
330°	-1.0
345°	-0.512
360°	0

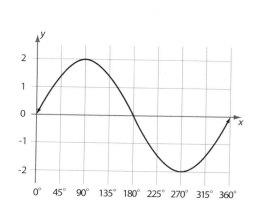

5. $y = \cos 4x$

x	y
0°	1.0
15°	0.5
30°	-0.5
45°	-1.0
60°	-0.5
75°	0.5
90°	1.0
105°	0.5
120°	-0.5
135°	-1.0
150°	-0.5
165°	0.5
180°	1.0
195°	0.5
210°	-0.5
225°	-1.0
240°	-0.5
255°	0.5
270°	1.0
285°	0.5
300°	-0.5
315°	-1.0
330°	-0.5
345°	0.5
360°	1.0

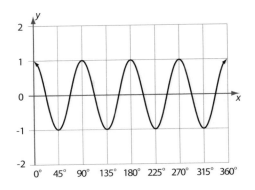

6. $y = 2 \tan x$

x	y
0°	0
15°	0.536
30°	1.154
45°	2.0
60°	3.464
75°	7.464
90°	undefined
105°	-7.464
120°	-3.464
135°	-2.0
150°	-1.154
165°	-0.536
180°	0
195°	0.536
210°	1.154
225°	2.0
240°	3.464
255°	7.464
270°	undefined
285°	-7.464
300°	-3.464
315°	-2.0
330°	-1.154
345°	-0.536
360°	0

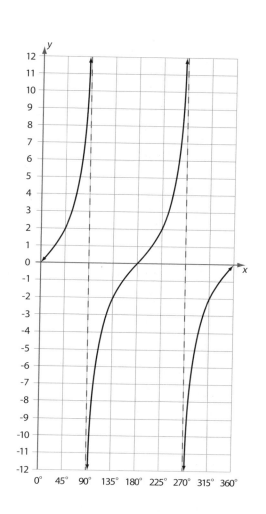

7. $y = \sin x + 3$

x	y
0°	3.0
15°	3.259
30°	3.5
45°	3.707
60°	3.866
75°	3.966
90°	4.0
105°	3.966
120°	3.866
135°	3.707
150°	3.5
165°	3.259
180°	3.0
195°	2.741
210°	2.5
225°	2.293
240°	2.134
255°	2.034
270°	2.0
285°	2.034
300°	2.134
315°	2.293
330°	2.5
345°	2.741
360°	3.0

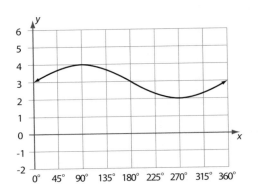

8. $y = \cot x$

x	y
0°	undefined
15°	3.731
30°	1.733
45°	1.0
60°	0.577
75°	0.268
90°	0
105°	-0.268
120°	-0.577
135°	-1.0
150°	-1.733
165°	-3.731
180°	undefined
195°	3.731
210°	1.733
225°	1.0
240°	0.577
255°	0.268
270°	0
285°	-0.268
300°	-0.577
315°	-1.0
330°	-1.733
345°	-3.731
360°	undefined

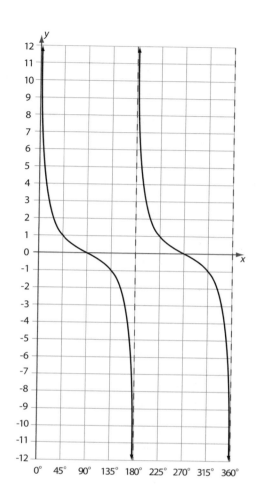

Notes

9. $y = \sec x$

x	y
0°	1.0
15°	1.035
30°	1.155
45°	1.414
60°	2.0
75°	3.861
90°	undefined
105°	-3.861
120°	-2.0
135°	-1.414
150°	-1.155
165°	-1.035
180°	-1.0
195°	-1.035
210°	-1.155
225°	-1.414
240°	-2.0
255°	-3.861
270°	undefined
285°	3.861
300°	2.0
315°	1.414
330°	1.155
345°	1.035
360°	1.0

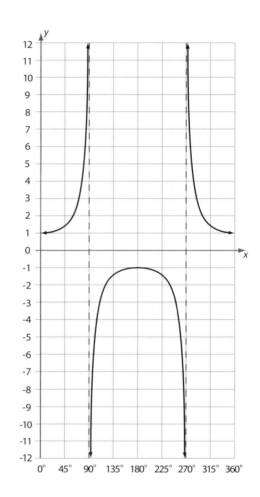

10. $y = \csc x$

x	y
0°	undefined
15°	3.861
30°	2.0
45°	1.414
60°	1.155
75°	1.035
90°	1.0
105°	1.035
120°	1.155
135°	1.414
150°	2.0
165°	3.861
180°	undefined
195°	-3.861
210°	-2.0
225°	-1.414
240°	-1.155
255°	-1.035
270°	-1.0
285°	-1.035
300°	-1.155
315°	-1.414
330°	-2.0
345°	-3.861
360°	undefined

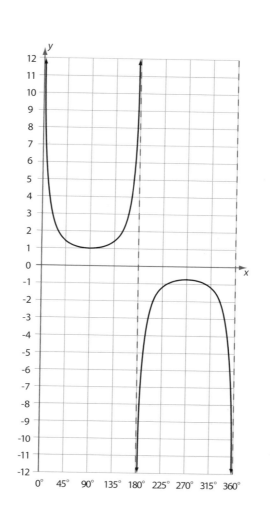

GRAPHING FUNCTIONS III: SHIFT PROPERTIES

Use the given graphs and shift properties to sketch a graph of each of the shifted functions.

Shift Properties

Given the graph of a function $f(x)$,

a) $f(x)+a$ - shifts the graph vertically by a.

b) $f(x+a)$ - shifts the graph horizontally by $-a$.

c) $f(-x)$ - rotates the graph around the y - axis.

d) $-f(x)$ - rotates the graph around the x - axis.

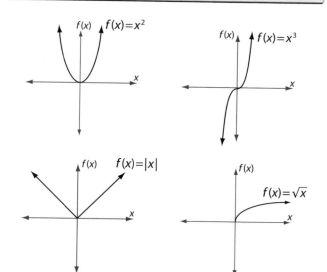

Shifted Functions

1. $f(x)=x^2+1$

2. $f(x)=x^3-2$

3. $f(x)=(x-1)^2$

4. $f(x)=|x|+3$

5. $f(x)=\sqrt{x}-1$

6. $f(x)=-x^2$

7. $f(x)=-x^3$

8. $f(x)=(x+2)^2-4$

9. $f(x)=-|x|+5$

10. $f(x)=-(x+1)^3+2$

Notes

Solutions

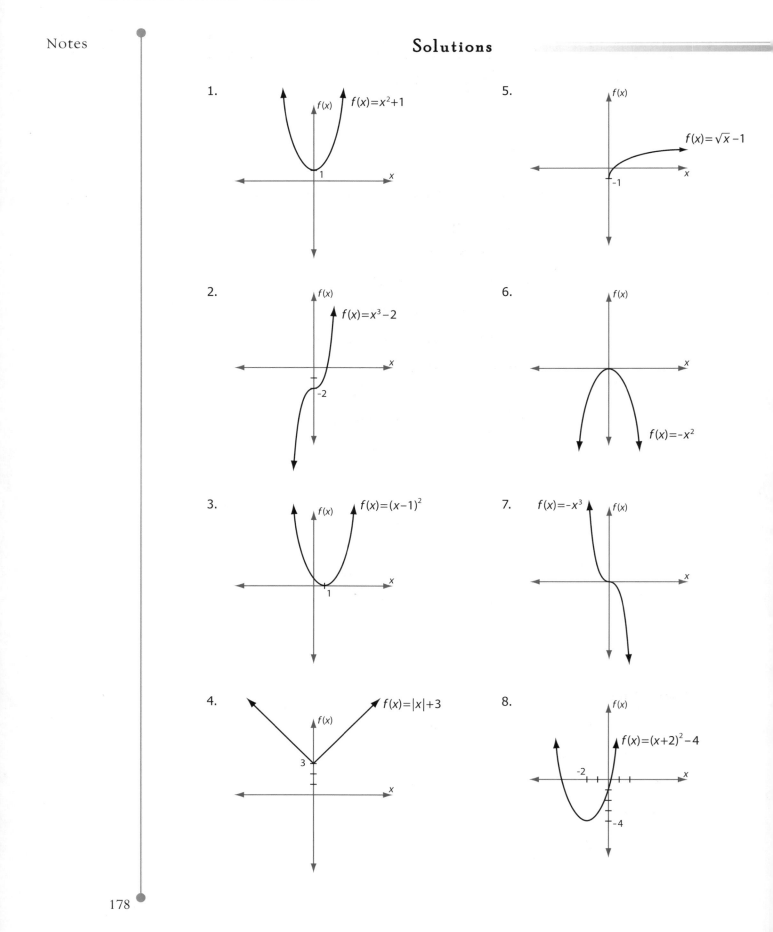

1. $f(x)=x^2+1$

2. $f(x)=x^3-2$

3. $f(x)=(x-1)^2$

4. $f(x)=|x|+3$

5. $f(x)=\sqrt{x}-1$

6. $f(x)=-x^2$

7. $f(x)=-x^3$

8. $f(x)=(x+2)^2-4$

9.

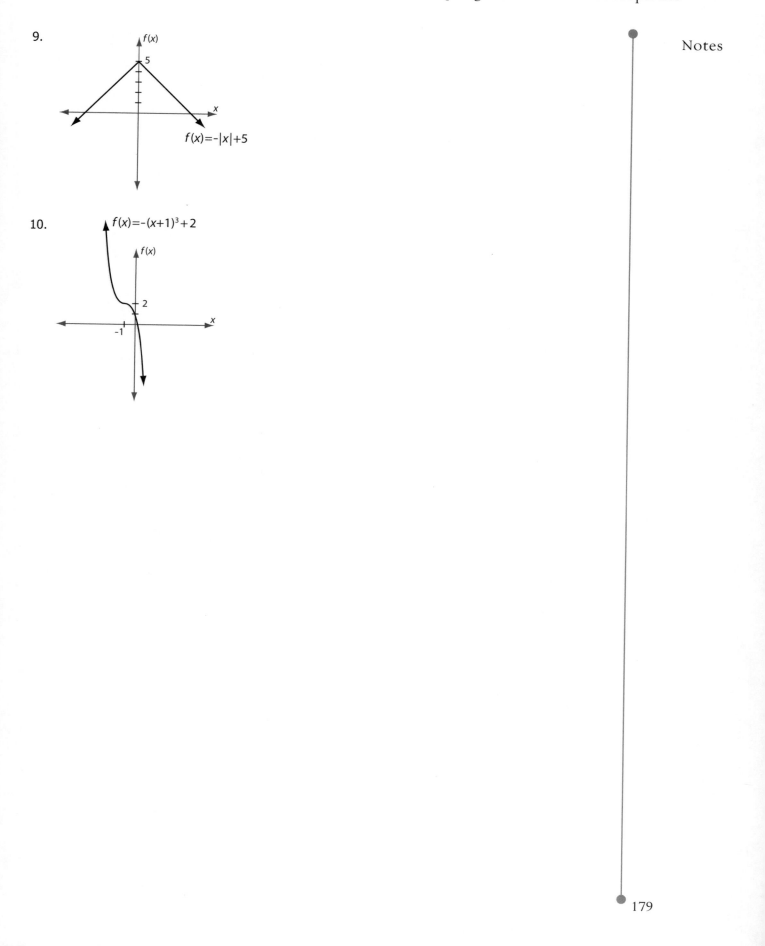

$f(x)=-|x|+5$

10.

$f(x)=-(x+1)^3+2$

GRAPHING COMPLEX NUMBERS

37

Graph the following complex numbers.

1. $2 + 5i$

2. $4 - 6i$

3. $-2 + i$

4. $-3 - i$

5. $1.5 - 2.5i$

6. $\sqrt{3} + \sqrt{2}\,i$

7. $4i$

8. $-5i$

9. $2 - \dfrac{1}{3}i$

10. $\dfrac{\sqrt{3}}{2} + \dfrac{\sqrt{2}}{2}i$

Notes

Notes

Solutions

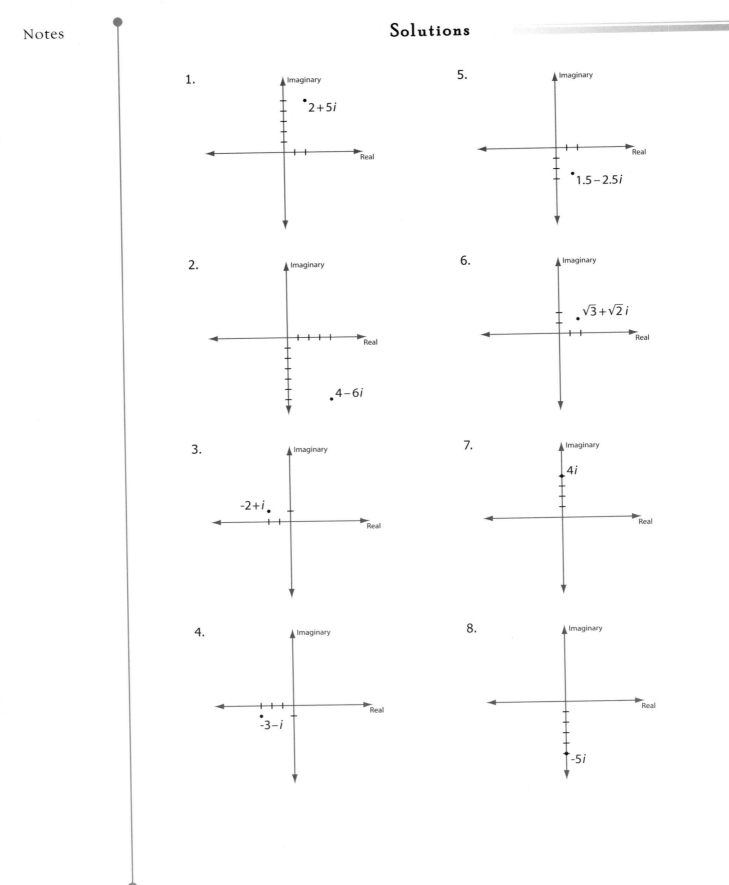

1. 2+5i

2. 4-6i

3. -2+i

4. -3-i

5. 1.5-2.5i

6. √3+√2 i

7. 4i

8. -5i

9.

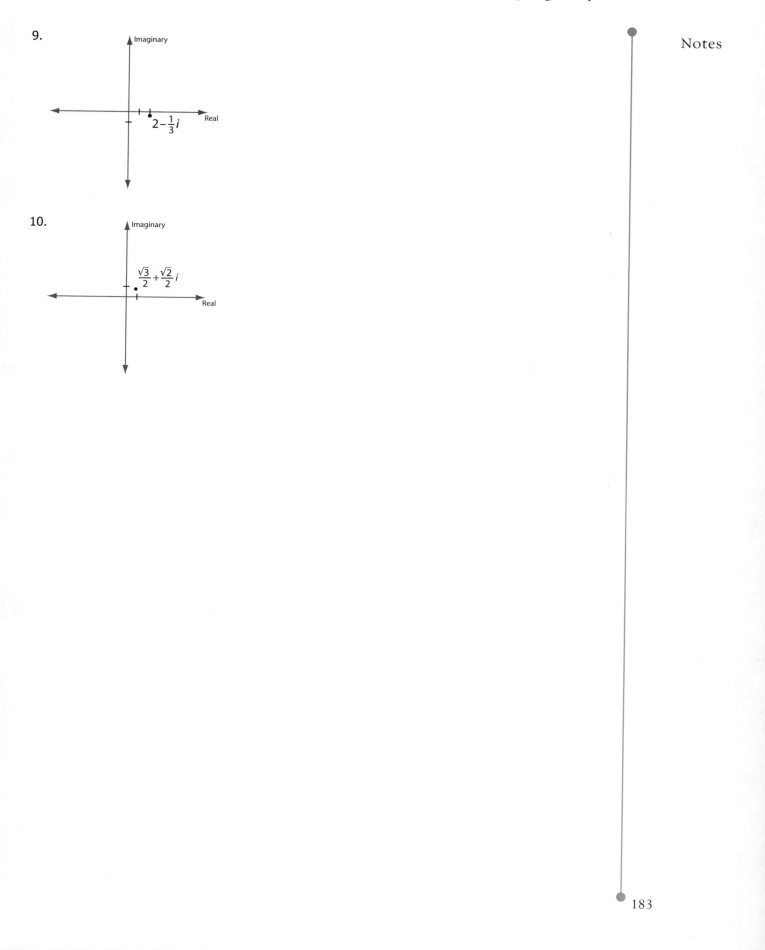

$2-\frac{1}{3}i$

10.

$\frac{\sqrt{3}}{2}+\frac{\sqrt{2}}{2}i$

POLAR COORDINATES I: PLOTTING POLAR POINTS

38

Plot the following polar points.

1. $(3, 30°)$

2. $(4, 60°)$

3. $(-2, 45°)$

4. $(2, -30°)$

5. $(-4, -60°)$

6. $\left(2, \dfrac{\pi}{6}\right)$

7. $\left(3, \dfrac{\pi}{2}\right)$

8. $(-6, \pi)$

9. $\left(3, -\dfrac{\pi}{3}\right)$

10. $\left(-2, -\dfrac{3\pi}{4}\right)$

Solutions

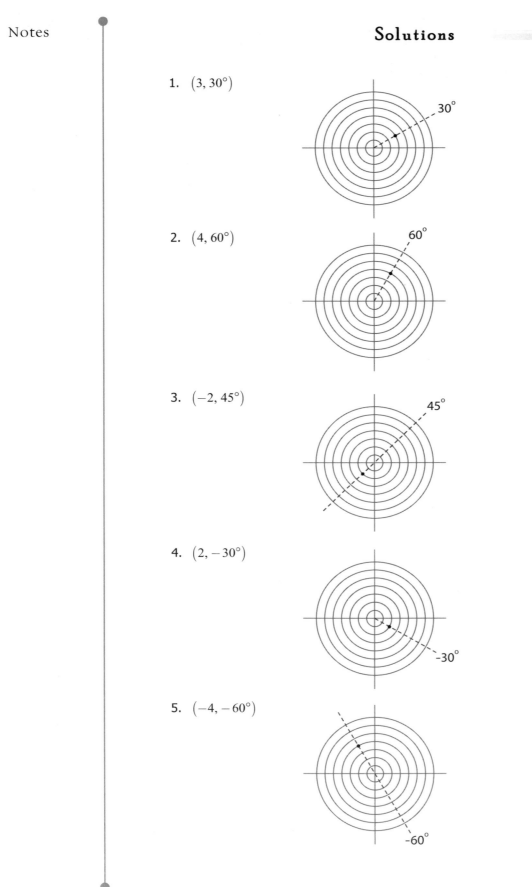

1. $(3, 30°)$

2. $(4, 60°)$

3. $(-2, 45°)$

4. $(2, -30°)$

5. $(-4, -60°)$

6. $\left(2, \dfrac{\pi}{6}\right)$

7. $\left(3, \dfrac{\pi}{2}\right)$

8. $(-6, \pi)$

9. $\left(3, -\dfrac{\pi}{3}\right)$

10. $\left(-2, -\dfrac{3\pi}{4}\right)$

Notes

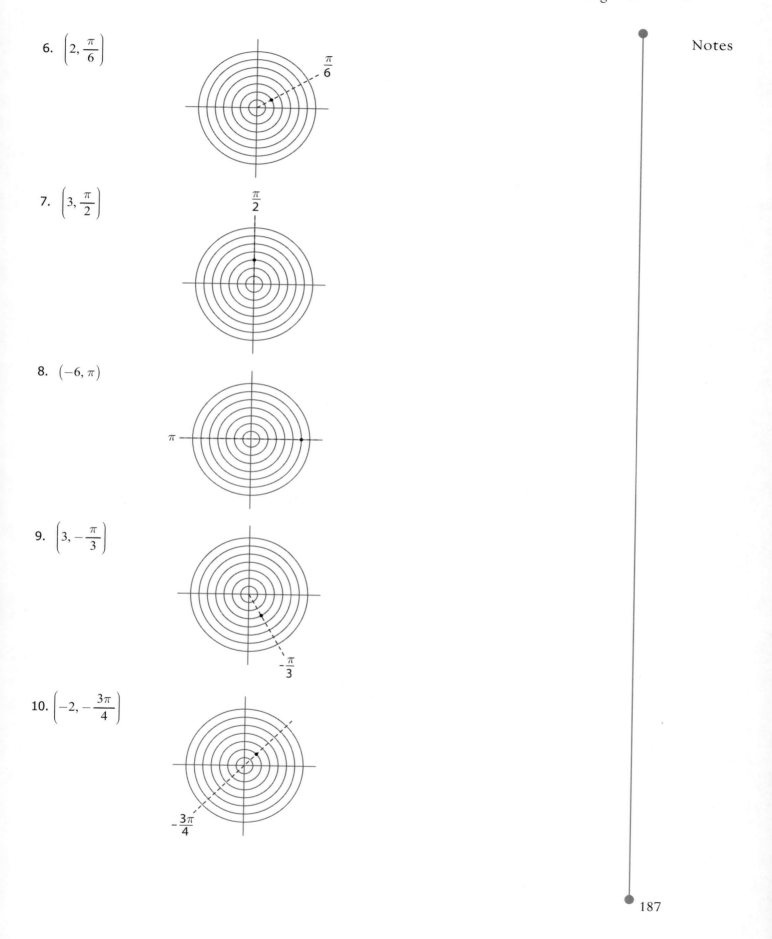

Convert the following rectangular coordinates into their polar form.

> Converting from rectangular coordinates into polar coordinates :
>
> $$r = \sqrt{x^2 + y^2} \qquad \theta = \tan^{-1}\left(\frac{y}{x}\right)$$

1. $(3, 4)$

2. $(2, 6)$

3. $(-2, 5)$

4. $(5, 0)$

5. $(0, 3)$

Convert the following polar coordinates into their rectangular form.

> Converting from polar coordinates into rectangular coordinates :
>
> $$x = r\cos\theta \qquad y = r\sin\theta$$

6. $(2, 30°)$

7. $(3, 65°)$

8. $(-4, 20°)$

9. $\left(8, \dfrac{3\pi}{4}\right)$

10. $\left(-2, \dfrac{\pi}{6}\right)$

Notes

Answer Key

1. $(5, 53.13°)$

2. $\left(2\sqrt{10}, 71.56°\right)$

3. $\left(\sqrt{29}, 111.8°\right)$

4. $(5, 0°)$

5. $(3, 90°)$

6. $(1.732, 1)$

7. $(1, 269, 2.718)$

8. $(-3.759, -1.368)$

9. $(-5.656, 5.656)$

10. $(-1.732, -1)$

Solutions

1. $(3, 4)$

$$r = \sqrt{x^2 + y^2} \qquad \theta = \tan^{-1}\left(\frac{y}{x}\right)$$

$$r = \sqrt{3^2 + 4^2} \qquad \theta = \tan^{-1}\left(\frac{4}{3}\right)$$

$$r = \sqrt{9 + 16} \qquad \theta = 53.13°$$

$$r = \sqrt{25}$$

$$r = 5$$

Thus,

$$(r, \theta) = (5, 53.13°)$$

2. $(2, 6)$

$$r = \sqrt{x^2 + y^2} \qquad \theta = \tan^{-1}\left(\frac{y}{x}\right)$$

$$r = \sqrt{2^2 + 6^2} \qquad \theta = \tan^{-1}\left(\frac{6}{2}\right)$$

$$r = \sqrt{4 + 6} \qquad \theta = \tan^{-1}(3)$$

$$r = \sqrt{40} \qquad \theta = 71.56°$$

$$r = \sqrt{4 \cdot 10}$$

$$r = \sqrt{4} \cdot \sqrt{10}$$

$$r = 2\sqrt{10}$$

Thus,

$$(r, \theta) = \left(2\sqrt{10}, 71.56°\right)$$

3. $(-2, 5)$

$$r = \sqrt{x^2 + y^2} \qquad \theta = \tan^{-1}\left(\frac{y}{x}\right)$$

$$r = \sqrt{(-2)^2 + 5^2} \qquad \theta = \tan^{-1}\left(\frac{5}{-2}\right)$$

$$r = \sqrt{4 + 25} \qquad \theta = -68.2°$$

$$r = \sqrt{29}$$

calculation cont. on next page...

Solution #3 from previous page...

Since our point is in the second quadrant (it has a negative x and a positive y) the angle is measured from $180°$.

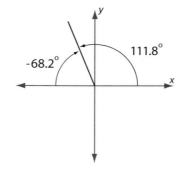

Thus,

$$(r,\theta)=\left(\sqrt{29},111.8°\right)$$

4. $(5,0)$

$$r=\sqrt{x^2+y^2} \qquad \theta=\tan^{-1}\left(\frac{y}{x}\right)$$

$$r=\sqrt{5^2+0^2} \qquad \theta=\tan^{-1}\left(\frac{0}{5}\right)$$

$$r=\sqrt{25} \qquad \theta=\tan^{-1}(0)$$

$$r=5 \qquad \theta=0°$$

Thus,

$$(r,\theta)=(5,0°)$$

5. $(0,3)$

$$r=\sqrt{0^2+3^2} \qquad \theta=\tan^{-1}\left(\frac{3}{0}\right)$$

$$r=\sqrt{3^2}$$

$$r=3$$

calculation cont. on next page...

Solution #5 from previous page...

Although we cannot divide by zero, we can still deduce the angle by graphing the point $(0, 3)$.

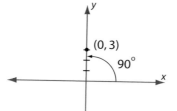

Since the point lies on the positive y-axis, it has a polar angle of $90°$.

Thus,

$$(r, \theta) = (3, 90°)$$

6. $(2, 30°)$

$x = r \cos \theta \qquad y = r \sin \theta$

$x = 2 \cos 30° \qquad y = 2 \sin 30°$

$x = 2(0.866) \qquad y = 2(0.5)$

$x = 1.732 \qquad y = 1$

Thus,

$$(x, y) = (1.732, 1)$$

7. $(3, 65°)$

$x = r \cos \theta \qquad y = r \sin \theta$

$x = 3 \cos 65° \qquad y = 3 \sin 65°$

$x = 3(0.423) \qquad y = 3(0.906)$

$x = 1.269 \qquad y = 2.718$

Thus,

$$(x, y) = (1, 269, 2.718)$$

8. $(-4, 20°)$

$x = r \cos \theta \qquad y = r \sin \theta$

$x = -4 \cos 20° \qquad y = -4 \sin 20°$

$x = -3.759 \qquad y = -1.368$

Thus,

$$(x, y) = (-3.759, -1.368)$$

9. $\left(8, \dfrac{3\pi}{4}\right)$

$x = r\cos\theta \qquad\qquad y = r\sin\theta$

$x = 8\cos\dfrac{3\pi}{4} \qquad\qquad y = 8\sin\dfrac{3\pi}{4}$

$x = 8(-0.707) \qquad\qquad y = 8(-0.707)$

$x = -5.656 \qquad\qquad y = 5.656$

Thus,

$(x, y) = (-5.656, 5.656)$

10. $\left(-2, \dfrac{\pi}{6}\right)$

$x = r\cos\theta \qquad\qquad y = r\sin\theta$

$x = -2\cos\dfrac{\pi}{6} \qquad\qquad y = -2\sin\dfrac{\pi}{6}$

$x = -2(0.866) \qquad\qquad y = -2(0.5)$

$x = -1.732 \qquad\qquad y = -1.0$

Thus,

$(x, y) = (-1.732, -1.0)$

CONVERTING BETWEEN RECTANGULAR AND POLAR COMPLEX NUMBERS

40

Convert the following rectangular complex numbers into their polar form.

> General form of a rectangular complex number :
> $$z = a + bi$$
>
> To convert a rectangular complex number into a polar complex number :
> $$r = \sqrt{a^2 + b^2} \qquad \theta = \tan^{-1}\left(\frac{b}{a}\right)$$
>
> General form of a polar complex number :
> $$z = r\left(\cos\theta + i\sin\theta\right)$$

1. $3 + 4i$

2. $2 + i$

3. $4 - i$

4. $-1 - i$

5. $3i$

6. $-4i$

7. $\sqrt{3} + i$

8. $\dfrac{1}{2} + \dfrac{1}{3}i$

9. 8

10. $2.4 + 3.8i$

Convert the following polar complex numbers into their rectangular form.

11. $z = 2\left(\cos 30° + i\sin 30°\right)$

12. $z = 5\left(\cos 45° + i\sin 45°\right)$

13. $z = 10\left(\cos 180° + i\sin 180°\right)$

14. $z = 4\left(\cos\dfrac{\pi}{4} + i\sin\dfrac{\pi}{4}\right)$

15. $z = 6\left(\cos\dfrac{\pi}{3} + i\sin\dfrac{\pi}{3}\right)$

16. $z = -4\left(\cos 20° + i\sin 20°\right)$

17. $z = 8\left(\cos 150° + i\sin 150°\right)$

18. $z = -6\left(\cos 210° + i\sin 210°\right)$

19. $z = 7\left(\cos\dfrac{3\pi}{4} + i\sin\dfrac{3\pi}{4}\right)$

20. $z = -2\left(\cos\dfrac{3\pi}{2} + i\sin\dfrac{3\pi}{2}\right)$

Notes

Answer Key

1. $z = 5\left(\cos 53.13° + i \sin 53.13°\right)$

2. $z = \sqrt{5}\left(\cos 26.56° + i \sin 26.56°\right)$

3. $z = \sqrt{17}\left(\cos 345.96° + i \sin 345.96°\right)$

4. $z = \sqrt{2}\left(\cos 225° + i \sin 225°\right)$

5. $z = 3\left(\cos 90° + i \sin 90°\right)$

6. $z = 4\left(\cos 270° + i \sin 270°\right)$

7. $z = 2\left(\cos 30° + i \sin 30°\right)$

8. $z = \dfrac{\sqrt{13}}{6}\left(\cos 33.7° + i \sin 33.7°\right)$

9. $z = 8\left(\cos 0° + i \sin 0°\right)$

10. $z = 4.49\left(\cos 57.67° + i \sin 57.67°\right)$

11. $z = 1.732 + i$

12. $z = 3.535 + 3.535i$

13. $z = -10$

14. $z = 2.828 + 2.828i$

15. $z = 3 + 5.196i$

16. $z = -3.76 - 1.368i$

17. $z = -6.928 + 4i$

18. $z = 5.196 + 3i$

19. $z = -4.949 + 4.949i$

20. $z = 2i$

Solutions

1. $3 + 4i$

    $\uparrow \quad \uparrow$
    $a \quad \downarrow b$

    $r = \sqrt{a^2 + b^2}$ $\qquad \theta = \tan^{-1}\left(\dfrac{b}{a}\right)$

    $r = \sqrt{3^2 + 4^2}$ $\qquad \theta = \tan^{-1}\left(\dfrac{4}{3}\right)$

    $r = \sqrt{9 + 16}$ $\qquad \theta = 53.13°$

    $r = \sqrt{25}$

    $r = 5$

Thus,

$z = r(\cos\theta + i\sin\theta)$

$z = 5(\cos 53.13° + i\sin 53.13°)$

2. $2 + i$

    $\uparrow \quad \uparrow$
    $a \quad \downarrow b = 1$

    $r = \sqrt{a^2 + b^2}$ $\qquad \theta = \tan^{-1}\left(\dfrac{b}{a}\right)$

    $r = \sqrt{2^2 + 1^2}$ $\qquad \theta = \tan^{-1}\left(\dfrac{1}{2}\right)$

    $r = \sqrt{4 + 1}$ $\qquad \theta = 26.56°$

    $r = \sqrt{5}$

Thus,

$z = r(\cos\theta + i\sin\theta)$

$z = \sqrt{5}(\cos 26.56° + i\sin 26.56°)$

3. $4 - i$

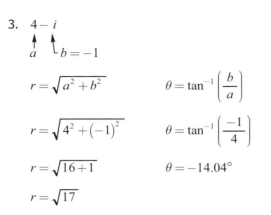

$$r = \sqrt{a^2 + b^2} \qquad \theta = \tan^{-1}\left(\frac{b}{a}\right)$$

$$r = \sqrt{4^2 + (-1)^2} \qquad \theta = \tan^{-1}\left(\frac{-1}{4}\right)$$

$$r = \sqrt{16 + 1} \qquad \theta = -14.04°$$

$$r = \sqrt{17}$$

Since the rectangular complex number has a positive real part and a negative imaginary part, it lies in the 4th quadrant. Consequently, the negative angle is measured from 0.

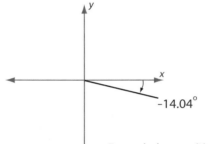

Recorded as positive angle $\theta = 345.96°$

Thus,

$$z = r\left(\cos\theta + i\sin\theta\right)$$

$$z = \sqrt{17}\left(\cos 345.96° + i\sin 345.96°\right)$$

4. $-1 - i$

$$r = \sqrt{a^2 + b^2} \qquad \theta = \tan^{-1}\left(\frac{b}{a}\right)$$

$$r = \sqrt{(-1)^2 + (-1)^2} \qquad \theta = \tan^{-1}\left(\frac{-1}{1}\right)$$

$$r = \sqrt{1 + 1} \qquad \theta = \tan^{-1}\left(-1\right)$$

$$r = \sqrt{2} \qquad \theta = -45°$$

calculation cont. on next page...

Solution #4 from previous page...

Since the rectangular complex number has a negative real part and a negative imaginary part, it lies in the 3rd quadrant. Consequently, the negative angle is measured from $180°$.

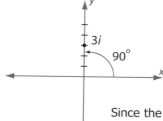

Recorded as positive angle $\theta = 225°$

Thus,

$$z = r\left(\cos\theta + i\sin\theta\right)$$

$$z = \sqrt{2}\left(\cos 225° + i\sin 225°\right)$$

5. $3i$

$$a = 0 \quad b = 3$$

$$r = \sqrt{a^2 + b^2} \qquad \theta = \tan^{-1}\left(\frac{b}{a}\right)$$

$$r = \sqrt{0^2 + 3^2} \qquad \theta = \tan^{-1}\left(\frac{3}{0}\right)$$

$$r = \sqrt{3^2}$$

$$r = 3$$

Although we cannot divide by zero, we can deduce the angle by graphing the rectangular complex point $z = 3i$.

Since the point lies on the positive y-axis, it has a polar angle of $90°$.

Thus,

$$z = r\left(\cos\theta + i\sin\theta\right)$$

$$z = 3\left(\cos 90° + i\sin 90°\right)$$

Notes

6. $-4i$

$a = 0 \qquad b = -4$

$r = \sqrt{a^2 + b^2}$ $\qquad\qquad \theta = \tan^{-1}\left(\dfrac{b}{a}\right)$

$r = \sqrt{0^2 + (-4)^2}$ $\qquad \theta = \tan^{-1}\left(\dfrac{-4}{0}\right)$

$r = \sqrt{(-4)^2}$

$r = 4$

Although we cannot divide by zero, we can deduce the angle by graphing the rectangular complex point $z = -4i$.

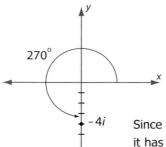

Since the point lies on the positive y-axis,
it has a polar angle of $270°$.

Thus,

$z = r(\cos\theta + i\sin\theta)$

$z = 4(\cos 270° + i\sin 270°)$

7. $\sqrt{3} + i$

$\qquad a \qquad b = 1$

$r = \sqrt{a^2 + b^2}$ $\qquad\qquad \theta = \tan^{-1}\left(\dfrac{b}{a}\right)$

$r = \sqrt{\left(\sqrt{3}\right)^2 + 1^2}$ $\qquad \theta = \tan^{-1}\left(\dfrac{1}{\sqrt{3}}\right)$

$r = \sqrt{3 + 1}$ $\qquad\qquad\quad \theta = 30°$

$r = \sqrt{4}$

$r = 2$

Thus,

$z = r(\cos\theta + i\sin\theta)$

$z = 2(\cos 30° + i\sin 30°)$

8. $\frac{1}{2} + \frac{1}{3}i$

$\uparrow_a \quad \uparrow_b$

$r = \sqrt{a^2 + b^2}$ $\qquad\qquad \theta = \tan^{-1}\left(\frac{b}{a}\right)$

$r = \sqrt{\left(\frac{1}{2}\right)^2 + \left(\frac{1}{3}\right)^2}$ $\qquad \theta = \tan^{-1}\left(\dfrac{\frac{1}{3}}{\frac{1}{2}}\right)$

$r = \sqrt{\frac{1}{4} + \frac{1}{9}}$ $\qquad\qquad \theta = \tan^{-1}\left(\frac{1}{3} \cdot \frac{2}{1}\right)$

$r = \sqrt{\frac{9}{36} + \frac{4}{36}}$ $\qquad\qquad \theta = \tan^{-1}\left(\frac{2}{3}\right)$

$r = \sqrt{\frac{13}{36}}$ $\qquad\qquad\qquad \theta = 33.7°$

$r = \frac{\sqrt{13}}{\sqrt{36}}$

$r = \frac{\sqrt{13}}{6}$

Thus,

$z = r(\cos\theta + i\sin\theta)$

$z = \frac{\sqrt{13}}{6}(\cos 33.7° + i\sin 33.7°)$

9. 8

$a = 8 \quad b = 0$

$r = \sqrt{a^2 + b^2}$ $\qquad\qquad \theta = \tan^{-1}\left(\frac{b}{a}\right)$

$r = \sqrt{8^2 + 0}$ $\qquad\qquad \theta = \tan^{-1}\left(\frac{0}{8}\right)$

$r = \sqrt{8^2}$ $\qquad\qquad\qquad \theta = \tan^{-1}(0)$

$r = 8$ $\qquad\qquad\qquad\quad \theta = 0°$

Thus,

$z = r(\cos\theta + i\sin\theta)$

$z = 8(\cos 0° + i\sin 0°)$

10. $2.4 + 3.8i$

$$r = \sqrt{a^2 + b^2} \qquad\qquad \theta = \tan^{-1}\left(\frac{b}{a}\right)$$

$$r = \sqrt{(2.4)^2 + (3.8)^2} \qquad\qquad \theta = \tan^{-1}\left(\frac{3.8}{2.4}\right)$$

$$r = \sqrt{5.76 + 14.44} \qquad\qquad \theta = \tan^{-1}(1.58)$$

$$r = \sqrt{20.2} \qquad\qquad \theta = 57.67°$$

$$r = 4.49$$

Thus,

$$z = r(\cos\theta + i\sin\theta)$$

$$z = 4.49(\cos 57.67° + i\sin 57.67°)$$

11. $z = 2(\cos 30° + i\sin 30°)$

$$z = 2(0.866 + i(0.5))$$

$$z = 1.732 + i$$

12. $z = 5(\cos 45° + i\sin 45°)$

$$z = 5(0.707 + i(0.707))$$

$$z = 3.535 + 3.535i$$

13. $z = 10(\cos 180° + i\sin 180°)$

$$z = 10(-1 + 0)$$

$$z = -10$$

14. $z = 4\left(\cos\dfrac{\pi}{4} + i\sin\dfrac{\pi}{4}\right)$

$$z = 4(0.707 + i(0.707))$$

$$z = 2.828 + 2.828i$$

15. $z = 6\left(\cos\dfrac{\pi}{3} + i\sin\dfrac{\pi}{3}\right)$

$$z = 6(0.5 + i(0.866))$$

$$z = 3 + 5.196i$$

16. $z = -4(\cos 20° + i\sin 20°)$

$z = -4(0.94 + 0.342i)$

$z = -3.76 - 1.368i$

17. $z = 8(\cos 150° + i\sin 150°)$

$z = 8(-0.866 + i(0.5))$

$z = -6.928 + 4i$

18. $z = -6(\cos 210° + i\sin 210°)$

$z = -6(-0.866 + i(-0.5))$

$z = 5.196 + 3i$

19. $z = 7\left(\cos\dfrac{3\pi}{4} + i\sin\dfrac{3\pi}{4}\right)$

$z = 7(-0.707 + i(0.707))$

$z = -4.949 + 4.949i$

20. $z = -2\left(\cos\dfrac{3\pi}{2} + i\sin\dfrac{3\pi}{2}\right)$

$z = -2(0 + i(-1))$

$z = 2i$

PRODUCTS AND QUOTIENTS OF POLAR COMPLEX NUMBERS

41

Find $z_1 \cdot z_2$ and $\dfrac{z_1}{z_2}$ for each of the following.

> Given two polar complex numbers $z_1 = r_1 \left(\cos \theta_1 + i \sin \theta_1 \right)$ and $z_2 = r_2 \left(\cos \theta_2 + i \sin \theta_2 \right)$:
>
> $$z_1 \cdot z_2 = r_1 r_2 \left[\cos \left(\theta_1 + \theta_2 \right) + i \sin \left(\theta_1 + \theta_2 \right) \right]$$
>
> $$\frac{z_1}{z_2} = \frac{r_1}{r_2} = \left[\cos \left(\theta_1 - \theta_2 \right) + i \sin \left(\theta_1 - \theta_2 \right) \right]$$

1. $z_1 = 12 \left(\cos 20° + i \sin 20° \right)$

   $z_2 = 2 \left(\cos 5° + i \sin 5° \right)$

2. $z_1 = 6 \left(\cos 75° + i \sin 75° \right)$

   $z_2 = 3 \left(\cos 20° + i \sin 20° \right)$

3. $z_1 = 2 \left(\cos 15° + i \sin 15° \right)$

   $z_2 = 4 \left(\cos 10° + i \sin 10° \right)$

4. $z_1 = 3 \left(\cos \dfrac{\pi}{12} + i \sin \dfrac{\pi}{12} \right)$

   $z_2 = 4 \left(\cos \dfrac{\pi}{3} + i \sin \dfrac{\pi}{3} \right)$

5. $z_1 = 5 \left[\cos \left(-\dfrac{\pi}{6} \right) + i \sin \left(-\dfrac{\pi}{6} \right) \right]$

   $z_2 = 10 \left[\cos \left(\dfrac{\pi}{4} \right) + i \sin \left(\dfrac{\pi}{4} \right) \right]$

Notes

Answer Key

1. $z_1 \cdot z_2 = 24\left(\cos 25° + i\sin 25°\right)$

   $\dfrac{z_1}{z_2} = 6\left(\cos 15° + i\sin 15°\right)$

2. $z_1 \cdot z_2 = 18\left(\cos 95° + i\sin 95°\right)$

   $\dfrac{z_1}{z_2} = 2\left(\cos 55° + i\sin 55°\right)$

3. $z_1 \cdot z_2 = 8\left(\cos 25° + i\sin 25°\right)$

   $\dfrac{z_1}{z_2} = \dfrac{1}{2}\left(\cos 5° + i\sin 5°\right)$

4. $z_1 \cdot z_2 = 12\left(\cos \dfrac{5\pi}{12} + i\sin \dfrac{5\pi}{12}\right)$

   $\dfrac{z_1}{z_2} = \dfrac{3}{4}\left[\cos\left(-\dfrac{\pi}{4}\right) + i\sin\left(-\dfrac{\pi}{4}\right)\right]$

5. $z_1 \cdot z_2 = 50\left(\cos \dfrac{\pi}{12} + i\sin \dfrac{\pi}{12}\right)$

   $\dfrac{z_1}{z_2} = \dfrac{1}{2}\left[\cos\left(-\dfrac{5\pi}{12}\right) + i\sin\left(-\dfrac{5\pi}{12}\right)\right]$

Solutions

1. $z_1 = 12\left(\cos 20° + i \sin 20°\right)$

   $z_2 = 2\left(\cos 5° + i \sin 5°\right)$

   $z_1 \cdot z_2 = 12 \cdot 2\left[\cos\left(20° + 5°\right) + i \sin\left(20° + 5°\right)\right]$

   $z_1 \cdot z_2 = 24\left(\cos 25° + i \sin 25°\right)$

   $\dfrac{z_1}{z_2} = \dfrac{12}{2}\left[\cos\left(20° - 5°\right) + i \sin\left(20° - 5°\right)\right]$

   $\dfrac{z_1}{z_2} = 6\left(\cos 15° + i \sin 15°\right)$

2. $z_1 = 6\left(\cos 75° + i \sin 75°\right)$

   $z_2 = 3\left(\cos 20° + i \sin 20°\right)$

   $z_1 \cdot z_2 = 6 \cdot 3\left[\cos\left(75° + 20°\right) + i \sin\left(75° + 20°\right)\right]$

   $z_1 \cdot z_2 = 18\left(\cos 95° + i \sin 95°\right)$

   $\dfrac{z_1}{z_2} = \dfrac{6}{3}\left[\cos\left(75° - 20°\right) + i \sin\left(75° - 20°\right)\right]$

   $\dfrac{z_1}{z_2} = 2\left(\cos 55° + i \sin 55°\right)$

3. $z_1 = 2\left(\cos 15° + i \sin 15°\right)$

   $z_2 = 4\left(\cos 10° + i \sin 10°\right)$

   $z_1 \cdot z_2 = 2 \cdot 4\left[\cos\left(15° + 10°\right) + i \sin\left(15° + 10°\right)\right]$

   $z_1 \cdot z_2 = 8\left(\cos 25° + i \sin 25°\right)$

   $\dfrac{z_1}{z_2} = \dfrac{2}{4}\left[\cos\left(15° - 10°\right) + i \sin\left(15° - 10°\right)\right]$

   $\dfrac{z_1}{z_2} = \dfrac{1}{2}\left(\cos 5° + i \sin 5°\right)$

4. $z_1 = 3\left(\cos\dfrac{\pi}{12} + i\sin\dfrac{\pi}{12}\right)$

$z_2 = 4\left(\cos\dfrac{\pi}{3} + i\sin\dfrac{\pi}{3}\right)$

$z_1 \cdot z_2 = 3\cdot 4\left[\cos\left(\dfrac{\pi}{12} + \dfrac{\pi}{3}\right) + i\sin\left(\dfrac{\pi}{12} + \dfrac{\pi}{3}\right)\right]$

$z_1 \cdot z_2 = 12\left[\cos\left(\dfrac{\pi}{12} + \dfrac{4\pi}{12}\right) + i\sin\left(\dfrac{\pi}{12} + \dfrac{4\pi}{12}\right)\right]$

$z_1 \cdot z_2 = 12\left(\cos\dfrac{5\pi}{12} + i\sin\dfrac{5\pi}{12}\right)$

$\dfrac{z_1}{z_2} = \dfrac{3}{4}\left[\cos\left(\dfrac{\pi}{12} - \dfrac{\pi}{3}\right) + i\sin\left(\dfrac{\pi}{12} - \dfrac{\pi}{3}\right)\right]$

$\dfrac{z_1}{z_2} = \dfrac{3}{4}\left[\cos\left(\dfrac{\pi}{12} - \dfrac{4\pi}{12}\right) + i\sin\left(\dfrac{\pi}{12} - \dfrac{4\pi}{12}\right)\right]$

$\dfrac{z_1}{z_2} = \dfrac{3}{4}\left[\cos\left(-\dfrac{3\pi}{12}\right) + i\sin\left(-\dfrac{3\pi}{12}\right)\right]$

$\dfrac{z_1}{z_2} = \dfrac{3}{4}\left[\cos\left(-\dfrac{\pi}{4}\right) + i\sin\left(-\dfrac{\pi}{4}\right)\right]$

5. $z_1 = 5\left[\cos\left(-\dfrac{\pi}{6}\right) + i\sin\left(-\dfrac{\pi}{6}\right)\right]$

$z_2 = 10\left[\cos\left(\dfrac{\pi}{4}\right) + i\sin\left(\dfrac{\pi}{4}\right)\right]$

$z_1 \cdot z_2 = 5\cdot 10\left[\cos\left(-\dfrac{\pi}{6} + \dfrac{\pi}{4}\right) + i\sin\left(-\dfrac{\pi}{6} + \dfrac{\pi}{4}\right)\right]$

$z_1 \cdot z_2 = 50\left[\cos\left(-\dfrac{2\pi}{12} + \dfrac{3\pi}{12}\right) + i\sin\left(-\dfrac{2\pi}{12} + \dfrac{3\pi}{12}\right)\right]$

$z_1 \cdot z_2 = 50\left(\cos\dfrac{\pi}{12} + i\sin\dfrac{\pi}{12}\right)$

$\dfrac{z_1}{z_2} = \dfrac{5}{10}\left[\cos\left(-\dfrac{\pi}{6} - \dfrac{\pi}{4}\right) + i\sin\left(-\dfrac{\pi}{6} - \dfrac{\pi}{4}\right)\right]$

$\dfrac{z_1}{z_2} = \dfrac{1}{2}\left[\cos\left(-\dfrac{2\pi}{12} - \dfrac{3\pi}{12}\right) + i\sin\left(-\dfrac{2\pi}{12} - \dfrac{3\pi}{12}\right)\right]$

$\dfrac{z_1}{z_2} = \dfrac{1}{2}\left[\cos\left(-\dfrac{5\pi}{12}\right) + i\sin\left(-\dfrac{5\pi}{12}\right)\right]$

DeMoivre's Theorem

42

Use DeMoivre's Theorem to find each of the following.

> **DeMoivre's Theorem**
>
> For a polar complex number $z = r(\cos\theta + i\sin\theta)$:
> $$z^n = r^n(\cos n\theta + i\sin n\theta)$$

1. If $z = 2(\cos 10° + i\sin 10°)$, find z^4

2. If $z = -3(\cos 40° + i\sin 40°)$, find z^3

3. If $z = \sqrt{2}(\cos 30° + i\sin 30°)$, find z^6

4. If $z = -\sqrt{5}(\cos 110° + i\sin 110°)$, find z^4

Use DeMoivre's Theorem to find each of the following. Record your final answer in rectangular form.

5. $(1+i)^4$

6. $(\sqrt{2}+i)^6$

7. $(-\sqrt{3}+\sqrt{2}i)^4$

8. $(3+4i)^5$

9. $(2-i)^7$

10. $(1-\sqrt{2}i)^6$

Notes

Answer Key

1. $z^4 = 16\left(\cos 40° + i \sin 40°\right)$

2. $z^3 = -27\left(\cos 120° + i \sin 120°\right)$

3. $z^6 = 8\left(\cos 180° + i \sin 180°\right)$

4. $z^4 = 25\left(\cos 440° + i \sin 440°\right)$

5. $z^4 = -4$

6. $z^6 = -22.95 - 14.04i$

7. $z^4 = -22.975 - 9.825i$

8. $z^5 = -237.5 - 3115.6i$

9. $z^7 = -278.1 + 28.79i$

10. $z^6 = 23.0 + 14.1i$

Solutions

1. $z = 2(\cos 10° + i \sin 10°)$

   $z^4 = 2^4 \left[\cos 4(10°) + i \sin 4(10°)\right]$

   $z^4 = 16(\cos 40° + i \sin 40°)$

2. $z = -3(\cos 40° + i \sin 40°)$

   $z^3 = (-3)^3 \left[\cos 3(40°) + i \sin 3(40°)\right]$

   $z^3 = -27(\cos 120° + i \sin 120°)$

3. $z = \sqrt{2}(\cos 30° + i \sin 30°)$

   $z^6 = \left(\sqrt{2}\right)^6 \left[\cos 6(30°) + i \sin 6(30°)\right]$

   $z^6 = \left(2^{\frac{1}{2}}\right)^6 (\cos 180° + i \sin 180°)$

   $z^6 = 2^3 (\cos 180° + i \sin 180°)$

   $z^6 = 8(\cos 180° + i \sin 180°)$

4. $z = -\sqrt{5}(\cos 110° + i \sin 110°)$

   $z^4 = \left(-\sqrt{5}\right)^4 \left[\cos 4(110°) + i \sin 4(110°)\right]$

   $z^4 = \left(-5^{\frac{1}{2}}\right)^4 (\cos 440° + i \sin 440°)$

   $z^4 = 5^2 (\cos 440° + i \sin 440°)$

   $z^4 = 25(\cos 440° + i \sin 440°)$

5. $(1+i)^4$

First, we convert the rectangular complex number $z = 1+i$ into its polar form:

$$z = 1 + i$$

$$\underset{\underset{a}{\uparrow}}{} \quad \underset{\underset{b=1}{\uparrow}}{}$$

$$r = \sqrt{a^2 + b^2} \qquad\qquad \theta = \tan^{-1}\left(\frac{b}{a}\right)$$

$$r = \sqrt{1^2 + 1^2} \qquad\qquad \theta = \tan^{-1}\left(\frac{1}{1}\right)$$

$$r = \sqrt{2} \qquad\qquad\qquad \theta = 45°$$

Thus,

$$z = r\left(\cos\theta + i\sin\theta\right)$$

$$z = \sqrt{2}\left(\cos 45° + i\sin 45°\right)$$

Next, we use DeMoivre's Theorem to incorporate the exponent:

$$z = \sqrt{2}\left(\cos 45° + i\sin 45°\right)$$

$$z^4 = \left(\sqrt{2}\right)^4\left[\cos 4\left(45°\right) + i\sin 4\left(45°\right)\right]$$

$$z^4 = \left(2^{\frac{1}{2}}\right)^4\left(\cos 180° + i\sin 180°\right)$$

Lastly, we convert our polar complex number into its rectangular form by calculating the sine and cosine of the angle and incorporating the coefficient:

$$z^4 = 2^2\left(-1 + i\left(0\right)\right)$$

$$z^4 = 4\left(-1 + 0\right)$$

$$z^4 = -4$$

6. $\left(\sqrt{2}+i\right)^6$

First, we convert the rectangular complex number $z = \sqrt{2}+i$ into its polar form:

$$z = \sqrt{2} + i$$

$$\underset{\underset{a}{\uparrow}}{} \quad \underset{\underset{b=1}{\uparrow}}{}$$

calculation cont. on next page...

Solution #6 from previous page...

$$r = \sqrt{a^2 + b^2} \qquad\qquad \theta = \tan^{-1}\left(\frac{b}{a}\right)$$

$$r = \sqrt{\left(\sqrt{2}\right)^2 + 1^2} \qquad\qquad \theta = \tan^{-1}\left(\frac{1}{\sqrt{2}}\right)$$

$$r = \sqrt{2 + 1} \qquad\qquad \theta = \tan^{-1}(0.707)$$

$$r = \sqrt{3} \qquad\qquad \theta = 35.26°$$

Thus,

$$z = r\left(\cos\theta + i\sin\theta\right)$$

$$z = \sqrt{3}\left(\cos 35.26° + i\sin 35.26°\right)$$

Next, we use DeMoivre's Theorem to incorporate the exponent:

$$z^6 = \left(\sqrt{3}\right)^6 \left[\cos 6\left(35.26°\right) + i\sin 6\left(35.26°\right)\right]$$

$$z^6 = \left(3^{\frac{1}{2}}\right)^6 \left(\cos 211.56° + i\sin 211.56°\right)$$

Lastly, we convert our polar complex number into its rectangular form by calculating the sine and cosine of the angle and incorporating the coefficient:

$$z^6 = 3^3 \left[-0.85 + i(-0.52)\right]$$

$$z^6 = 27\left(-0.85 - 0.52i\right)$$

$$z^6 = -22.95 - 14.04i$$

7. $\left(-\sqrt{3} + \sqrt{2}\,i\right)^4$

First, we convert the rectangular complex number $z = -\sqrt{3} + \sqrt{2}\,i$ into its polar form:

$$z = -\sqrt{3} + \sqrt{2}\,i$$
$$\underset{a}{\uparrow} \qquad \underset{b}{\uparrow}$$

$$r = \sqrt{a^2 + b^2} \qquad\qquad \theta = \tan^{-1}\left(\frac{\sqrt{2}}{-\sqrt{3}}\right)$$

$$r = \sqrt{\left(-\sqrt{3}\right)^2 + \left(\sqrt{2}\right)^2} \qquad\qquad \theta = \tan^{-1}(-0.816)$$

$$r = \sqrt{3 + 2} \qquad\qquad \theta = -39.21°$$

$$r = \sqrt{5}$$

calculation cont. on next page...

Solution #7 from previous page...

Since the complex number has a negative real component $\left(-\sqrt{3}\right)$ and a positive imaginary component, it lies in the 2nd quadrant:

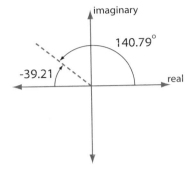

Using the positive angle, $\theta = 140.79°$, we get,

$$z = r\left(\cos\theta + i\sin\theta\right)$$

$$z = \sqrt{5}\left(\cos 140.79° + i\sin 140.79°\right)$$

Next, we use DeMoivre's Theorem to incorporate the exponent:

$$z = \sqrt{5}\left(\cos 140.79° + i\sin 140.79°\right)$$

$$z^4 = \left(\sqrt{5}\right)^4\left[\cos 4\left(140.79°\right) + i\sin 4\left(140.79°\right)\right]$$

$$z^4 = \left(5^{\frac{1}{2}}\right)^4\left(\cos 563.16° + i\sin 563.16°\right)$$

$$z^4 = 5^2\left(\cos 563.16° + i\sin 563.16°\right)$$

$$z^4 = 25\left(\cos 563.16° + i\sin 563.16°\right)$$

Since $360°$ is a full rotation around the circle, we can express $563.16°$ as $203.16°$:

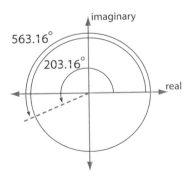

Thus,

$$z^4 = 25\left(\cos 203.16° + i\sin 203.16°\right)$$

calculation cont. on next page...

Solution #7 from previous page...

Lastly, we convert our polar complex number into its rectangular form by calculating the sine and cosine of the angle and incorporating the coefficient:

$$z^4 = 25\left[-0.919 + i\left(-0.393\right)\right]$$

$$z^4 = -22.975 - 9.825i$$

8. $(3 + 4i)^5$

First, we convert the rectangular complex number $z = 3 + 4i$ into its polar form:

$$z = 3 + 4i$$
$$\underset{a}{\uparrow} \quad \underset{b}{\uparrow}$$

$$r = \sqrt{a^2 + b^2} \qquad\qquad \theta = \tan^{-1}\left(\frac{b}{a}\right)$$

$$r = \sqrt{3^2 + b^2} \qquad\qquad \theta = \tan^{-1}\left(\frac{4}{3}\right)$$

$$r = \sqrt{9 + 16} \qquad\qquad \theta = 53.13°$$

$$r = \sqrt{25}$$

$$r = 5$$

Thus,

$$z = r\left(\cos\theta + i\sin\theta\right)$$

$$z = 5\left(\cos 53.13° + i\sin 53.13°\right)$$

Next, we use DeMoivre's Theorem to incorporate the exponent:

$$z^5 = 5^5\left[\cos 5\left(53.13°\right) + i\sin 5\left(53.13°\right)\right]$$

$$z^5 = 3125\left(\cos 265.65° + i\sin 265.65°\right)$$

Lastly, we convert our polar complex number into its rectangular form by calculating the sine and cosine of the angle and incorporating the coefficient:

$$z^5 = 3125\left(\cos 265.65° + i\sin 265.65°\right)$$

$$z^5 = 3125\left[-0.076 + i\left(-0.997\right)\right]$$

$$z^5 = -237.5 - 3115.6i$$

9. $(2-i)^7$

First, we convert the rectangular complex number $z = 2-i$ into its polar form:

$$z = 2 - i$$

$$\underset{a}{\uparrow} \quad \underset{b=-1}{\uparrow}$$

$$r = \sqrt{a^2 + b^2} \qquad\qquad \theta = \tan^{-1}\left(\frac{b}{a}\right)$$

$$r = \sqrt{2^2 + (-1)^2} \qquad\qquad \theta = \tan^{-1}\left(\frac{-1}{2}\right)$$

$$r = \sqrt{4+1} \qquad\qquad \theta = -26.56°$$

$$r = \sqrt{5}$$

With a positive real component (2) and a negative imaginary component (-1) the complex number lies in the 4th quadrant.

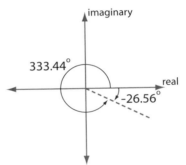

Using the positive angle, $\theta = 333.44°$, we get,

$$z = r(\cos\theta + i\sin\theta)$$

$$z = \sqrt{5}\left(\cos 333.44° + i\sin 333.44°\right)$$

Next, we use DeMoivre's Theorem to incorporate the exponent:

$$z = \sqrt{5}\left(\cos 333.44° + i\sin 333.44°\right)$$

$$z^7 = \left(\sqrt{5}\right)^7\left[\cos 7\left(333.44°\right) + i\sin 7\left(333.44°\right)\right]$$

$$z^7 = 279.5\left(\cos 2334.08° + i\sin 2334.08°\right)$$

(Notice that since the exponent was odd (7), we calculated $(5)^7$ directly rather than using a fractional exponent as in previous exercises.)

Realizing that $2160°$ correspondes to six full rotations around the circle, we can express the angle as:

$$\theta = 2334.08° - 2160°$$

$$\theta = 174.08°$$

calculation cont. on next page...

Solution #9 from previous page...

Thus,

$$z^7 = 279.5\left(\cos 174.08° + i \sin 174.08°\right)$$

Lastly, we convert our polar complex number into its rectangular form by calculating the sine and cosine of the angle and incorporating the coefficient:

$$z^7 = 279.5\left(\cos 174.08° + i \sin 174.08°\right)$$

$$z^7 = 279.5\left[-0.995 + i\left(0.103\right)\right]$$

$$z^7 = -278.1 + 28.79i$$

10. $\left(1 - \sqrt{2}\,i\right)^6$

First, we convert the rectangular complex number $z = 1 - \sqrt{2}\,i$ into its polar form:

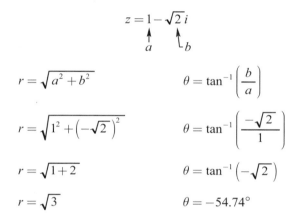

$$r = \sqrt{a^2 + b^2} \qquad\qquad \theta = \tan^{-1}\left(\frac{b}{a}\right)$$

$$r = \sqrt{1^2 + \left(-\sqrt{2}\right)^2} \qquad\qquad \theta = \tan^{-1}\left(\frac{-\sqrt{2}}{1}\right)$$

$$r = \sqrt{1+2} \qquad\qquad \theta = \tan^{-1}\left(-\sqrt{2}\right)$$

$$r = \sqrt{3} \qquad\qquad \theta = -54.74°$$

With a positive real component $\left(1\right)$ and a negative imaginary component $\left(-\sqrt{2}\right)$ the complex number lies in the 4th quadrant.

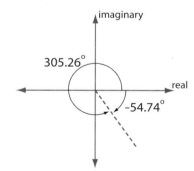

Using the positive angle, $\theta = 305.26°$, we get,

$$z = r\left(\cos\theta + i \sin\theta\right)$$

$$z = \sqrt{3}\left(\cos 305.26° + i \sin 305.26°\right)$$

calculation cont. on next page...

Solution #10 from previous page...

Next, we use DeMoivre's Theorem to incorporate the exponent:

$$z = \sqrt{3}\left(\cos 305.26° + i\sin 305.26°\right)$$

$$z^6 = \left(\sqrt{3}\right)^6\left[\cos 6\left(305.26°\right) + i\sin 6\left(305.26°\right)\right]$$

$$z^6 = \left(3^{\frac{1}{2}}\right)^6\left(\cos 1831.56° + i\sin 1831.56°\right)$$

$$z^6 = 3^3\left(\cos 1831.56° + i\sin 1831.56°\right)$$

$$z^6 = 27\left(\cos 1831.56° + i\sin 1831.56°\right)$$

Realizing that $1800°$ corresponds to five full rotations around the circle, we can express the angle as:

$$\theta = 1831.56° - 1800°$$

$$\theta = 31.56°$$

Thus,

$$z^6 = 27\left(\cos 31.56° + i\sin 31.56°\right)$$

Lastly, we convert our polar complex number into its rectangular form by calculating the sine and cosine of the angle and incorporating the coefficient:

$$z^6 = 27\left(\cos 31.56° + i\sin 31.56°\right)$$

$$z^6 = 27\left[0.852 + i\left(0.523\right)\right]$$

$$z^6 = 23.0 + 14.1i$$

ADDING, SUBTRACTING, AND MULTIPLYING MATRICES

Add, subtract, or multiply the following matrices.

1. $\begin{bmatrix} 1 & 3 \\ 4 & 2 \end{bmatrix} + \begin{bmatrix} 3 & 7 \\ 5 & 6 \end{bmatrix}$

2. $\begin{bmatrix} -3 & 0 \\ 1 & 5 \end{bmatrix} + \begin{bmatrix} 2 & 6 \\ -4 & 1 \end{bmatrix}$

3. $\begin{bmatrix} 1 & 2 & 5 \\ -3 & 0 & 4 \end{bmatrix} + \begin{bmatrix} 3 & -4 & 1 \\ 0 & 7 & -3 \end{bmatrix}$

4. $\begin{bmatrix} 6 \\ 2 \\ 1 \end{bmatrix} + \begin{bmatrix} -4 \\ 3 \\ 0 \end{bmatrix}$

5. $\begin{bmatrix} 3 & 5 \\ 2 & 6 \end{bmatrix} - \begin{bmatrix} 1 & 4 \\ 1 & 2 \end{bmatrix}$

6. $\begin{bmatrix} 2 & -1 & 6 \\ 4 & -5 & -3 \end{bmatrix} - \begin{bmatrix} 5 & 3 & -5 \\ -2 & 0 & 3 \end{bmatrix}$

7. $\begin{bmatrix} 1 & 3 & 4 \\ 4 & -6 & 0 \\ 5 & 7 & -1 \end{bmatrix} - \begin{bmatrix} -3 & 2 & 1 \\ 0 & 2 & 5 \\ 1 & -2 & 4 \end{bmatrix}$

8. $\begin{bmatrix} 1 & 3 \\ 2 & 5 \end{bmatrix}\begin{bmatrix} 2 & 1 \\ 1 & 4 \end{bmatrix}$

9. $\begin{bmatrix} 3 & 4 & -1 \\ -2 & 5 & 0 \end{bmatrix}\begin{bmatrix} 3 & 2 \\ -4 & 5 \\ 6 & 2 \end{bmatrix}$

10. $\begin{bmatrix} 3 & 1 & 3 \\ 0 & 1 & 2 \\ 5 & 1 & 1 \end{bmatrix}\begin{bmatrix} 4 & 1 & 2 \\ 2 & 0 & 1 \\ 3 & -1 & 6 \end{bmatrix}$

Notes

Answer Key

1. $\begin{bmatrix} 1 & 3 \\ 4 & 2 \end{bmatrix} + \begin{bmatrix} 3 & 7 \\ 5 & 6 \end{bmatrix} = \begin{bmatrix} 4 & 10 \\ 9 & 8 \end{bmatrix}$

2. $\begin{bmatrix} -3 & 0 \\ 1 & 5 \end{bmatrix} + \begin{bmatrix} 2 & 6 \\ -4 & 1 \end{bmatrix} = \begin{bmatrix} -1 & 6 \\ -3 & 6 \end{bmatrix}$

3. $\begin{bmatrix} 1 & 2 & 5 \\ -3 & 0 & 4 \end{bmatrix} + \begin{bmatrix} 3 & -4 & 1 \\ 0 & 7 & -3 \end{bmatrix} = \begin{bmatrix} 4 & -2 & 6 \\ -3 & 7 & 1 \end{bmatrix}$

4. $\begin{bmatrix} 6 \\ 2 \\ 1 \end{bmatrix} + \begin{bmatrix} -4 \\ 3 \\ 0 \end{bmatrix} = \begin{bmatrix} 2 \\ 5 \\ 1 \end{bmatrix}$

5. $\begin{bmatrix} 3 & 5 \\ 2 & 6 \end{bmatrix} - \begin{bmatrix} 1 & 4 \\ 1 & 2 \end{bmatrix} = \begin{bmatrix} 2 & 1 \\ 1 & 4 \end{bmatrix}$

6. $\begin{bmatrix} 2 & -1 & 6 \\ 4 & -5 & -3 \end{bmatrix} - \begin{bmatrix} 5 & 3 & -5 \\ -2 & 0 & 3 \end{bmatrix} = \begin{bmatrix} -3 & -4 & 11 \\ 6 & -5 & -6 \end{bmatrix}$

7. $\begin{bmatrix} 1 & 3 & 4 \\ 4 & -6 & 0 \\ 5 & 7 & -1 \end{bmatrix} - \begin{bmatrix} -3 & 2 & 1 \\ 0 & 2 & 5 \\ 1 & -2 & 4 \end{bmatrix} = \begin{bmatrix} 4 & 1 & 3 \\ 4 & -8 & -5 \\ 4 & 9 & -5 \end{bmatrix}$

8. $\begin{bmatrix} 1 & 3 \\ 2 & 5 \end{bmatrix}\begin{bmatrix} 2 & 1 \\ 1 & 4 \end{bmatrix} = \begin{bmatrix} 5 & 13 \\ 9 & 22 \end{bmatrix}$

9. $\begin{bmatrix} 3 & 4 & -1 \\ -2 & 5 & 0 \end{bmatrix}\begin{bmatrix} 3 & 2 \\ -4 & 5 \\ 6 & 2 \end{bmatrix} = \begin{bmatrix} -13 & 24 \\ -26 & 21 \end{bmatrix}$

10. $\begin{bmatrix} 3 & 1 & 3 \\ 0 & 1 & 2 \\ 5 & 1 & 1 \end{bmatrix}\begin{bmatrix} 4 & 1 & 2 \\ 2 & 0 & 1 \\ 3 & -1 & 6 \end{bmatrix} = \begin{bmatrix} 23 & 0 & 25 \\ 8 & -2 & 13 \\ 25 & 4 & 17 \end{bmatrix}$

Solutions

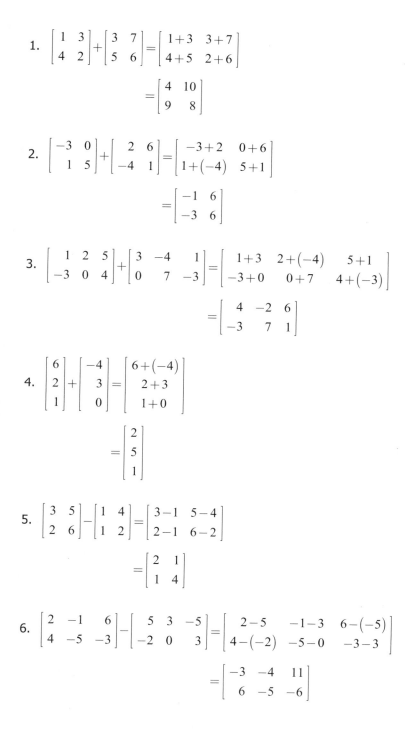

1. $\begin{bmatrix} 1 & 3 \\ 4 & 2 \end{bmatrix} + \begin{bmatrix} 3 & 7 \\ 5 & 6 \end{bmatrix} = \begin{bmatrix} 1+3 & 3+7 \\ 4+5 & 2+6 \end{bmatrix}$

$= \begin{bmatrix} 4 & 10 \\ 9 & 8 \end{bmatrix}$

2. $\begin{bmatrix} -3 & 0 \\ 1 & 5 \end{bmatrix} + \begin{bmatrix} 2 & 6 \\ -4 & 1 \end{bmatrix} = \begin{bmatrix} -3+2 & 0+6 \\ 1+(-4) & 5+1 \end{bmatrix}$

$= \begin{bmatrix} -1 & 6 \\ -3 & 6 \end{bmatrix}$

3. $\begin{bmatrix} 1 & 2 & 5 \\ -3 & 0 & 4 \end{bmatrix} + \begin{bmatrix} 3 & -4 & 1 \\ 0 & 7 & -3 \end{bmatrix} = \begin{bmatrix} 1+3 & 2+(-4) & 5+1 \\ -3+0 & 0+7 & 4+(-3) \end{bmatrix}$

$= \begin{bmatrix} 4 & -2 & 6 \\ -3 & 7 & 1 \end{bmatrix}$

4. $\begin{bmatrix} 6 \\ 2 \\ 1 \end{bmatrix} + \begin{bmatrix} -4 \\ 3 \\ 0 \end{bmatrix} = \begin{bmatrix} 6+(-4) \\ 2+3 \\ 1+0 \end{bmatrix}$

$= \begin{bmatrix} 2 \\ 5 \\ 1 \end{bmatrix}$

5. $\begin{bmatrix} 3 & 5 \\ 2 & 6 \end{bmatrix} - \begin{bmatrix} 1 & 4 \\ 1 & 2 \end{bmatrix} = \begin{bmatrix} 3-1 & 5-4 \\ 2-1 & 6-2 \end{bmatrix}$

$= \begin{bmatrix} 2 & 1 \\ 1 & 4 \end{bmatrix}$

6. $\begin{bmatrix} 2 & -1 & 6 \\ 4 & -5 & -3 \end{bmatrix} - \begin{bmatrix} 5 & 3 & -5 \\ -2 & 0 & 3 \end{bmatrix} = \begin{bmatrix} 2-5 & -1-3 & 6-(-5) \\ 4-(-2) & -5-0 & -3-3 \end{bmatrix}$

$= \begin{bmatrix} -3 & -4 & 11 \\ 6 & -5 & -6 \end{bmatrix}$

7. $\begin{bmatrix} 1 & 3 & 4 \\ 4 & -6 & 0 \\ 5 & 7 & -1 \end{bmatrix} - \begin{bmatrix} -3 & 2 & 1 \\ 0 & 2 & 5 \\ 1 & -2 & 4 \end{bmatrix} = \begin{bmatrix} 1-(-3) & 3-2 & 4-1 \\ 4-0 & -6-2 & 0-5 \\ 5-1 & 7-(-2) & -1-4 \end{bmatrix}$

$= \begin{bmatrix} 4 & 1 & 3 \\ 4 & -8 & -5 \\ 4 & 9 & -5 \end{bmatrix}$

8. $\begin{bmatrix} 1 & 3 \\ 2 & 5 \end{bmatrix} \begin{bmatrix} 2 & 1 \\ 1 & 4 \end{bmatrix} = \begin{bmatrix} 1(2)+3(1) & 1(1)+3(4) \\ 2(2)+5(1) & 2(1)+5(4) \end{bmatrix}$

$= \begin{bmatrix} 5 & 13 \\ 9 & 22 \end{bmatrix}$

9. $\begin{bmatrix} 3 & 4 & -1 \\ -2 & 5 & 0 \end{bmatrix} \begin{bmatrix} 3 & 2 \\ -4 & 5 \\ 6 & 2 \end{bmatrix} = \begin{bmatrix} 3(3)+4(-4)+(-1)(6) & 3(2)+4(5)+(-1)(2) \\ (-2)(3)+5(-4)+0(6) & (-2)(2)+5(5)+0(2) \end{bmatrix}$

$= \begin{bmatrix} 9-16-6 & 6+20-2 \\ -6-20+0 & -4+25+0 \end{bmatrix}$

$= \begin{bmatrix} -13 & 24 \\ -26 & 21 \end{bmatrix}$

10. $\begin{bmatrix} 3 & 1 & 3 \\ 0 & 1 & 2 \\ 5 & 1 & 1 \end{bmatrix} \begin{bmatrix} 4 & 1 & 2 \\ 2 & 0 & 1 \\ 3 & -1 & 6 \end{bmatrix} = \begin{bmatrix} 3(4)+1(2)+3(3) & 3(1)+1(0)+3(-1) & 3(2)+1(1)+3(6) \\ 0(4)+1(2)+2(3) & 0(1)+1(0)+2(-1) & 0(2)+1(1)+2(6) \\ 5(4)+1(2)+1(3) & 5(1)+1(0)+1(-1) & 5(2)+1(1)+1(6) \end{bmatrix}$

$= \begin{bmatrix} 12+2+9 & 3+0-3 & 6+1+18 \\ 0+2+6 & 0+0-2 & 0+1+12 \\ 20+2+3 & 5+0-1 & 10+1+6 \end{bmatrix}$

$= \begin{bmatrix} 23 & 0 & 25 \\ 8 & -2 & 13 \\ 25 & 4 & 17 \end{bmatrix}$

Calculate each of the following determinants.

1. $\begin{vmatrix} 2 & 1 \\ 3 & 4 \end{vmatrix}$

2. $\begin{vmatrix} -1 & 3 \\ -2 & 4 \end{vmatrix}$

3. $\begin{vmatrix} a & b \\ c & d \end{vmatrix}$

4. $\begin{vmatrix} 2 & \dfrac{1}{2} \\ 3 & \dfrac{1}{3} \end{vmatrix}$

5. $\begin{vmatrix} 0.7 & 1.2 \\ 1.5 & 0.9 \end{vmatrix}$

6. $\begin{vmatrix} 1 & 2 & 1 \\ 1 & 3 & 4 \\ 5 & 2 & 1 \end{vmatrix}$

7. $\begin{vmatrix} 2 & 0 & 3 \\ -1 & -2 & 4 \\ 0 & 1 & 2 \end{vmatrix}$

8. $\begin{vmatrix} 3 & 1 & 4 \\ 2 & 7 & 0 \\ -1 & 5 & -4 \end{vmatrix}$

9. $\begin{vmatrix} a & b & c \\ d & e & f \\ g & h & i \end{vmatrix}$

10. $\begin{vmatrix} 1 & 2 & 1 & 3 \\ -2 & 0 & 4 & 3 \\ 1 & -1 & 0 & 2 \\ -3 & 1 & 4 & 0 \end{vmatrix}$

Notes

Answer Key

1. $\begin{vmatrix} 2 & 1 \\ 3 & 4 \end{vmatrix} = 5$

2. $\begin{vmatrix} -1 & 3 \\ -2 & 4 \end{vmatrix} = 2$

3. $\begin{vmatrix} a & b \\ c & d \end{vmatrix} = ad - bc$

4. $\begin{vmatrix} 2 & \frac{1}{2} \\ 3 & \frac{1}{3} \end{vmatrix} = \frac{-5}{6}$

5. $\begin{vmatrix} 0.7 & 1.2 \\ 1.5 & 0.9 \end{vmatrix} = -1.17$

6. $\begin{vmatrix} 1 & 2 & 1 \\ 1 & 3 & 4 \\ 5 & 2 & 1 \end{vmatrix} = 20$

7. $\begin{vmatrix} 2 & 0 & 3 \\ -1 & -2 & 4 \\ 0 & 1 & 2 \end{vmatrix} = -19$

8. $\begin{vmatrix} 3 & 1 & 4 \\ 2 & 7 & 0 \\ -1 & 5 & -4 \end{vmatrix} = -8$

9. $\begin{vmatrix} a & b & c \\ d & e & f \\ g & h & i \end{vmatrix} = aei - afh - bdi + bgf + cdh - cge$

10. $\begin{vmatrix} 1 & 2 & 1 & 3 \\ -2 & 0 & 4 & 3 \\ 1 & -1 & 0 & 2 \\ -3 & 1 & 4 & 0 \end{vmatrix} = -14$

Solutions

1. $\begin{vmatrix} 2 & 1 \\ 3 & 4 \end{vmatrix} = 2(4) - 3(1) = 8 - 3 = 5$

2. $\begin{vmatrix} -1 & 3 \\ -2 & 4 \end{vmatrix} = (-1)(4) - (-2)(3) = -4 + 6 = 2$

3. $\begin{vmatrix} a & b \\ c & d \end{vmatrix} = ad - bc$

4. $\begin{vmatrix} 2 & \dfrac{1}{2} \\ 3 & \dfrac{1}{3} \end{vmatrix} = 2\left(\dfrac{1}{3}\right) - 3\left(\dfrac{1}{2}\right) = \dfrac{2}{3} - \dfrac{3}{2} = \dfrac{4}{6} - \dfrac{9}{6} = \dfrac{-5}{6}$

5. $\begin{vmatrix} 0.7 & 1.2 \\ 1.5 & 0.9 \end{vmatrix} = (0.7)(0.9) - (1.2)(1.5) = 0.63 - 1.8 = -1.17$

6. $\begin{vmatrix} 1 & 2 & 1 \\ 1 & 3 & 4 \\ 5 & 2 & 1 \end{vmatrix}$

Expanding across the top row of the matrix yields:

$$\begin{vmatrix} 1 & 2 & 1 \\ 1 & 3 & 4 \\ 5 & 2 & 1 \end{vmatrix} = 1 \begin{vmatrix} 3 & 4 \\ 2 & 1 \end{vmatrix} - 2 \begin{vmatrix} 1 & 4 \\ 5 & 1 \end{vmatrix} + 1 \begin{vmatrix} 1 & 3 \\ 5 & 2 \end{vmatrix}$$

Calculating each of the 2 x 2 determinants yields:

$$= 1\big(3(1) - 2(4)\big) - 2\big(1(1) - 5(4)\big) + 1\big(1(2) - 5(3)\big)$$

$$= (3 - 8) - 2(1 - 20) + (2 - 15)$$

$$= (-5) - 2(-19) + (-13)$$

$$= -5 + 38 - 13$$

$$= 20$$

7. $\begin{vmatrix} 2 & 0 & 3 \\ -1 & -2 & 4 \\ 0 & 1 & 2 \end{vmatrix}$

Expanding across the top row of the matrix yields:

$$\begin{vmatrix} 2 & 0 & 3 \\ -1 & -2 & 4 \\ 0 & 1 & 2 \end{vmatrix} = 2 \begin{vmatrix} -2 & 4 \\ 1 & 2 \end{vmatrix} - 0 \begin{vmatrix} -1 & 4 \\ 0 & 2 \end{vmatrix} + 3 \begin{vmatrix} -1 & -2 \\ 0 & 1 \end{vmatrix}$$

or,

$$2 \begin{vmatrix} -2 & 4 \\ 1 & 2 \end{vmatrix} + 3 \begin{vmatrix} -1 & -2 \\ 0 & 1 \end{vmatrix}$$

calculation cont. on next page...

Solution #7 from previous page...

Calculating each of the 2 x 2 determinants yields:

$$= 2\big((-2)(2) - 1(4)\big) + 3\big((-1)(1) - 0(-2)\big)$$

$$= 2(-4 - 4) + 3(-1 + 0)$$

$$= 2(-8) + 3(-1)$$

$$= -16 - 3$$

$$= -19$$

8. $\begin{vmatrix} 3 & 1 & 4 \\ 2 & 7 & 0 \\ -1 & 5 & -4 \end{vmatrix}$

Expanding across the top row of the matrix yields:

$$\begin{vmatrix} 3 & 1 & 4 \\ 2 & 7 & 0 \\ -1 & 5 & -4 \end{vmatrix} = 3\begin{vmatrix} 7 & 0 \\ 5 & -4 \end{vmatrix} - 1\begin{vmatrix} 2 & 0 \\ -1 & -4 \end{vmatrix} + 4\begin{vmatrix} 2 & 7 \\ -1 & 5 \end{vmatrix}$$

Calculating each of the 2 x 2 determinants yields:

$$= 3\big(7(-4) - 5(0)\big) - 1\big(2(-4) - (-1)(0)\big) + 4\big(2(5) - (-1)(7)\big)$$

$$= 3(-28 - 0) - (-8 - 0) + 4(10 + 7)$$

$$= 3(-28) - (-8) + 4(17)$$

$$= -84 + 8 + 68$$

$$= -8$$

9. $\begin{vmatrix} a & b & c \\ d & e & f \\ g & h & i \end{vmatrix}$

Expanding across the top row of the matrix yields:

$$\begin{vmatrix} a & b & c \\ d & e & f \\ g & h & i \end{vmatrix} = a\begin{vmatrix} e & f \\ h & i \end{vmatrix} - b\begin{vmatrix} d & f \\ g & i \end{vmatrix} + c\begin{vmatrix} d & e \\ g & h \end{vmatrix}$$

Calculating each of the 2 x 2 determinants yields:

$$= a(ei - fh) - b(di - gf) + c(dh - ge)$$

$$= aei - afh - bdi + bgf + cdh - cge$$

10.
$$\begin{vmatrix} 1 & 2 & 1 & 3 \\ -2 & 0 & 4 & 3 \\ 1 & -1 & 0 & 2 \\ -3 & 1 & 4 & 0 \end{vmatrix}$$

Expanding across the top row of the matrix yields the 3 x 3 determinants:

$$\begin{vmatrix} 1 & 2 & 1 & 3 \\ -2 & 0 & 4 & 3 \\ 1 & -1 & 0 & 2 \\ -3 & 1 & 4 & 0 \end{vmatrix} = 1\begin{vmatrix} 0 & 4 & 3 \\ -1 & 0 & 2 \\ 1 & 4 & 0 \end{vmatrix} - 2\begin{vmatrix} -2 & 4 & 3 \\ 1 & 0 & 2 \\ -3 & 4 & 0 \end{vmatrix} + 1\begin{vmatrix} -2 & 0 & 3 \\ 1 & -1 & 2 \\ -3 & 1 & 0 \end{vmatrix} - 3\begin{vmatrix} -2 & 0 & 4 \\ 1 & -1 & 0 \\ -3 & 1 & 4 \end{vmatrix}$$

Next, we expand each of the 3 x 3 determinants using the top row of each.

$$= 1\left[0\begin{vmatrix} 0 & 2 \\ 4 & 0 \end{vmatrix} - 4\begin{vmatrix} -1 & 2 \\ 1 & 0 \end{vmatrix} + 3\begin{vmatrix} -1 & 0 \\ 1 & 4 \end{vmatrix} \right] - 2\left[-2\begin{vmatrix} 0 & 2 \\ 4 & 0 \end{vmatrix} - 4\begin{vmatrix} 1 & 2 \\ -3 & 0 \end{vmatrix} + 3\begin{vmatrix} 1 & 0 \\ -3 & 4 \end{vmatrix} \right]$$

$$+ 1\left[-2\begin{vmatrix} -1 & 2 \\ 1 & 0 \end{vmatrix} - 0\begin{vmatrix} 1 & 2 \\ -3 & 0 \end{vmatrix} + 3\begin{vmatrix} 1 & -1 \\ -3 & 1 \end{vmatrix} \right] - 3\left[-2\begin{vmatrix} -1 & 0 \\ 1 & 4 \end{vmatrix} - 0\begin{vmatrix} 1 & 0 \\ -3 & 4 \end{vmatrix} + 4\begin{vmatrix} 1 & -1 \\ -3 & 1 \end{vmatrix} \right]$$

Calculating each of the 2 x 2 determinants that does not have a zero multiplier yields:

$$= \left[-4\left(-1(0) - 1(2) \right) + 3\left(-1(4) - 1(0) \right) \right]$$

$$- 2\left[-2\left(0(0) - 4(2) \right) - 4\left(1(0) - (-3)(2) \right) + 3\left(1(4) - (-3)(0) \right) \right]$$

$$+ \left[-2\left(-1(0) - 1(2) \right) + 3\left(1(1) - (-3)(-1) \right) \right]$$

$$- 3\left[-2\left(-1(4) - 1(0) \right) + 4\left(1(1) - (-3)(-1) \right) \right]$$

$$= \left[-4(-2) + 3(-4) \right] - 2\left[-2(-8) - 4(6) + 3(4) \right] + \left[-2(-2) + 3(-2) \right] - 3\left[-2(-4) + 4(-2) \right]$$

$$= (8 - 12) - 2(16 - 24 + 12) + (4 - 6) - 3(8 - 8)$$

$$= -4 - 2(4) - 2 - 3(0)$$

$$= -4 - 8 - 2$$

$$= -14$$

45

SIMULTANEOUS EQUATIONS I: METHOD OF ADDITION, METHOD OF SUBSTITUTION, AND CRAMER'S RULE

Solve the following systems of equations using:
a. The Method of Addition
b. The Method of Substitution
c. Cramer's Rule

The Method of Addition

1. Add the two equations.

Note: It may be necessary to multiply one or both of the equations by a factor before adding equations.

2. Solve the resulting equations for the remaining variable.

3. Take the value of the variable found in Step 2 and insert it into either equation to find the value of the other variable.

The Method of Substitution

1. Choose the simpler of the two equations and solve it for one of the variables.

2. Take the result from Step 1 and substitute it into the other equation. This substitution will produce an equation with only one variable.

3. Solve the equation produced in Step 2.

4. Take the result from Step 3 and insert it into the equation produced in Step 1 to find the value of the other variable.

Cramer's Rule

$$a_1 x + b_1 y = c_1$$

$$a_2 x + b_2 y = c_2$$

$$x = \frac{\begin{vmatrix} c_1 & b_1 \\ c_2 & b_2 \end{vmatrix}}{\begin{vmatrix} a_1 & b_1 \\ a_2 & b_2 \end{vmatrix}} \qquad y = \frac{\begin{vmatrix} a_1 & c_1 \\ a_2 & c_2 \end{vmatrix}}{\begin{vmatrix} a_1 & b_1 \\ a_2 & b_2 \end{vmatrix}}$$

* Note that the solutions in this section are grouped by the method used to solve the system.

1. $x + y = 4$
   $2x - y = -1$

2. $x - y = 3$
   $x + 2y = 0$

3. $2x + y = 2$
   $x - 3y = -6$

4. $5x - 3y = 0$
   $2x + 2y = -16$

5. $2x + 3y = 2$
   $4x - 6y = 0$

6. $x + y = 10$
   $3x + 12y = 12$

7. $\frac{1}{2}x + \frac{1}{4}y = 3$
   $\frac{3}{4}x - \frac{1}{2}y = 1$

8. $\frac{1}{2}x + 8y = 2$
   $x - y = \frac{33}{4}$

9. $10x + \frac{1}{3}y = -1$
   $5x + 2y = -\frac{23}{2}$

10. $5x + 7y = 6$
    $15x - 14y = -2$

Notes

Answer Key

The Method of Addition

1(a). $x = 1, y = 3$

2(a). $x = 2, y = -1$

3(a). $x = 0, y = 2$

4(a). $x = -3, y = -5$

5(a). $x = \dfrac{1}{2}, y = \dfrac{1}{3}$

6(a). $x = 12, y = -2$

7(a). $x = 4, y = 4$

8(a). $x = 8, y = -\dfrac{1}{4}$

9(a). $x = \dfrac{1}{10}, y = -6$

10(a). $x = \dfrac{2}{5}, y = \dfrac{4}{7}$

The Method of Substitution

1(b). $x = 1, y = 3$

2(b). $x = 2, y = -1$

3(b). $x = 0, y = 2$

4(b). $x = -3, y = -5$

5(b). $x = \dfrac{1}{2}, y = \dfrac{1}{3}$

6(b). $x = 12, y = -2$

7(b). $x = 4, y = 4$

8(b). $x = 8, y = -\dfrac{1}{4}$

9(b). $x = \dfrac{1}{10}, y = -6$

10(b). $x = \dfrac{2}{5}, y = \dfrac{4}{7}$

Cramer's Rule

1(c). $x = 1, y = 3$

2(c). $x = 2, y = -1$

3(c). $x = 0, y = 2$

4(c). $x = -3, y = -5$

5(c). $x = \dfrac{1}{2}, y = \dfrac{1}{3}$

6(c). $x = 12, y = -2$

7(c). $x = 4, y = 4$

8(c). $x = 8, y = -\dfrac{1}{4}$

9(c). $x = \dfrac{1}{10}, y = -6$

10(c). $x = \dfrac{2}{5}, y = \dfrac{4}{7}$

Solutions

The Method of Addition

1(a). $x + y = 4$

$2x - y = -1$

Add the two equations to cancel y and then solve for x:

$$x + y = 4$$
$$\underline{2x - y = -1}$$
$$3x + 0 = 3$$
$$3x = 3$$
$$x = 1$$

Inserting the result for x into the equation, we find y:

$$x + y = 4$$
$$1 + y = 4$$
$$1 + y - 1 = 4 - 1$$
$$y = 3$$

Solution: $x = 1$, $y = 3$

2(a). $x - y = 3$

$x + 2y = 0$

First, multiply the bottom equation by -1, yielding:

$$x - y = 3$$
$$-x - 2y = 0$$

Next, add the two equations to eliminate x and find y:

$$x - y = 3$$
$$\underline{-x - 2y = 0}$$
$$0 - 3y = 3$$
$$-3y = 3$$
$$\frac{-3y}{-3} = \frac{3}{-3}$$
$$y = -1$$

calculation cont. on next page...

Solution #2(a) from previous page...

Inserting the result for y into the top equation, we find x:

$$x - y = 3$$

$$x - (-1) = 3$$

$$x + 1 = 3$$

$$x + 1 - 1 = 3 - 1$$

$$x = 2$$

Solution: $x = 2$, $y = -1$

3(a). $2x + y = 2$

$x - 3y = -6$

We begin by multiplying the top equation by 3, yielding:

$$6x + 3y = 6$$

$$x - 3y = -6$$

Next, we add the two equations to cancel y and then solve for x:

$$6x + 3y = 6$$

$$\underline{x - 3y = -6}$$

$$7x + 0 = 0$$

$$7x = 0$$

$$\frac{7x}{7} = \frac{0}{7}$$

$$x = 0$$

Inserting the result for x into the bottom equation, we find y:

$$x - 3y = -6$$

$$0 - 3y = -6$$

$$-3y = -6$$

$$\frac{-3y}{-3} = \frac{-6}{-3}$$

$$y = 2$$

Solution: $x = 0$, $y = 2$

4(a). $5x - 3y = 0$

$2x + 2y = -16$

Multiplying the top equation by 2 and the bottom equation by 3, we get:

$$10x - 6y = 0$$

$$6x + 6y = -48$$

Adding the two equations to cancel y and then solving for x, we get:

$$10x - 6y = 0$$

$$\underline{6x + 6y = -48}$$

$$16x + 0 = -48$$

$$16x = -48$$

$$\frac{16x}{16} = \frac{-48}{16}$$

$$x = -3$$

Inserting the result for x into the *original* bottom equation, we find y:

$$2x + 2y = -16$$

$$2(-3) + 2y = -16$$

$$-6 + 2y = -16$$

$$-6 + 2y = 6 = 16 + 6$$

$$2y = 10$$

$$\frac{2y}{2} = \frac{-10}{2}$$

$$y = -5$$

Solution: $x = -3$, $y = -5$

5(a). $2x + 3y = 2$

$4x - 6y = 0$

Multiplying the top equation by 2 yields:

$$4x + 6y = 4$$

$$4x - 6y = 0$$

calculation cont. on next page...

Notes

Solution #5(a) from previous page...

Adding the two equations to cancel y and then solving for x yields:

$$4x + 6y = 4$$

$$\underline{4x - 6y = 0}$$

$$8x + 0 = 4$$

$$8x = 4$$

$$\frac{8x}{8} = \frac{4}{8}$$

$$x = \frac{1}{2}$$

Inserting the result for x into the *original* top equation, we find y:

$$2x + 3y = 2$$

$$2\left(\frac{1}{2}\right) + 3y = 2$$

$$1 + 3y - 1 = 2 - 1$$

$$3y = 1$$

$$\frac{3y}{3} = \frac{1}{3}$$

$$y = \frac{1}{3}$$

Solution: $x = \dfrac{1}{2}$, $y = \dfrac{1}{3}$

6(a). $x + y = 10$

$3x + 12y = 12$

First, we multiply the top equation by -3, yielding:

$$-3x - 3y = -30$$

$$3x + 12y = 12$$

Adding the two equations to cancel x and then solving for y, we get:

$$-3x - 3y = -30$$

$$\underline{3x + 12y = 12}$$

$$0 + 9y = -18$$

$$9y = -18$$

$$\frac{9y}{9} = \frac{-18}{9}$$

$$y = -2$$

calculation cont. on next page...

Solution #6(a) from previous page...

Inserting the result for y into the *original* top equation, we find x:

$$x + y = 10$$

$$x + (-2) = 10$$

$$x - 2 = 10$$

$$x - 2 + 2 = 10 + 2$$

$$x = 12$$

Solution: $x = 12$, $y = -2$

7(a). $\dfrac{1}{2}x + \dfrac{1}{4}y = 3$

$\dfrac{3}{4}x - \dfrac{1}{2}y = 1$

Multiplying the top equation by 4 and the bottom equation by 2 yields:

$$2x + y = 12 \quad \textbf{A}$$

$$\frac{3}{2}x - y = 2$$

Adding the two equations to cancel y and then solving for x, we get:

$$2x + y = 12$$

$$\frac{3}{2}x - y = 2$$

$$\rule{3cm}{0.4pt}$$

$$\frac{7}{2}x + 0 = 14$$

$$\frac{7}{2}x = 14$$

$$\frac{\frac{7}{2}x}{\frac{7}{2}} = \frac{14}{\frac{7}{2}}$$

$$x = \frac{14}{1} \cdot \frac{2}{7}$$

$$x = 4$$

calculation cont. on next page...

Notes

Solution #7(a) from previous page...

Inserting the result for x into Equation Ⓐ, we find y:

$$2x + y = 12$$

$$2(4) + y = 12$$

$$8 + y = 12$$

$$8 + y - 8 = 12 - 8$$

$$y = 4$$

Solution: $x = 4$, $y = 4$

8(a). $\dfrac{1}{2}x + 8y = 2$

$x - y = \dfrac{33}{4}$

First, we multiply the top equation by -2 yielding:

$$-x - 16y = -4$$

$$x - y = \frac{33}{4}$$

Adding the two equations to cancel x and then solving for y, we get:

$$-x - 16y = -4$$

$$\underline{\quad x - y = \frac{33}{4}\quad}$$

$$0 - 17y = \frac{17}{4}$$

$$-17y = \frac{17}{4}$$

$$\frac{-17y}{-17} = \frac{\frac{17}{4}}{-17}$$

$$y = \frac{17}{4} \cdot \frac{1}{-17}$$

$$y = \frac{-1}{4}$$

calculation cont. on next page...

Solution #8(a) from previous page...

Inserting the result for y into the bottom equation, we find x:

$$x - y = \frac{33}{4}$$

$$x - \left(\frac{-1}{4}\right) = \frac{33}{4}$$

$$x + \frac{1}{4} = \frac{33}{4}$$

$$x + \frac{1}{4} - \frac{1}{4} = \frac{33}{4} - \frac{1}{4}$$

$$x = \frac{32}{4}$$

$$x = 8$$

Solution: $x = 8$, $y = -\frac{1}{4}$

9(a). $10x + \frac{1}{3}y = -1$

$5x + 2y = -\frac{23}{2}$

We begin by multiplying the bottom equation by -2, yielding:

$$10x + \frac{1}{3}y = -1$$

$$-10x - 4y = 23$$

Next, we add the two equations to cancel x and then solve for y:

$$10x + \frac{1}{3}y = -1$$

$$\underline{-10x - 4y = 23}$$

$$0 - \frac{11}{3}y = 22$$

$$-\frac{11}{3}y = 22$$

$$\frac{-\frac{11}{3}}{-\frac{11}{3}}y = \frac{22}{-\frac{11}{3}}$$

$$y = \frac{22}{1} \cdot \left(-\frac{3}{11}\right)$$

$$y = -6$$

calculation cont. on next page...

Notes

Solution #9(a) from previous page...

Inserting the result for y into the top equation, we find x:

$$10x + \frac{1}{3}y = -1$$

$$10x + \frac{1}{3}y(-6) = -1$$

$$10x - 2 = -1$$

$$10x - 2 + 2 = -1 + 2$$

$$10x = 1$$

$$\frac{10x}{10} = \frac{1}{10}$$

$$x = \frac{1}{10}$$

Solution: $x = \frac{1}{10}$, $y = -6$

10(a). $5x + 7y = 6$

$15x - 14y = -2$

We begin by multiplying the top equation by -3, yielding:

$$-15x - 21y = -18$$

$$15x - 14y = -2$$

Next, we add the two equations to cancel x and then solve for y:

$$-15x - 21y = -18$$

$$\underline{15x - 14y = -2}$$

$$0 - 35y = -20$$

$$-35y = -20$$

$$\frac{-35y}{-35} = \frac{-20}{-35}$$

$$y = \frac{4}{7}$$

calculation cont. on next page...

Solution #10(a) from previous page...

Inserting the result for y into the *original* top equation, we find x:

$$5x + 7y = 6$$

$$5x + 7\left(\frac{4}{7}\right) = 6$$

$$5x + 4 = 6$$

$$5x + 4 - 4 = 6 - 4$$

$$5x = 2$$

$$\frac{5x}{5} = \frac{2}{5}$$

$$x = \frac{2}{5}$$

Solution: $x = \dfrac{2}{5}$, $y = \dfrac{4}{7}$

The Method of Substitution

1(b). $x + y = 4$

$2x - y = -1$

Solving the top equation for x, we get:

$$x + y = 4$$

$$x + y - y = 4$$

$$x = 4 - y \quad \boxed{\text{A}}$$

Substituting this result into the bottom equation, we find y:

$$2x - y = -1$$

$$2(4 - y) - y = -1$$

$$8 - 2y - y = -1$$

$$8 - 3y = -1$$

$$8 - 3y - 8 = -1 - 8$$

$$-3y = -9$$

$$\frac{-3y}{-3} = \frac{-9}{-3}$$

$$y = 3$$

calculation cont. on next page...

Solution #1(b) from previous page...

Lastly, we find x by substituting the result for y back into Equation Ⓐ:

$$x = 4 - y$$

$$x = 4 - 3$$

$$x = 1$$

Solution: $x = 1, y = 3$

2(b). $x - y = 3$

$x + 2y = 0$

Solving the top equation for x, we get:

$$x - y = 3$$

$$x - y + y = 3 + y$$

$$x = 3 + y \quad Ⓑ$$

Substituting this result into the bottom equation, we find y:

$$x + 2y = 0$$

$$(3 + y) + 2y = 0$$

$$3 + 3y = 0$$

$$3 + 3y - 3 = 0 - 3$$

$$3y = -3$$

$$\frac{3y}{3} = \frac{-3}{3}$$

$$y = -1$$

Lastly, we find x by substituting the result for y back into Equation Ⓑ:

$$x = 3 + y$$

$$x = 3 + (-1)$$

$$x = 3 - 1$$

$$x = 2$$

Solution: $x = 2, y = -1$

3(b). $2x + y = 2$

$x - 3y = -6$

Solving the top equation for y, we get:

$$2x = y = 2$$

$$2x + y - 2x = 2 - 2x$$

$$y = 2 - 2x \quad \text{C}$$

Substituting this result into the bottom equation, we find x:

$$x - 3y = -6$$

$$x - 3(2 - 2x) = -6$$

$$x - 6 + 6x = -6$$

$$7x - 6 = -6$$

$$7x - 6 + 6 = -6 + 6$$

$$7x = 0$$

$$\frac{7x}{7} = \frac{0}{7}$$

$$x = 0$$

Inserting the result for x into Equation C, we find y:

$$y = 2 - 2x$$

$$y = 2 - 2(0)$$

$$y = 2 - 0$$

$$y = 2$$

Solution: $x = 0$, $y = 2$

4(b). $5x - 3y = 0$

$2x + 2y = -16$

Solving the bottom equation for x, we get:

$$2x + 2y = -16$$

$$2x + 2y - 2y = -16 - 2y$$

$$2x = -16 - 2y$$

$$\frac{2x}{2} = \frac{-16 - 2y}{2}$$

$$x = -8 - y \quad \text{D}$$

calculation cont. on next page...

Solution #4(b) from previous page...

Substituting this result into the top equation, we find y:

$$5x - 3y = 0$$

$$5(-8 - y) - 3y = 0$$

$$-40 - 5y - 3y = 0$$

$$-40 - 8y = 0$$

$$-40 - 8y + 40 = 0 + 40$$

$$-8y = 40$$

$$\frac{-8y}{-8} = \frac{40}{-8}$$

$$y = -5$$

Inserting the result for y into Equation ⒟ , we find x:

$$x = -8 - y$$

$$x = -8 - (-5)$$

$$x = -8 + 5$$

$$x = -3$$

Solution: $x = -3$, $y = -5$

5(b). $2x + 3y = 2$

$4x - 6y = 0$

Solving the top equation for x, we get:

$$2x + 3y = 2$$

$$2x + 3y - 3y = 2 - 3y$$

$$2x = 2 - 3y$$

$$\frac{2x}{2} = \frac{2 - 3y}{2}$$

$$x = 1 - \frac{3}{2}y \quad ⒠$$

calculation cont. on next page...

Solution #5(b) from previous page...

Substituting this result into the bottom equation, we find y:

$$4x - 6y = 0$$

$$4\left(1 - \frac{3}{2}y\right) - 6y = 0$$

$$4 - 6y - 6y = 0$$

$$4 - 12y = 0$$

$$4 - 12y - 4 = 0 - 4$$

$$-12y = -4$$

$$\frac{-12}{-12} = \frac{-4}{-12}$$

$$y = \frac{1}{3}$$

Inserting the result for y into Equation $\boxed{E}$, we find x:

$$x = 1 - \frac{3}{2}y$$

$$x = 1 - \frac{3}{2}\left(\frac{1}{3}\right)$$

$$x = 1 - \frac{1}{2}$$

$$x = \frac{1}{2}$$

Solution: $x = \dfrac{1}{2}, y = \dfrac{1}{3}$

6(b). $x + y = 10$

$3x + 12y = 12$

Solving the top equation for x:

$$x + y = 10$$

$$x + y - y = 10 - y$$

$$x = 10 - y \quad \boxed{F}$$

calculation cont. on next page...

Solution #6(b) from previous page...

Substituting this result into the bottom equation, we find y:

$$3x + 12y = 12$$

$$3(10 - y) + 12y = 12$$

$$30 - 3y + 12y = 12$$

$$30 + 9y = 12$$

$$30 + 9y - 30 = 12 - 30$$

$$9y = -18$$

$$\frac{9y}{9} = \frac{-18}{9}$$

$$y = -2$$

Inserting the result for y into Equation $\boxed{F}$, we find x:

$$x = 10 - y$$

$$x = 10 - (-2)$$

$$x = 10 + 2$$

$$x = 12$$

Solution: $x = 12$, $y = -2$

7(b). $\dfrac{1}{2}x + \dfrac{1}{4}y = 3$

$\dfrac{3}{4}x - \dfrac{1}{2}y = 1$

Solving the top equation for y, we get:

$$\frac{1}{2}x + \frac{1}{4}y = 3$$

$$\frac{1}{2}x + \frac{1}{4}y - \frac{1}{2}x = 3 - \frac{1}{2}x$$

$$\frac{1}{4}y = 3 - \frac{1}{2}x$$

$$4\left(\frac{1}{4}y\right) = 4\left(3 - \frac{1}{2}x\right)$$

$$y = 12 - 2x \qquad \boxed{G}$$

calculation cont. on next page...

Solution #7(b) from previous page...

Substituting this result into the bottom equation, we find x:

$$\frac{3}{4}x - \frac{1}{2}y = 1$$

$$\frac{3}{4}x - \frac{1}{2}(12 - 2x) = 1$$

$$\frac{3}{4}x - 6 + x = 1$$

$$\frac{7}{4}x - 6 = 1$$

$$\frac{7}{4}x - 6 + 6 = 1 + 6$$

$$\frac{7}{4}x = 7$$

$$\frac{\frac{7}{4}x}{\frac{7}{4}} = \frac{7}{\frac{7}{4x}}$$

$$x = \frac{7}{1} \cdot \frac{4}{7}$$

$$x = 4$$

Inserting the result for x into Equation $\boxed{G}$, we find y:

$$y = 12 - 2x$$

$$y = 12 - 2(4)$$

$$y = 12 - 8$$

$$y = 4$$

Solution: $x = 4$, $y = 4$

8(b). $\dfrac{1}{2}x + 8y = 2$

$x - y = \dfrac{33}{4}$

Solving the bottom equation for x, we get:

$$x - y = \frac{33}{4}$$

$$x - y + y = \frac{33}{4} + y$$

$$x = \frac{33}{4} + y \qquad \boxed{H}$$

calculation cont. on next page...

Solution #8(b) from previous page...

Substituting this result into the top equation, we find y:

$$\frac{1}{2}x + 8y = 2$$

$$\frac{1}{2}\left(\frac{33}{4} + y\right) + 8y = 2$$

$$\frac{33}{8} + \frac{1}{2}y + 8y = 2$$

$$\frac{33}{8} + \frac{17}{2}y = 2$$

$$\frac{33}{8} + \frac{17}{2}y - \frac{33}{8} = 2 - \frac{33}{8}$$

$$\frac{17}{2}y = \frac{16}{8} - \frac{33}{8}$$

$$\frac{17}{2}y = -\frac{17}{8}$$

$$\frac{\frac{17}{2}}{\frac{17}{2}} = \frac{-\frac{17}{8}}{\frac{17}{2}}$$

$$y = -\frac{17}{8} \cdot \frac{2}{17}$$

$$y = -\frac{2}{8}$$

$$y = -\frac{1}{4}$$

Inserting the result for y into Equation $\boxed{H}$, we find x:

$$x = \frac{33}{4} + y$$

$$x = \frac{33}{4} + \left(-\frac{1}{4}\right)$$

$$x = \frac{33}{4} - \frac{1}{4}$$

$$x = \frac{32}{4}$$

$$x = 8$$

Solution: $x = 8$, $y = -\frac{1}{4}$

9(b). $10x + \dfrac{1}{3}y = -1$

$5x + 2y = -\dfrac{23}{2}$

Solving the top equation for y:

$$10x + \frac{1}{3}y = -1$$

$$10x + \frac{1}{3}y - 10x = -1 - 10x$$

$$\frac{1}{3}y = -1 - 10x$$

$$3\left(\frac{1}{3}y\right) = 3(-1 - 10x)$$

$$y = -3 - 30x \qquad \boxed{\text{I}}$$

Substituting this result into the bottom equation, we find x:

$$5x + 2y = -\frac{23}{2}$$

$$5x + 2(-3 - 30x) = -\frac{23}{2}$$

$$5x - 6 - 60x = -\frac{23}{2}$$

$$-55x - 6 = -\frac{23}{2}$$

$$-55x - 6 + 6 = -\frac{23}{2} + 6$$

$$-55x = -\frac{23}{2} + \frac{12}{2}$$

$$-55x = -\frac{11}{2}$$

$$\frac{-55x}{-55} = \frac{-\dfrac{11}{2}}{-55}$$

$$x = -\frac{11}{2} \cdot \frac{1}{-55}$$

$$x = \frac{1}{10}$$

calculation cont. on next page...

Notes

Solution #9(b) from previous page...

Inserting the result for x into Equation $\boxed{\text{I}}$, we find y:

$$y = -3 - 30x$$

$$y = -3 - 30\left(\frac{1}{10}\right)$$

$$y = -3 - 3$$

$$y = -6$$

Solution: $x = \dfrac{1}{10}$, $y = -6$

10(b). $5x + 7y = 6$

$15x - 14y = -2$

Solving the top equation for x, we get:

$$5x + 7y = 6$$

$$5x + 7y - 7y = 6 - 7y$$

$$5x = 6 - 7y$$

$$x = \frac{6 - 7y}{5} \qquad \boxed{\text{J}}$$

Substituting this result into the bottom equation, we find y:

$$15x - 14y = -2$$

$$15\left(\frac{6 - 7y}{5}\right) - 14y = -2$$

$$3(6 - 7y) - 14y = -2$$

$$18 - 21y - 14y = -2$$

$$18 - 35y = -2$$

$$18 - 35y - 18 = -2 - 18$$

$$-35y = -20$$

$$\frac{-35y}{-35} = \frac{-20}{-35}$$

$$y = \frac{4}{7}$$

calculation cont. on next page...

Solution #10(b) from previous page...

Inserting the result for y into Equation **J**, we find x:

$$x = \frac{6 - 7y}{5}$$

$$x = \frac{6 - 7\left(\dfrac{4}{7}\right)}{5}$$

$$x = \frac{6 - 4}{5}$$

$$x = \frac{2}{5}$$

Solution: $x = \dfrac{2}{5}$, $y = \dfrac{4}{7}$

Cramer's Rule

1(c). $x + y = 4$

$2x - y = -1$

$$x = \frac{\begin{vmatrix} 4 & 1 \\ -1 & -1 \end{vmatrix}}{\begin{vmatrix} 1 & 1 \\ 2 & -1 \end{vmatrix}} \qquad y = \frac{\begin{vmatrix} 1 & 4 \\ 2 & -1 \end{vmatrix}}{\begin{vmatrix} 1 & 1 \\ 2 & -1 \end{vmatrix}}$$

Evaluating each of the determinants:

$$\begin{vmatrix} 4 & 1 \\ -1 & -1 \end{vmatrix} = 4(-1) - (-1)(1) = -4 - (-1) = 4 + 1 = -3$$

$$\begin{vmatrix} 1 & 4 \\ 2 & -1 \end{vmatrix} = 1(-1) - 2(4) = -1 - 8 = -9$$

$$\begin{vmatrix} 1 & 1 \\ 2 & -1 \end{vmatrix} = 1(-1) - 2(1) = -1 - 2 = -3$$

Thus,

$$x = \frac{-3}{-3} = 1$$

$$y = \frac{-9}{-3} = 3$$

Solution: $x = 1$, $y = 3$

2(c). $x - y = 3$

$x + 2y = 0$

$$x = \frac{\begin{vmatrix} 3 & -1 \\ 0 & 2 \end{vmatrix}}{\begin{vmatrix} 1 & -1 \\ 1 & 2 \end{vmatrix}} \qquad y = \frac{\begin{vmatrix} 1 & 3 \\ 1 & 0 \end{vmatrix}}{\begin{vmatrix} 1 & -1 \\ 1 & 2 \end{vmatrix}}$$

Evaluating each of the determinants:

$$\begin{vmatrix} 3 & -1 \\ 0 & 2 \end{vmatrix} = 3(2) - 0(-1) = 6 + 0 = 6$$

$$\begin{vmatrix} 1 & 3 \\ 1 & 0 \end{vmatrix} = 1(0) - 1(3) = 0 - 3 = -3$$

$$\begin{vmatrix} 1 & -1 \\ 1 & 2 \end{vmatrix} = 1(2) - 1(-1) = 2 + = 3$$

Thus,

$$x = \frac{6}{3} \qquad y = \frac{-3}{3}$$

$$x = 2 \qquad y = -1$$

Solution: $x = 2, y = -1$

3(c). $2x + y = 2$

$x - 3y = -6$

$$x = \frac{\begin{vmatrix} 2 & 1 \\ -6 & -3 \end{vmatrix}}{\begin{vmatrix} 2 & 1 \\ 1 & -3 \end{vmatrix}} \qquad y = \frac{\begin{vmatrix} 2 & 2 \\ 1 & -6 \end{vmatrix}}{\begin{vmatrix} 2 & 1 \\ 1 & -3 \end{vmatrix}}$$

Evaluating each of the determinants:

$$\begin{vmatrix} 2 & 1 \\ -6 & -3 \end{vmatrix} = 2(-3) - (-6)(1) = -6 - (-6) = -6 + 6 = 0$$

$$\begin{vmatrix} 2 & 2 \\ 1 & -6 \end{vmatrix} = 2(-6) - 1(2) = -12 - 2 = -14$$

$$\begin{vmatrix} 2 & 1 \\ 1 & -3 \end{vmatrix} = 2(-3) - 1(1) = -6 - 1 = -7$$

Thus,

$$x = \frac{0}{-7} \qquad y = \frac{-14}{-7}$$

$$x = 0 \qquad y = -2$$

Solution: $x = 0, y = 2$

4(c). $5x - 3y = 0$

$2x + 2y = -16$

$$x = \frac{\begin{vmatrix} 0 & -3 \\ -16 & 2 \end{vmatrix}}{\begin{vmatrix} 5 & -3 \\ 2 & 2 \end{vmatrix}} \qquad y = \frac{\begin{vmatrix} 5 & 0 \\ 2 & -16 \end{vmatrix}}{\begin{vmatrix} 5 & -3 \\ 2 & 2 \end{vmatrix}}$$

Evaluating each of the determinants:

$$\begin{vmatrix} 0 & -3 \\ -16 & 2 \end{vmatrix} = 0(2) - (-16)(-3) = 0 - 48 = -48$$

$$\begin{vmatrix} 5 & 0 \\ 2 & -16 \end{vmatrix} = 5(-16) - 2(0) = -80 - 0 = -80$$

$$\begin{vmatrix} 5 & -3 \\ 2 & 2 \end{vmatrix} = 5(2) - 2(-3) = 10 + 6 = 16$$

Thus,

$$x = \frac{-48}{16} \qquad y = \frac{-80}{16}$$

$$x = -3 \qquad y = -5$$

Solution: $x = -3$, $y = -5$

5(c). $2x + 3y = 2$

$4x - 6y = 0$

$$x = \frac{\begin{vmatrix} 2 & 3 \\ 0 & -6 \end{vmatrix}}{\begin{vmatrix} 2 & 3 \\ 4 & -6 \end{vmatrix}} \qquad y = \frac{\begin{vmatrix} 2 & 2 \\ 4 & 0 \end{vmatrix}}{\begin{vmatrix} 2 & 3 \\ 4 & -6 \end{vmatrix}}$$

Evaluating each of the determinants:

$$\begin{vmatrix} 2 & 3 \\ 0 & -6 \end{vmatrix} = 2(-6) - 0(3) = -12 - 0 = -12$$

$$\begin{vmatrix} 2 & 2 \\ 4 & 0 \end{vmatrix} = 2(0) - 4(2) = 0 - 8 = -8$$

$$\begin{vmatrix} 2 & 3 \\ 4 & -6 \end{vmatrix} = 2(-6) - 4(3) = -12 - 12 = -24$$

calculation cont. on next page...

Solution #5(c) from previous page...

Thus,

$$x = \frac{-12}{-24} \qquad y = \frac{-8}{-24}$$

$$x = \frac{1}{2} \qquad y = \frac{1}{3}$$

Solution: $x = \dfrac{1}{2}$, $y = \dfrac{1}{3}$

6(c). $x + y = 10$

$3x + 12y = 12$

$$x = \frac{\begin{vmatrix} 10 & 1 \\ 12 & 12 \end{vmatrix}}{\begin{vmatrix} 1 & 1 \\ 3 & 12 \end{vmatrix}} \qquad\qquad y = \frac{\begin{vmatrix} 1 & 10 \\ 3 & 12 \end{vmatrix}}{\begin{vmatrix} 1 & 1 \\ 3 & 12 \end{vmatrix}}$$

Evaluating each of the determinants:

$$\begin{vmatrix} 10 & 3 \\ 12 & 12 \end{vmatrix} = 10(12) - 12(1) = 120 - 12 = 108$$

$$\begin{vmatrix} 1 & 10 \\ 3 & 12 \end{vmatrix} = 1(12) - 3(10) = 12 - 30 = -18$$

$$\begin{vmatrix} 1 & 1 \\ 3 & 12 \end{vmatrix} = 1(12) - 3(1) = 12 - 3 = 9$$

Thus,

$$x = \frac{108}{9} \qquad\qquad y = \frac{-18}{9}$$

$$x = 12 \qquad\qquad y = -2$$

Solution: $x = 12$, $y = -2$

7(c). $\dfrac{1}{2}x + \dfrac{1}{4}y = 3$

$\dfrac{3}{4}x - \dfrac{1}{2}y = 1$

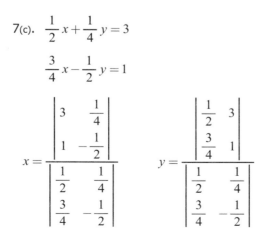

calculation cont. on next page...

Solution #7(c) from previous page...

Evaluating each of the determinants:

$$\begin{vmatrix} 3 & \dfrac{1}{4} \\ 1 & -\dfrac{1}{2} \end{vmatrix} = 3\left(-\dfrac{1}{2}\right) - 1\left(\dfrac{1}{4}\right) = -\dfrac{3}{2} - \dfrac{1}{4} = -\dfrac{6}{4} - \dfrac{1}{4} = -\dfrac{7}{4}$$

$$\begin{vmatrix} \dfrac{1}{2} & 3 \\ \dfrac{3}{4} & 1 \end{vmatrix} = \dfrac{1}{2}(1) - \dfrac{3}{4}(3) = \dfrac{1}{2} - \dfrac{9}{4} = \dfrac{2}{4} - \dfrac{9}{4} = -\dfrac{7}{4}$$

$$\begin{vmatrix} \dfrac{1}{2} & \dfrac{1}{4} \\ \dfrac{3}{4} & -\dfrac{1}{2} \end{vmatrix} = \dfrac{1}{2}\left(-\dfrac{1}{2}\right) - \dfrac{3}{4}\left(\dfrac{1}{4}\right) = -\dfrac{1}{4} - \dfrac{3}{16} = -\dfrac{4}{16} - \dfrac{3}{16} = -\dfrac{7}{16}$$

Thus,

$$x = \dfrac{-\dfrac{7}{4}}{-\dfrac{7}{16}} \qquad\qquad y = \dfrac{-\dfrac{7}{4}}{-\dfrac{7}{16}}$$

$$x = -\dfrac{7}{4}\left(-\dfrac{16}{7}\right) \qquad\qquad y = -\dfrac{7}{4}\left(-\dfrac{16}{7}\right)$$

$$x = 4 \qquad\qquad y = 4$$

Solution: $x = 4$, $y = 4$

8(c). $\dfrac{1}{2}x + 8y = 2$

$x - y = \dfrac{33}{4}$

$$x = \dfrac{\begin{vmatrix} 2 & 8 \\ \dfrac{33}{4} & -1 \end{vmatrix}}{\begin{vmatrix} \dfrac{1}{2} & 8 \\ 1 & -1 \end{vmatrix}} \qquad\qquad y = \dfrac{\begin{vmatrix} \dfrac{1}{2} & 2 \\ 1 & \dfrac{33}{4} \end{vmatrix}}{\begin{vmatrix} \dfrac{1}{2} & 8 \\ 1 & -1 \end{vmatrix}}$$

calculation cont. on next page...

Solution #8(c) from previous page...

Evaluating each of the determinants:

$$\begin{vmatrix} 2 & 8 \\ \dfrac{33}{4} & -1 \end{vmatrix} = 2(-1) - \dfrac{33}{4}(8) = -2 - 66 = -68$$

$$\begin{vmatrix} \dfrac{1}{2} & 2 \\ 1 & \dfrac{33}{4} \end{vmatrix} = \dfrac{1}{2}\left(\dfrac{33}{4}\right) - 1(2) = \dfrac{33}{8} - 2 = \dfrac{33}{8} - \dfrac{16}{8} = \dfrac{17}{8}$$

$$\begin{vmatrix} \dfrac{1}{2} & 8 \\ 1 & -1 \end{vmatrix} = \dfrac{1}{2}(-1) - 1(8) = -\dfrac{1}{2} - 8 = -\dfrac{17}{2}$$

Thus,

$$x = \dfrac{-68}{-\dfrac{17}{2}} = \dfrac{-68}{1}\left(-\dfrac{2}{17}\right) = 8$$

$$y = \dfrac{\dfrac{17}{8}}{-\dfrac{17}{2}} = \dfrac{17}{8}\left(-\dfrac{2}{17}\right) = -\dfrac{1}{4}$$

Solution: $x = 8,\ y = -\dfrac{1}{4}$

9(c). $10x + \dfrac{1}{3}y = -1$

$5x + 2y = -\dfrac{23}{2}$

$$x = \dfrac{\begin{vmatrix} -1 & \dfrac{1}{3} \\ -\dfrac{23}{2} & 2 \end{vmatrix}}{\begin{vmatrix} 10 & \dfrac{1}{3} \\ 5 & 2 \end{vmatrix}} \qquad y = \dfrac{\begin{vmatrix} 10 & -1 \\ 5 & -\dfrac{23}{2} \end{vmatrix}}{\begin{vmatrix} 10 & \dfrac{1}{3} \\ 5 & 2 \end{vmatrix}}$$

calculation cont. on next page...

Solution #9(c) from previous page...

Evaluating each of the determinants:

$$\begin{vmatrix} -1 & \dfrac{1}{3} \\ -\dfrac{23}{2} & 2 \end{vmatrix} = -1(2) - \left(-\dfrac{23}{2}\right)\left(\dfrac{1}{3}\right) = -2 + \dfrac{23}{6} = \dfrac{-12}{6} + \dfrac{23}{6} = \dfrac{11}{6}$$

$$\begin{vmatrix} 10 & -1 \\ 5 & -\dfrac{23}{2} \end{vmatrix} = 10\left(-\dfrac{23}{2}\right) - 5(-1) = -115 + 5 = -110$$

$$\begin{vmatrix} 10 & \dfrac{1}{3} \\ 5 & 2 \end{vmatrix} = 10(2) - 5\left(\dfrac{1}{3}\right) = 20 - \dfrac{5}{3} = \dfrac{60}{3} - \dfrac{5}{3} = \dfrac{55}{3}$$

Thus,

$$x = \dfrac{\dfrac{11}{6}}{\dfrac{55}{3}} = \dfrac{11}{6} \cdot \dfrac{3}{55} = \dfrac{1}{10}$$

$$y = \dfrac{-110}{\dfrac{55}{3}} = \dfrac{-110}{1} \cdot \dfrac{3}{55} = -6$$

Solution: $x = \dfrac{1}{10}, \ y = -6$

10(c). $5x + 7y = 6$

$15x - 14y = -2$

$$x = \dfrac{\begin{vmatrix} 6 & 7 \\ -2 & -14 \end{vmatrix}}{\begin{vmatrix} 5 & 7 \\ 15 & -14 \end{vmatrix}} \qquad y = \dfrac{\begin{vmatrix} 5 & 6 \\ 15 & -2 \end{vmatrix}}{\begin{vmatrix} 5 & 7 \\ 15 & -14 \end{vmatrix}}$$

Evaluating each of the determinants:

$$\begin{vmatrix} 6 & 7 \\ -2 & -14 \end{vmatrix} = 6(-14) - (-2)(7) = -84 + 14 = -70$$

$$\begin{vmatrix} 5 & 6 \\ 15 & -2 \end{vmatrix} = 5(-2) - 15(6) = -10 - 90 = -100$$

$$\begin{vmatrix} 5 & 7 \\ 15 & -14 \end{vmatrix} = 5(-14) - 15(7) = -70 - 105 = -175$$

calculation cont. on next page...

Notes

Solution #10(c) from previous page...

Thus,

$$x = \frac{-70}{-175} = \frac{2}{5}$$

$$y = \frac{-100}{-175} = \frac{4}{7}$$

Solution: $x = \frac{2}{5}$, $y = \frac{4}{7}$

46

SIMULTANEOUS EQUATIONS II: GAUSS-JORDAN ELIMINATION

Construct the augmented matrix for each of the following systems of equations.

Notes

1. $2x + 3y = 9$

   $4x + 7y = 5$

2. $4x + 2y + 7z = 2$

   $-3x + 5y - 8z = 6$

   $5x + y + z = -1$

3. $2x = 7$

   $3x - 5z = 9$

   $2y + 8z = -4$

4. $4x + 8y - 2z + 6w = 9$

   $3x - w = -9$

   $2x - 3y + z = 15$

   $7y + 10z = 1$

Solve the following systems of equations, 5 - 8, using Gauss-Jordan Elimination.

Solving a system of equations using Gauss-Jordan Elimination

1. Construct the augmented matrix that represents the system.
2. Put the system into *reduced row-echelon form*:

$$\begin{bmatrix} 1 & 0 & \cdots & 0 & \cdot \\ 0 & 1 & 0 \cdots & & \cdot \\ \cdot & 0 & \cdot & 0 & \cdot \\ 0 & \cdots & 0 & 1 & \cdot \end{bmatrix}$$

   using the following rules:
   a) Any two rows of the matrix may be interchanged.
   b) A row may be multiplied by a *non-zero* constant.
   c) A row may be multipled by a non-zero constant and then added to another row.

---

5. $x - 5y = -13$

   $3x + 2y = 12$

6. $2x + 3y = 6$

   $x - y = \dfrac{1}{2}$

7. $2y + z = 4$

   $2x - 3z = 16$

   $x - y = 6$

8. $2x + y + z = 4$

   $-3x + 2y - 2z = -10$

   $x - 2y + 3z = 7$

Notes

1. $\begin{bmatrix} 2 & 3 & | & 9 \\ 4 & 7 & | & 5 \end{bmatrix}$

2. $\begin{bmatrix} 4 & 2 & 7 & | & 2 \\ -3 & 5 & -8 & | & 6 \\ 5 & 1 & 1 & | & -1 \end{bmatrix}$

3. $\begin{bmatrix} 2 & 0 & 0 & | & 7 \\ 3 & 0 & -5 & | & 9 \\ 0 & 2 & 8 & | & -4 \end{bmatrix}$

4. $\begin{bmatrix} 4 & 8 & -2 & 6 & | & 9 \\ 3 & 0 & 0 & -1 & | & -9 \\ 2 & -3 & 1 & 0 & | & 15 \\ 0 & 7 & 10 & 0 & | & 1 \end{bmatrix}$

5. $x = 2, y = 3$

6. $x = \dfrac{3}{2}, y = 1$

7. $x = 8, y = 2, z = 0$

8. $x = 2, y = -1, z = 1$

Solutions

1. $\begin{bmatrix} 2 & 3 & | & 9 \\ 4 & 7 & | & 5 \end{bmatrix}$

2. $\begin{bmatrix} 4 & 2 & 7 & | & 2 \\ -3 & 5 & -8 & | & 6 \\ 5 & 1 & 1 & | & -1 \end{bmatrix}$

3. $\begin{bmatrix} 2 & 0 & 0 & | & 7 \\ 3 & 0 & -5 & | & 9 \\ 0 & 2 & 8 & | & -4 \end{bmatrix}$

4. $\begin{bmatrix} 4 & 8 & -2 & 6 & | & 9 \\ 3 & 0 & 0 & -1 & | & -9 \\ 2 & -3 & 1 & 0 & | & 15 \\ 0 & 7 & 10 & 0 & | & 1 \end{bmatrix}$

5. First, we construct the augmented matrix for the system:

$$\begin{bmatrix} 1 & -5 & | & -13 \\ 3 & 2 & | & 12 \end{bmatrix}$$

Since we already have a 1 in the top, left entry, our next task is to get a 0 under it using the allowed rules. This can be accomplished by multiplying the top row by -3 and adding it to the bottom row.

$$\begin{bmatrix} 1 & -5 & | & -13 \\ 0 & 17 & | & 51 \end{bmatrix}$$

Since 51 is 3 x 17, a simple way to get a 1 in the 2nd row, 2nd column without introducing ungainly fractions is to multiply the bottom row by 1/17, yielding:

$$\begin{bmatrix} 1 & -5 & | & -13 \\ 0 & 1 & | & 3 \end{bmatrix}$$

To get a zero in Row 1, Column 2, we multiply the bottom row by 5 and add it to the top row:

$$\begin{bmatrix} 1 & 0 & | & 2 \\ 0 & 1 & | & 3 \end{bmatrix}$$

Thus,
$$x = 2, \, y = 3$$

6. First, we construct the augmented matrix for the system:

$$\begin{bmatrix} 2 & 3 & | & 6 \\ 1 & -1 & | & \dfrac{1}{2} \end{bmatrix}$$

To get a 1 in Row 1, Column 1, we simply interchange the two rows of the matrix.

$$\begin{bmatrix} 1 & -1 & | & \dfrac{1}{2} \\ 2 & 3 & | & 6 \end{bmatrix}$$

calculation cont. on next page...

Solution #6 from previous page...

To get a 0 in Row 2, Column 1, we multiply the top row by -2 and add it to the bottom row.

$$\left[\begin{array}{cc|c} 1 & -1 & \dfrac{1}{2} \\ 0 & 5 & 5 \end{array}\right]$$

To get a 1 in Row 2, Column 2, we multiply the bottom row by 1/5:

$$\left[\begin{array}{cc|c} 1 & -1 & \dfrac{1}{2} \\ 0 & 1 & 1 \end{array}\right]$$

Lastly, to get a 0 in Row 1, Column 2, we add the bottom row to the top row:

$$\left[\begin{array}{cc|c} 1 & 0 & \dfrac{3}{2} \\ 0 & 1 & 1 \end{array}\right]$$

Thus,

$$x = \frac{3}{2}, \, y = 1$$

7. We begin by constructing the augmented matrix for the system:

$$\left[\begin{array}{ccc|c} 0 & 2 & 1 & 4 \\ 2 & 0 & -3 & 16 \\ 1 & -1 & 0 & 6 \end{array}\right]$$

To get a 1 in Row 1, Column 1, we simply interchange the 1st and 3rd rows.

$$\left[\begin{array}{ccc|c} 1 & -1 & 0 & 6 \\ 2 & 0 & -3 & 16 \\ 0 & 2 & 1 & 4 \end{array}\right]$$

Next, we get a 0 in Row 2, Column 1 by multiplying the top row by -2 and adding it to the 2nd row.

$$\left[\begin{array}{ccc|c} 1 & -1 & 0 & 6 \\ 0 & 2 & -3 & 4 \\ 0 & 2 & 1 & 4 \end{array}\right]$$

To get a 1 in Row 2, Column 2, we multiply the 2nd row by 1/2.

$$\left[\begin{array}{ccc|c} 1 & -1 & 0 & 6 \\ 0 & 1 & -\dfrac{3}{2} & 2 \\ 0 & 2 & 1 & 4 \end{array}\right]$$

calculation cont. on next page...

Solution #7 from previous page...

Adding the 2nd row to the 1st row produces a 0 in Row 1, Column 2.

$$\begin{bmatrix} 1 & 0 & -\dfrac{3}{2} & \bigg| & 8 \\ 0 & 1 & -\dfrac{3}{2} & \bigg| & 2 \\ 0 & 2 & 1 & \bigg| & 4 \end{bmatrix}$$

To get a 0 in Row 3, Column 2, we multiply the 2nd row by -2 and add it to the 3rd row:

$$\begin{bmatrix} 1 & 0 & -\dfrac{3}{2} & \bigg| & 8 \\ 0 & 1 & -\dfrac{3}{2} & \bigg| & 2 \\ 0 & 0 & 4 & \bigg| & 0 \end{bmatrix}$$

To get a 1 in Row 3, Column 3, we multiply the 3rd row by 1/4:

$$\begin{bmatrix} 1 & 0 & -\dfrac{3}{2} & \bigg| & 8 \\ 0 & 1 & -\dfrac{3}{2} & \bigg| & 2 \\ 0 & 0 & 1 & \bigg| & 0 \end{bmatrix}$$

Multiplying the 3rd row by 3/2 and adding it to both the 1st and 2nd rows produces zeros in both Row 1, Column 3 and Row 2, Column 3:

$$\begin{bmatrix} 1 & 0 & 0 & | & 8 \\ 0 & 1 & 0 & | & 2 \\ 0 & 0 & 1 & | & 0 \end{bmatrix}$$

Thus,

$$x = 8, \, y = 2, \, z = 0$$

8. We begin by constructing the augmented matrix for the system:

$$\begin{bmatrix} 2 & 1 & 1 & | & 4 \\ -3 & 2 & -2 & | & -10 \\ 1 & -2 & 3 & | & 7 \end{bmatrix}$$

To get a 1 in Row 1, Column 1, we simply interchange the 1st and 3rd rows.

$$\begin{bmatrix} 1 & -2 & 3 & | & 7 \\ -3 & 2 & -2 & | & -10 \\ 2 & 1 & 1 & | & 4 \end{bmatrix}$$

To get a 0 in Row 2, Column 1, we multiply the top row by 3 and add it to the 2nd row:

$$\begin{bmatrix} 1 & -2 & 3 & | & 7 \\ 0 & -4 & 7 & | & 11 \\ 2 & 1 & 1 & | & 4 \end{bmatrix}$$

calculation cont. on next page...

Solution #8 from previous page...

To get a 0 in Row 3, Column 1, we multiply the top row by -2 and add it to the 3rd row:

$$\begin{bmatrix} 1 & -2 & 3 & | & 7 \\ 0 & -4 & 7 & | & 11 \\ 0 & 5 & -5 & | & -10 \end{bmatrix}$$

To get a 1 in Row 2, Column 2, we first interchange the 2nd and 3rd rows,

$$\begin{bmatrix} 1 & -2 & 3 & | & 7 \\ 0 & 5 & -5 & | & -10 \\ 0 & -4 & 7 & | & 11 \end{bmatrix}$$

and then multiply the new 2nd row by 1/5:

$$\begin{bmatrix} 1 & -2 & 3 & | & 7 \\ 0 & 1 & -1 & | & -2 \\ 0 & -4 & 7 & | & 11 \end{bmatrix}$$

To get a 0 in Row 1, Column 2, we multiply the 2nd row by 2 and add it to the top row:

$$\begin{bmatrix} 1 & 0 & 1 & | & 3 \\ 0 & 1 & -1 & | & -2 \\ 0 & -4 & 7 & | & 11 \end{bmatrix}$$

To get a 0 in Row 3, Column 2, we multiply the 2nd row by 4 and add it to the 3rd row:

$$\begin{bmatrix} 1 & 0 & 1 & | & 3 \\ 0 & 1 & -1 & | & -2 \\ 0 & 0 & 3 & | & 3 \end{bmatrix}$$

To get a 1 in Row 3, Column 3, we multiply the 3rd row by 1/3:

$$\begin{bmatrix} 1 & 0 & 1 & | & 3 \\ 0 & 1 & -1 & | & -2 \\ 0 & 0 & 1 & | & 1 \end{bmatrix}$$

Adding the 3rd row to the 2nd row produces a zero in Row 2, Column 3.

$$\begin{bmatrix} 1 & 0 & 1 & | & 3 \\ 0 & 1 & 0 & | & -1 \\ 0 & 0 & 1 & | & 1 \end{bmatrix}$$

Lastly, to get a zero in Row 1, Column 3 we multiply the 3rd row by -1 and add it to the 1st row:

$$\begin{bmatrix} 1 & 0 & 0 & | & 2 \\ 0 & 1 & 0 & | & -1 \\ 0 & 0 & 1 & | & 1 \end{bmatrix}$$

Thus,

$$x = 2, \, y = -1, \, z = 1$$

FINDING THE TERMS OF A SEQUENCE

47

Write the 1st four terms of each of the following sequences.

Notes

1. $a_n = 3n + 2$

2. $a_n = n!$

3. $a_n = n^2$

4. $a_n = \dfrac{(n+1)!}{n!}$

5. $a_n = n^3 - n^2$

Write the 1st four terms of each of the following recursive sequences.

6. $a_n = 2a_{n-1}$ $a_1 = 3$ for $n \geq 2$

7. $a_n = \dfrac{1}{2}a_{n-1}$ $a_1 = 4$ for $n \geq 2$

8. $a_n = 3a_{n-1} + 4a_{n-2}$ $a_1 = 1,\ a_2 = -2$ for $n \geq 3$

9. $a_n = (a_{n-1})^2 + 1$ $a_1 = 1$ for $n \geq 2$

10. $a_n = (a_{n-1})(a_{n-2})$ $a_1 = -1,\ a_2 = 2$ for $n \geq 3$

Notes

Answer Key

1. $\{5, 8, 11, 14\}$

2. $\{1, 2, 6, 24\}$

3. $\{1, 4, 9, 16\}$

4. $\{2, 3, 4, 5\}$

5. $\{0, 4, 18, 48\}$

6. $\{3, 6, 12, 24\}$

7. $\left\{4, 2, 1, \dfrac{1}{2}\right\}$

8. $\{1, -2, -2, -14\}$

9. $\{1, 2, 5, 26\}$

10. $\{-1, 2, -2, -4\}$

Solutions

1. $a_n = 3n + 2$

   $a_1 = 3(1) + 2 = 5$

   $a_2 = 3(2) + 2 = 8$

   $a_3 = 3(3) + 2 = 11$

   $a_4 = 3(4) + 2 = 14$

   First four terms: $\{5, 8, 11, 14, ...\}$

2. $a_n = n!$

   $a_1 = 1! = 1$

   $a_2 = 2! = 2$

   $a_3 = 3! = 6$

   $a_4 = 4! = 24$

   First four terms: $\{1, 2, 6, 24, ...\}$

3. $a_n = n^2$

   $a_1 = 1^2 = 1$

   $a_2 = 2^2 = 4$

   $a_3 = 3^2 = 9$

   $a_4 = 4^2 = 16$

   First four terms: $\{1, 4, 9, 16, ...\}$

4. $a_n = \dfrac{(n+1)!}{n!}$

   $a_1 = \dfrac{(1+1)!}{1!} = \dfrac{2!}{1} = \dfrac{2}{1} = 2$

   $a_2 = \dfrac{(2+1)!}{2!} = \dfrac{3!}{2!} = 3$

   $a_3 = \dfrac{(3+1)!}{3!} = \dfrac{4!}{3!} = 4$

   $a_4 = \dfrac{(4+1)!}{4!} = \dfrac{5!}{4!} = 5$

   First four terms: $\{2, 3, 4, 5, ...\}$

5. $a_n = n^3 - n^2$

$a_1 = 1^3 - 1^2 = 0$

$a_2 = 2^3 - 2^2 = 8 - 4 = 4$

$a_3 = 3^3 - 3^2 = 27 - 9 = 18$

$a_4 = 4^3 - 4^2 = 64 - 16 = 48$

First four terms: $\{0, 4, 18, 48, ...\}$

6. $a_n = 2a_{n-1} \qquad a_1 = 3$ for $n \geq 2$

$a_2 = 2a$

$a_2 = 2(3) = 6$

$a_3 = 2a_2$

$a_3 = 2(6) = 12$

First four terms: $\{3, 6, 12, 24, ...\}$

$a_4 = 2a_3$

$a_4 = 2(12) = 24$

7. $a_n = \dfrac{1}{2} a_{n-1} \qquad a_1 = 4$ for $n \geq 2$

$a_2 = \dfrac{1}{2} a_1$

$a_2 = \dfrac{1}{2}(4) = 2$

$a_3 = \dfrac{1}{2} a_2$

$a_3 = \dfrac{1}{2}(2) = 1$

First four terms: $\left\{4, 2, 1, \dfrac{1}{2}, ...\right\}$

$a_4 = \dfrac{1}{2} a_3$

$a_4 = \dfrac{1}{2}(1) = \dfrac{1}{2}$

8. $a_n = 3a_{n-1} + 4a_{n-2}$ $\qquad a_1 = 1,\ a_2 = -2$ for $n \geq 3$

$a_3 = 3a_2 + 4a_1$

$a_3 = 3(-2) + 4(1)$

$a_3 = -6 + 4$

$a_3 = -2$

$a_4 = 3a_3 + 4a_2$

$a_4 = 3(-2) + 4(-2)$

$a_4 = -6 - 8$

$a_4 = -14$

First four terms: $\{1,\ -2,\ -2,\ -14,\ ...\}$

9. $a_n = (a_{n-1})^2 + 1$ $\qquad a_1 = 1$ for $n \geq 2$

$a_2 = (a_1)^2 + 1$

$a_2 = (1)^2 + 1$

$a_2 = 2$

$a_3 = (a_2)^2 + 1$

$a_3 = (2)^2 + 1$

$a_3 = 5$

$a_4 = (a_3)^2 + 1$

$a_4 = (5)^2 + 1$

$a_4 = 26$

First four terms: $\{1,\ 2,\ 5,\ 26,\ ...\}$

10. $a_n = (a_{n-1})(a_{n-2})$ $\qquad a_1 = -1,\ a_2 = 2$ for $n \geq 3$

$a_3 = (a_2)(a_1)$

$a_3 = (2)(-1)$

$a_3 = -2$

$a_4 = (a_3)(a_2)$

$a_4 = (-2)(2)$

$a_4 = -4$

First four terms: $\{-1,\ 2,\ -2,\ -4,\ ...\}$

48

SUMMATION
OF A SERIES

Calculate each of the following series.

1. $\displaystyle\sum_{n=1}^{5} n^2 - 1$

2. $\displaystyle\sum_{i=3}^{7} \frac{(-1)^i}{2}$

3. $\displaystyle\sum_{j=2}^{4} \frac{(j+1)!}{j!}$

4. $\displaystyle\sum_{i=3}^{6} \frac{1}{2}(i+1)$

5. $\displaystyle\sum_{i=-2}^{2} 2i$

6. $\displaystyle\sum_{t=2}^{6} \frac{1}{t}$

7. $\displaystyle\sum_{n=0}^{3} (n+2)^2$

8. $\displaystyle\sum_{i=-3}^{4} |i|$

9. $\displaystyle\sum_{k=2}^{6} \frac{k+1}{k}$

10. $\displaystyle\sum_{i=1}^{5} [i+0.5]$

Answer Key

1. $\displaystyle\sum_{n=1}^{5} n^2 - 1 = 50$

2. $\displaystyle\sum_{i=3}^{7} \frac{(-1)^i}{2} = -\frac{1}{2}$

3. $\displaystyle\sum_{j=2}^{4} \frac{(j+1)!}{j!} = 12$

4. $\displaystyle\sum_{i=3}^{6} \frac{1}{2}(i+1) = 11$

5. $\displaystyle\sum_{i=-2}^{2} 2i = 0$

6. $\displaystyle\sum_{t=2}^{6} \frac{1}{t} = 1\frac{9}{20}$

7. $\displaystyle\sum_{n=0}^{3} (n+2)^2 = 54$

8. $\displaystyle\sum_{i=-3}^{4} |i| = 16$

9. $\displaystyle\sum_{k=2}^{6} \frac{k+1}{k} = 6\frac{9}{20}$

10. $\displaystyle\sum_{i=1}^{5} [\![i+0.5]\!] = 15$

Solutions

1. $\displaystyle\sum_{n=1}^{5} n^2 - 1 = \left(1^2 - 1\right) + \left(2^2 - 1\right) + \left(3^2 - 1\right) + \left(4^2 - 1\right) + \left(5^2 - 1\right)$

$\displaystyle\sum_{n=1}^{5} n^2 - 1 = (1-1) + (4-1) + (9-1) + (16-1) + (25-1)$

$\displaystyle\sum_{n=1}^{5} n^2 - 1 = 0 + 3 + 8 + 15 + 24$

$\displaystyle\sum_{n=1}^{5} n^2 - 1 = 50$

2. $\displaystyle\sum_{i=3}^{7} \frac{(-1)^i}{2} = \frac{(-1)^3}{2} + \frac{(-1)^4}{2} + \frac{(-1)^5}{2} + \frac{(-1)^6}{2} + \frac{(-1)^7}{2}$

$\displaystyle\sum_{i=3}^{7} \frac{(-1)^i}{2} = -\frac{1}{2} + \frac{1}{2} - \frac{1}{2} + \frac{1}{2} - \frac{1}{2}$

$\displaystyle\sum_{i=3}^{7} \frac{(-1)^i}{2} = -\frac{1}{2}$

3. $\displaystyle\sum_{j=2}^{4} \frac{(j+1)!}{j!} = \frac{(2+1)!}{2!} + \frac{(3+1)!}{3!} + \frac{(4+1)!}{4!}$

$\displaystyle\sum_{j=2}^{4} \frac{(j+1)!}{j!} = \frac{3!}{2!} + \frac{4!}{3!} + \frac{5!}{4!}$

$\displaystyle\sum_{j=2}^{4} \frac{(j+1)!}{j!} = 3 + 4 + 5$

$\displaystyle\sum_{j=2}^{4} \frac{(j+1)!}{j!} = 12$

4. $\displaystyle\sum_{i=3}^{6} \frac{1}{2}(i+1) = \frac{1}{2}(3+1) + \frac{1}{2}(4+1) + \frac{1}{2}(5+1) + \frac{1}{2}(6+1)$

$\displaystyle\sum_{i=3}^{6} \frac{1}{2}(i+1) = \frac{1}{2}(4) + \frac{1}{2}(5) + \frac{1}{2}(6) + \frac{1}{2}(7)$

$\displaystyle\sum_{i=3}^{6} \frac{1}{2}(i+1) = 2 + \frac{5}{2} + 3 + \frac{7}{2}$

$\displaystyle\sum_{i=3}^{6} \frac{1}{2}(i+1) = 11$

5. $\displaystyle\sum_{i=-2}^{2} 2i = 2(-2) + 2(-1) + 2(0) + 2(1) + 2(2)$

$\displaystyle\sum_{i=-2}^{2} 2i = -4 - 2 + 0 + 2 + 4$

$\displaystyle\sum_{i=-2}^{2} 2i = 0$

6. $\displaystyle\sum_{t=2}^{6} \frac{1}{t} = \frac{1}{2} + \frac{1}{3} + \frac{1}{4} + \frac{1}{5} + \frac{1}{6}$ } to add the fractions, we use a common denominator of 60.

$\displaystyle\sum_{t=2}^{6} \frac{1}{t} = \frac{30}{60} + \frac{20}{60} + \frac{15}{60} + \frac{12}{60} + \frac{10}{60}$

$\displaystyle\sum_{t=2}^{6} \frac{1}{t} = \frac{87}{60} = 1\frac{27}{60} = 1\frac{9}{20}$

7. $\displaystyle\sum_{n=0}^{3} (n+2)^2 = (0+2)^2 + (1+2)^2 + (2+2)^2 + (3+2)^2$

$\displaystyle\sum_{n=0}^{3} (n+2)^2 = (2)^2 + (3)^2 + (4)^2 + (5)^2$

$\displaystyle\sum_{n=0}^{3} (n+2)^2 = 4 + 9 + 16 + 25$

$\displaystyle\sum_{n=0}^{3} (n+2)^2 = 54$

8. $\displaystyle\sum_{i=-3}^{4} |i| = |-3| + |-2| + |-1| + |0| + |1| + |2| + |3| + |4|$

$\displaystyle\sum_{i=-3}^{4} |i| = 3 + 2 + 1 + 0 + 1 + 2 + 3 + 4$

$\displaystyle\sum_{i=-3}^{4} |i| = 16$

9. $\displaystyle\sum_{k=2}^{6} \frac{k+1}{k} = \frac{2+1}{2} + \frac{3+1}{3} + \frac{4+1}{4} + \frac{5+1}{5} + \frac{6+1}{6}$

$\displaystyle\sum_{k=2}^{6} \frac{k+1}{k} = \frac{3}{2} + \frac{4}{3} + \frac{5}{4} + \frac{6}{5} + \frac{7}{6}$ } to add the fractions, we use a common denominator of 60.

$\displaystyle\sum_{k=2}^{6} \frac{k+1}{k} = \frac{90}{60} + \frac{80}{60} + \frac{75}{60} + \frac{72}{60} + \frac{70}{60}$

$\displaystyle\sum_{k=2}^{6} \frac{k+1}{k} = \frac{387}{60} = 6\frac{27}{60} = 6\frac{9}{20}$

10. $\displaystyle\sum_{i=1}^{5}\left[\!\left[i+0.5\right]\!\right]=\left[\!\left[1+0.5\right]\!\right]+\left[\!\left[2+0.5\right]\!\right]+\left[\!\left[3+0.5\right]\!\right]+\left[\!\left[4+0.5\right]\!\right]+\left[\!\left[5+0.5\right]\!\right]$

$\displaystyle\sum_{i=1}^{5}\left[\!\left[i+0.5\right]\!\right]=\left[\!\left[1.5\right]\!\right]+\left[\!\left[2.5\right]\!\right]+\left[\!\left[3.5\right]\!\right]+\left[\!\left[4.5\right]\!\right]+\left[\!\left[5.5\right]\!\right]$

$\displaystyle\sum_{i=1}^{5}\left[\!\left[i+0.5\right]\!\right]=1+2+3+4+5$

$\displaystyle\sum_{i=1}^{5}\left[\!\left[i+0.5\right]\!\right]=15$

Final Examination I

Note: In this first comprehensive final exam, the topics are grouped, but are not in the same order as presented in the book.

1. Given that $\sin\theta = 0.45$, find the angle θ.

2.

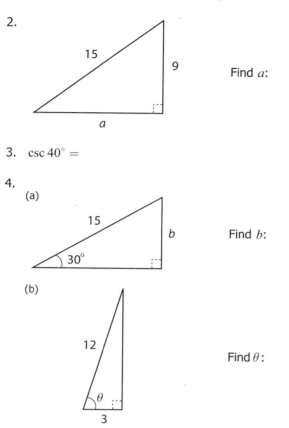

Find a:

3. $\csc 40° =$

4.

(a)

Find b:

(b)

Find θ:

5. Given that $\mathbf{v} = 4\mathbf{i} - 2\mathbf{j}$ and $\mathbf{w} = 3\mathbf{i} + 7\mathbf{j}$, find:

    (a) $\mathbf{v} + \mathbf{w}$ (c) $\mathbf{v} \cdot \mathbf{w}$

    (b) $\mathbf{v} - \mathbf{w}$ (d) $\|\mathbf{v}\|$

6. Identify the base and the exponent in the expression

$$\left(\frac{1}{2}\right)^5$$

7. Calculate the volume of a sphere of radius 6 in.

8. $\begin{vmatrix} 2 & -5 \\ 3 & -7 \end{vmatrix} =$

9. $4\begin{bmatrix} 3 & 4 & -2 \\ 1 & 0 & 5 \end{bmatrix} =$

10. $\begin{bmatrix} 3 & 4 & -1 \\ 5 & 2 & 0 \end{bmatrix}\begin{bmatrix} -2 & -5 \\ 6 & 8 \\ 3 & -3 \end{bmatrix} =$

11. Factor each of the following:

    (a) $x^2 - 9$

    (b) $x^3 + 8$

    (c) $4x^3 y^8 + 12x^4 y^3$

12. Determine if each of the following is a function of x.

    (a) $y = x^2 + 3$

    (b) $y^2 = x$

    (c) $y = \dfrac{4}{x}$

13. Determine if each of the following graphs is a function.

    (a)   (b)

    (c)   (d)

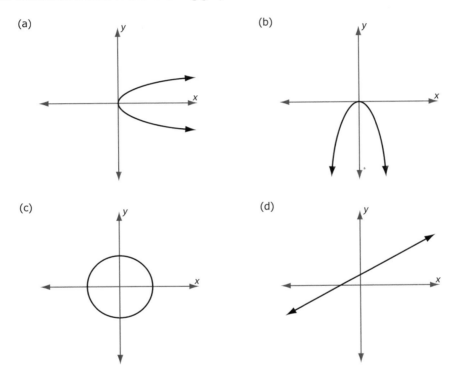

14. Find the distance and midpoint between the points $(2, -5)$ and $(6, 3)$.

15. $3\sqrt{2} + 5\sqrt{2} - \sqrt{2} =$

16. $\sqrt{8} \cdot \sqrt{2} =$

17. $\left(x^2 + 3x - 5\right)\left(x^3 - x^2 + 9\right) =$

18. $\left(4x^3 + 7x^2 - 5x + 1\right) - \left(x^3 - 9x^2 - 5\right) =$

19. Given that $z_1 = 1 + i$ and $z_2 = 2 - 3i$, find:

    (a) $z_1 + z_2$ (d) $\dfrac{z_1}{z_2}$

    (b) $4z_1$ (e) $(z_1)^6$

    (c) $z_1 \cdot z_2$

20. Translate each of the following exponential expressions into a logarithmic expression.

    (a) $3^4 = 81$

    (b) $\left(\dfrac{1}{2}\right)^3 = \dfrac{1}{8}$

    (c) $10^2 = 100$

    (d) $e^{2x} = v$

21. Translate each of the following logarithmic expressions into an exponential expression.

    (a) $\log_2 32 = 5$

    (b) $\text{Log}\,1000 = 3$

    (c) $\text{Ln}\,5 = x$

22. Combine $3 \log_2 x - \dfrac{1}{4} \log_2 y$ as far as possible using the properties of logarithms.

23. Solve each of the following.

    (a) $\log_2 (x - 1) = 3$

    (b) $5^{\frac{x}{2}} = 125$

    (c) $e^{7x} = 10$

    (d) $\text{Log}\,(4x + 9) = 2$

24. Solve each of the following.

    (a) $x - 3 = 9$ (d) $\dfrac{6}{x} = 18$

    (b) $4x = 20$ (e) $5x - 2 = 10$

    (c) $\dfrac{x}{3} = 2$ (f) $\dfrac{7x + 3}{5} = 1$

25. Solve each of the following quadratic equations using the indicated method.

    (a) $4x^2 = 100$ Square Root Method

    (b) $x^2 + 5x - 8 = 0$ Completing the Square

    (c) $x^2 + 4x + 3 = 0$ Factoring

    (d) $5x^2 + 9x = 10$ Quadratic Formula

26. Simply $\dfrac{x^{-2}x^5}{x^{-3}}$ as far as possible using the properties of exponents.

27. Convert $\dfrac{3\pi}{8}$ Rad into degrees.

28. Convert $225°$ into radians. Record your final answer in terms of π.

29. Sketch a graph of each of the following functions.

    (a) $f(x) = x - 3$

    (b) $f(x) = x^2$

    (c) $f(x) = x^3$

30. Solve each of the following systems of equations using the indicated method.

    (a) $x + y = -3$

         $2x + 3y = -11$ Method of Addition

    (b) $2x + y = 2$

         $3x - 4y = -19$ Method of Substitution

    (c) $6x + y = 0$

         $5x + 2y = -7$ Cramer's Rule

    (d) $x + y - z = 9$

         $2x - z = 8$ Gauss-Jordan Elimination

         $y + 2z = -5$

31. Convert the rectangular complex number $z = 3 + i$ into its polar form.

32. Convert the polar complex number $z = 3\left(\cos 20° + i\sin 20°\right)$ into its rectangular form.

33. $\displaystyle\sum_{i=1}^{4} \dfrac{(-1)^i}{i+1} =$

34. Calculate each of the following:

    (a) $_{10}C_3$

    (b) $_7P_5$

35. Given that the graph of $f(x)=|x|$ is

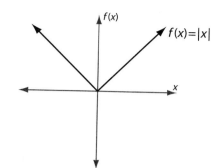

use the shift properties to sketch a graph of $f(x)=-|x|+2$.

36. Given that $z_1 = 10\left(\cos 60° + i\sin 60°\right)$ and $z_2 = 2\left(\cos 15° + i\sin 15°\right)$, find:

(a) $z_1 \cdot z_2$

(b) $\dfrac{z_1}{z_2}$

(c) $\left(z_2\right)^4$

37. Given that $f(x) = 3x^2 + 2x$ and $g(x) = x - 1$, find:

(a) $f \circ g(x)$

(b) $g \circ f(x)$

(c) $f \circ g(1)$

38. Plot the complex number $z = 5 - i$.

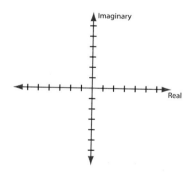

39. Write out the first four terms of the sequence $a_n = (n+1)! - n$.

40. Plot the polar point $(r, \theta) = (-3, 45°)$.

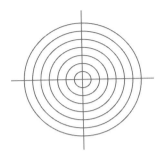

41. Convert the rectangular point $(x, y) = (1, 4)$ into polar coordinates.

42. Convert the polar point $(r, \theta) = (2, 35°)$ into rectangular coordinates.

43. Sketch a graph of each of the following trigonometric functions.

    (a) $y = \sin x$

    (b) $y = \cos x$

    (c) $y = \sin 2x$

    (d) $y = 4 \cos x$

44. Find the slope of each of the following lines.

    (a)   The line that passes through the points $(3, -4)$ and $(1, 6)$.

    (b)   The line $y = 4x + 1$.

    (c)   A line parallel to the line $y = 6x - 5$.

    (d)   A line perpendicular to the line $y = \dfrac{2}{3}x + 8$.

45. Write an equation for each of the following lines.

    (a)   The line with a slope of 5 and a y-intercept of 2.

    (b)   The line that passes through the points $(2, 4)$ and $(-1, 5)$.

    (c)   The line that is parallel to the line $y = 8x - 3$ that has a y-intercept of 3.

    (d)   The line that is perpendicular to the line $y = 5x + 7$ that passes through the point $(0, -6)$.

46. Write the equation of the circle that is centered at $(-2, 6)$ and has a radius of 4.

47. Solve the following inequality :

$$-4x + 6 < 8$$

1. $26.74°$

2. 12

3. 1.555

4.
 (a) 7.5
 (b) $75.52°$

5.
 (a) $7\mathbf{i}+5\mathbf{j}$
 (b) $\mathbf{i}-9\mathbf{j}$
 (c) -2
 (d) $2\sqrt{5}$

6. $\underbrace{\left(\frac{1}{2}\right)^{5}}$
 exponent (pointing to 5), base (pointing to $\frac{1}{2}$)

7. 288π in.^{3}

8. 1

9. $\begin{bmatrix} 12 & 16 & -8 \\ 4 & 0 & 20 \end{bmatrix}$

10. $\begin{bmatrix} 15 & 20 \\ 2 & -9 \end{bmatrix}$

11.
 (a) $(x+3)(x-3)$
 (b) $(x+2)(x^2-2x+4)$
 (c) $4x^3y^3(y^5+3x)$

12.
 (a) Function
 (b) Not a Function
 (c) Function

13.
 (a) Not a Function
 (b) Function
 (c) Not a Function
 (d) Function

14.
 Distance: $d=4\sqrt{5}$
 Midpoint: $(\bar{x},\bar{y})=(4,-1)$

15. $7\sqrt{2}$

16. 4

17. $x^5+2x^4-8x^3+14x^2+27x-45$

18. $3x^3+16x^2-5x+6$

19.
 (a) $3-2i$
 (b) $4+4i$
 (c) $5-i$
 (d) $-\frac{1}{13}+\frac{5}{13}i$
 (e) $-8i$

20.
 (a) $\log_3 81=4$
 (b) $\log_{\frac{1}{2}}\frac{1}{8}=3$
 (c) $\text{Log}\,100=2$
 (d) $\text{Ln}\,v=2x$

21.
 (a) $2^5=32$
 (b) $10^3=1000$
 (c) $e^x=5$

22. $\log_2\frac{x^3}{\sqrt[4]{y}}$

23.
 (a) 9
 (b) 6
 (c) 0.3
 (d) $22\frac{3}{4}$

24.
 (a) 12
 (b) 5
 (c) 6
 (d) $\frac{1}{3}$
 (e) $2\frac{2}{5}$
 (f) $\frac{2}{7}$

25.
(a) ± 5

(b) $\dfrac{-5+\sqrt{57}}{2}$ and $\dfrac{-5-\sqrt{57}}{2}$

(c) -1 and -3

(d) $\dfrac{-9+\sqrt{281}}{10}$ and $\dfrac{-9-\sqrt{281}}{10}$

26. x^6

27. $67.5°$

28. $\dfrac{5\pi}{4}$ Rad

29.
(a)

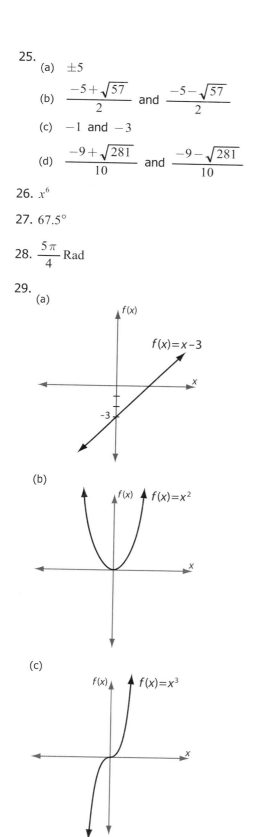

(b)

(c)

30.
(a) $x=2,\ y=-5$

(b) $x=-1,\ y=4$

(c) $x=1,\ y=-6$

(d) $x=2,\ y=3,\ z=-4$

31. $\sqrt{10}\left(\cos 18.43° + i\sin 18.43°\right)$

32. $2.8 + 1.02i$

33. $-\dfrac{13}{60}$

34.
(a) 120

(b) 720

35.

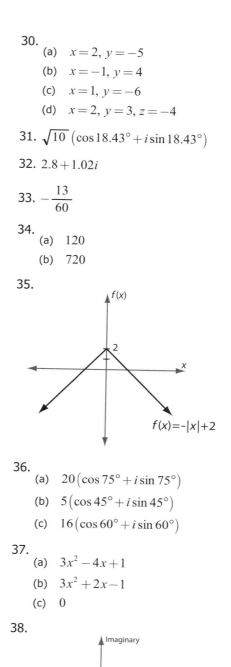

36.
(a) $20\left(\cos 75° + i\sin 75°\right)$

(b) $5\left(\cos 45° + i\sin 45°\right)$

(c) $16\left(\cos 60° + i\sin 60°\right)$

37.
(a) $3x^2 - 4x + 1$

(b) $3x^2 + 2x - 1$

(c) 0

38.

39. $\{1, 4, 21, 116\}$

40. $(-3, 45°)$

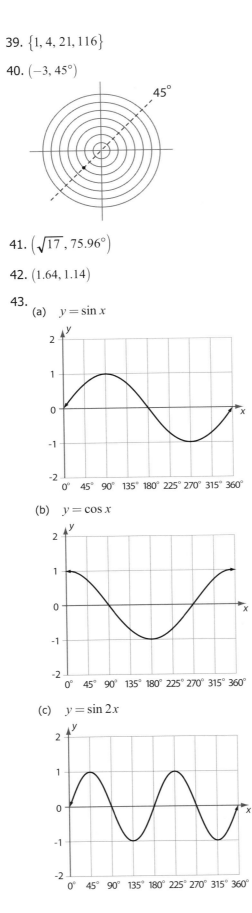

41. $\left(\sqrt{17}, 75.96°\right)$

42. $(1.64, 1.14)$

43.
(a) $y = \sin x$

(b) $y = \cos x$

(c) $y = \sin 2x$

(d) $y = 4\cos x$

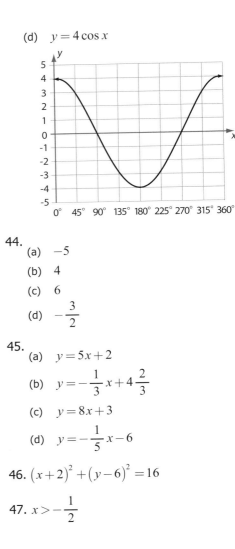

44.
(a) -5

(b) 4

(c) 6

(d) $-\dfrac{3}{2}$

45.
(a) $y = 5x + 2$

(b) $y = -\dfrac{1}{3}x + 4\dfrac{2}{3}$

(c) $y = 8x + 3$

(d) $y = -\dfrac{1}{5}x - 6$

46. $(x+2)^2 + (y-6)^2 = 16$

47. $x > -\dfrac{1}{2}$

1. $\sin \theta = 0.45$

   $\sin^{-1}(\sin \theta) = \sin^{-1}(0.45)$

   $\theta = 26.74°$

2. $a^2 + b^2 = c^2$

   $a^2 + 9^2 = 15^2$

   $a^2 + 81 = 225$

   $a^2 = 144$

   $\sqrt{a^2} = \sqrt{144}$

   $a = 12$

3. $\csc 40° = \dfrac{1}{\sin 40°} = \dfrac{1}{0.643} = 1.555$

4.
   (a)

   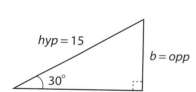

   $\sin \theta = \dfrac{opp}{hyp}$

   $\sin 30° = \dfrac{b}{15}$

   $15 \sin 30° = b$

   $15(0.5) = b$

   $7.5 = b$

   (b)

   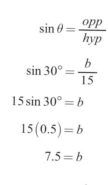

   $\cos \theta = \dfrac{adj}{hyp}$

   $\cos \theta = \dfrac{3}{12}$

   $\cos \theta = \dfrac{1}{4}$

   $\cos^{-1}(\cos \theta) = \cos^{-1}(0.25)$

   $\theta = 75.52°$

5.
   (a) $\mathbf{v} + \mathbf{w} = (4\mathbf{i} - 2\mathbf{j}) + (3\mathbf{i} + 7\mathbf{j})$

   $\mathbf{v} + \mathbf{w} = 4\mathbf{i} - 2\mathbf{j} + 3\mathbf{i} + 7\mathbf{j}$

   $\mathbf{v} + \mathbf{w} = 7\mathbf{i} + 5\mathbf{j}$

   (b) $\mathbf{v} - \mathbf{w} = (4\mathbf{i} - 2\mathbf{j}) - (3\mathbf{i} + 7\mathbf{j})$

   $\mathbf{v} - \mathbf{w} = 4\mathbf{i} - 2\mathbf{j} - 3\mathbf{i} - 7\mathbf{j}$

   $\mathbf{v} - \mathbf{w} = \mathbf{i} - 9\mathbf{j}$

(c) $\quad \mathbf{v} \bullet \mathbf{w} = (4\mathbf{i} - 2\mathbf{j}) \bullet (3\mathbf{i} + 7\mathbf{j})$

$\qquad \mathbf{v} \bullet \mathbf{w} = 4 \cdot 3 + (-2)(7)$

$\qquad \mathbf{v} \bullet \mathbf{w} = 12 - 14$

$\qquad \mathbf{v} \bullet \mathbf{w} = -2$

(d) $\quad \|\mathbf{v}\| = \sqrt{a^2 + b^2}$

$\qquad \|\mathbf{v}\| = \sqrt{4^2 + (-2)^2}$

$\qquad \|\mathbf{v}\| = \sqrt{16 + 4}$

$\qquad \|\mathbf{v}\| = \sqrt{20}$

$\qquad \|\mathbf{v}\| = 2\sqrt{5}$

6. $\left(\dfrac{1}{2}\right)^{5}$ ← exponent

  ↑ base

7. $V_{\text{sphere}} = \dfrac{4}{3}\pi r^3$

$\quad V_{\text{sphere}} = \dfrac{4}{3}\pi (6\,\text{in.})^3$

$\quad V_{\text{sphere}} = \dfrac{4}{3}\pi (216\,\text{in.}^3)$

$\quad V_{\text{sphere}} = 288\pi\,\text{in.}^3$

8. $\begin{vmatrix} 2 & -5 \\ 3 & -7 \end{vmatrix} = 2(-7) - 3(-5) = -14 + 15 = 1$

9. $4\begin{bmatrix} 3 & 4 & -2 \\ 1 & 0 & 5 \end{bmatrix} = \begin{bmatrix} 12 & 16 & -8 \\ 4 & 0 & 20 \end{bmatrix}$

10. $\begin{bmatrix} 3 & 4 & -1 \\ 5 & 2 & 0 \end{bmatrix}\begin{bmatrix} -2 & -5 \\ 6 & 8 \\ 3 & -3 \end{bmatrix} = \begin{bmatrix} 3(-2)+4(6)+(-1)(3) & 3(-5)+4(8)+(-1)(-3) \\ 5(-2)+2(6)+0(3) & 5(-5)+2(8)+0(-3) \end{bmatrix} = \begin{bmatrix} 15 & 20 \\ 2 & -9 \end{bmatrix}$

11.

(a) The difference of two squares :

$\quad x^2 - 9 = x^2 - 3^2 = (x+3)(x-3)$

(b)   The sum of two cubes:

$$x^3 + 8 = x^3 + 2^3 = (x+2)(x^2 - 2x + 4)$$

(c)   Common factors:

$$4x^3 y^8 + 12x^4 y^3 = 4x^3 y^3 (y^5 + 3x)$$

12.

(a)   Function

(b)   Not a Function

(c)   Function

13.

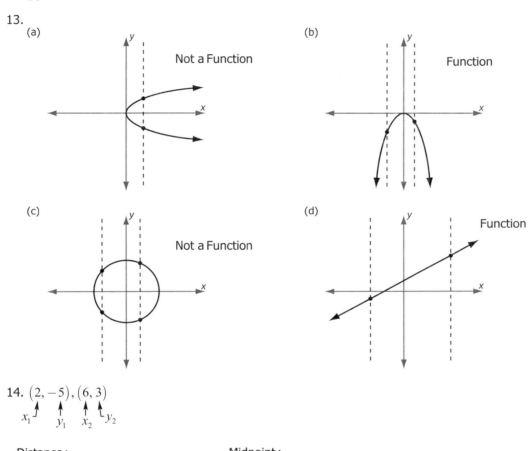

(a)   Not a Function

(b)   Function

(c)   Not a Function

(d)   Function

14. $(2, -5), (6, 3)$

$x_1 \quad y_1 \quad x_2 \quad y_2$

Distance:

$$d = \sqrt{(x_2 - x_1)^2 + (y_2 - y_1)^2}$$

$$d = \sqrt{(6-2)^2 + (3-(-5))^2}$$

$$d = \sqrt{(4)^2 + (8)^2}$$

$$d = \sqrt{16 + 64}$$

$$d = \sqrt{80}$$

$$d = 4\sqrt{5}$$

Midpoint:

$$(\bar{x}, \bar{y}) = \left(\frac{x_1 + x_2}{2}, \frac{y_1 + y_2}{2} \right)$$

$$(\bar{x}, \bar{y}) = \left(\frac{2+6}{2}, \frac{-5+3}{2} \right)$$

$$(\bar{x}, \bar{y}) = \left(\frac{8}{2}, \frac{-2}{2} \right)$$

$$(\bar{x}, \bar{y}) = (4, -1)$$

15. $3\sqrt{2} + 5\sqrt{2} - \sqrt{2} = 7\sqrt{2}$

16. $\sqrt{8} \cdot \sqrt{2} = \sqrt{8 \cdot 2} = \sqrt{16} = 4$

17. $\left(x^2 + 3x - 5\right)\left(x^3 - x^2 + 9\right) = x^2\left(x^3\right) + x^2\left(-x^2\right) + x^2\left(9\right) + 3x\left(x^3\right) + 3x\left(-x^2\right)$

$$+ 3x\left(9\right) + \left(-5\right)\left(x^3\right) + \left(-5\right)\left(-x^2\right) + \left(-5\right)\left(9\right)$$

$$= x^5 - x^4 + 9x^2 + 3x^4 - 3x^3 + 27x - 5x^3 + 5x^2 - 45$$

$$= x^5 + 2x^4 - 8x^3 + 14x^2 + 27x - 45$$

18. $\left(4x^3 + 7x^2 - 5x + 1\right) - \left(x^3 - 9x^2 - 5\right) = 4x^3 + 7x^2 - 5x + 1 - x^3 + 9x^2 + 5$

$$= 3x^3 + 16x^2 - 5x + 6$$

19.

(a) $z_1 + z_2 = \left(1 + i\right) + \left(2 - 3i\right)$

$z_1 + z_2 = 1 + i + 2 - 3i$

$z_1 + z_2 = 3 - 2i$

(b) $4z_1 = 4\left(1 + i\right)$

$4z_1 = 4 + 4i$

(c) $z_1 \cdot z_2 = \left(1 + i\right)\left(2 - 3i\right)$

$z_1 \cdot z_2 = 1\left(2\right) + 1\left(-3i\right) + i\left(2\right) + i\left(-3i\right)$

$z_1 \cdot z_2 = 2 - 3i + 2i - 3i^2$

$z_1 \cdot z_2 = 2 - i - 3\left(-1\right)$

$z_1 \cdot z_2 = 2 - i + 3$

$z_1 \cdot z_2 = 5 - i$

(d) $\dfrac{z_1}{z_2} = \dfrac{1 + i}{2 - 3i}$

$\dfrac{z_1}{z_2} = \dfrac{1 + i}{2 - 3i} \cdot \dfrac{2 + 3i}{2 + 3i}$

$\dfrac{z_1}{z_2} = \dfrac{\left(1 + i\right)\left(2 + 3i\right)}{\left(2 - 3i\right)\left(2 + 3i\right)}$

$\dfrac{z_1}{z_2} = \dfrac{1\left(2\right) + 1\left(3i\right) + i\left(2\right) + i\left(3i\right)}{2\left(2\right) + 2\left(3i\right) + \left(-3i\right)\left(2\right) + \left(-3i\right)\left(3i\right)}$

$\dfrac{z_1}{z_2} = \dfrac{2 + 3i + 2i + 3i^2}{4 + 6i - 6i - 9i^2}$

$\dfrac{z_1}{z_2} = \dfrac{2 + 5i + 3\left(-1\right)}{4 - 9\left(-1\right)}$

calculation cont. on next page...

Solution #19(d) from previous page...

$$\frac{z_1}{z_2} = \frac{2+5i-3}{4+9}$$

$$\frac{z_1}{z_2} = \frac{-1+5i}{13}$$

$$\frac{z_1}{z_2} = -\frac{1}{13} + \frac{5}{13}i$$

(e) $\left(z_1\right)^6 = \left(1+i\right)^6$

First, we convert $1+i$ into its polar form:

$$1 + i$$
$$\underset{a}{\uparrow} \quad \underset{b=1}{\uparrow}$$

$$r = \sqrt{a^2 + b^2} \qquad\qquad \theta = \tan^{-1}\left(\frac{b}{a}\right)$$

$$r = \sqrt{1^2 + 1^2} \qquad\qquad \theta = \tan^{-1}\left(\frac{1}{1}\right)$$

$$r = \sqrt{2} \qquad\qquad\qquad \theta = \tan^{-1}\left(1\right)$$

$$\theta = 45°$$

$$z = r\left(\cos\theta + i\sin\theta\right)$$

$$z = \sqrt{2}\left(\cos 45° + i\sin 45°\right)$$

Next, we incorporate the exponent of 6 using DeMoivre's Theorem:

$$z = \sqrt{2}\left(\cos 45° + i\sin 45°\right)$$

$$z^6 = \left(\sqrt{2}\right)^6 \left[\cos 6\left(45°\right) + i\sin 6\left(45°\right)\right]$$

$$z^6 = 8\left(\cos 270° + i\sin 270°\right)$$

Converting our answer back to rectangular form:

$$z^6 = 8\left[0 + i\left(-1\right)\right]$$

$$z^6 = 8\left(-i\right)$$

$$z^6 = -8i$$

20.

(a) $3^4 = 81 \Rightarrow \log_3 81 = 4$

(b) $\left(\frac{1}{2}\right)^3 = \frac{1}{8} \Rightarrow \log_{\frac{1}{2}} \frac{1}{8} = 3$

(c) $10^2 = 100 \Rightarrow \text{Log}\, 100 = 2$

(d) $e^{2x} = v \Rightarrow \text{Ln}\, v = 2x$

21.

(a) $\log_2 32 = 5 \Rightarrow 2^5 = 32$

(b) $\text{Log}\, 1000 = 3 \Rightarrow 10^3 = 1000$

(c) $\text{Ln}\, 5 = x \Rightarrow e^x = 5$

22. $3 \log_2 x - \dfrac{1}{4} \log_2 y = \log_2 x^3 - \log_2 y^{\frac{1}{4}}$

$$= \log_2 x^3 - \log_2 \sqrt[4]{y}$$

$$= \log_2 \frac{x^3}{\sqrt[4]{y}}$$

23.

(a) $\log_2 (x-1) = 3$

$$2^{\log_2 (x-1)} = 2^3$$

$$x - 1 = 8$$

$$x = 9$$

(b) $5^{\frac{x}{2}} = 125$

$$\log_5 5^{\frac{x}{2}} = \log_5 125$$

$$\frac{x}{2} = 3$$

$$x = 6$$

(c) $e^{7x} = 10$

$$\text{Ln}\, e^{7x} = \text{Ln}\, 10$$

$$7x = 2.3$$

$$x = 0.3$$

(d) $\text{Log}\,(4x+9) = 2$

$$10^{\text{Log}\,(4x+9)} = 10^2$$

$$4x + 9 = 100$$

$$4x = 91$$

$$x = \frac{91}{4}$$

$$x = 22\frac{3}{4}$$

24.

(a) $x - 3 = 9$

$x - 3 + 3 = 9 + 3$

$x = 12$

(b) $4x = 20$

$\dfrac{4x}{4} = \dfrac{20}{4}$

$x = 5$

(c) $\dfrac{x}{3} = 2$

$\dfrac{x}{3}(3) = 2(3)$

$x = 6$

(d) $\dfrac{6}{x} = 18$

$\dfrac{6}{x}(x) = 18x$

$6 = 18x$

$\dfrac{6}{18} = \dfrac{18x}{18}$

$\dfrac{1}{3} = x$

(e) $5x - 2 = 10$

$5x - 2 + 2 = 10 + 2$

$5x = 12$

$\dfrac{5x}{5} = \dfrac{12}{5}$

$x = \dfrac{12}{5} = 2\dfrac{2}{5}$

(f) $\dfrac{7x + 3}{5} = 1$

$\dfrac{7x + 3}{5}(5) = 1(5)$

$7x + 3 = 5$

$7x + 3 - 3 = 5 - 3$

$7x = 2$

$\dfrac{7x}{7} = \dfrac{2}{7}$

$x = \dfrac{2}{7}$

25.

(a) $4x^2 = 100$

$$\frac{4x^2}{4} = \frac{100}{4}$$

$$x^2 = 25$$

$$\sqrt{x^2} = \sqrt{25}$$

$$x = \pm 5$$

(b) $x^2 + 5x - 8 = 0$

$$x^2 + 5x = 8$$

Finding the term that must be added to both sides:

$$\left(\frac{5}{2}\right)^2 = \frac{25}{4}$$

$$\Rightarrow \qquad x^2 + 5x = 8$$

$$x^2 + 5x + \frac{25}{4} = 8 + \frac{25}{4}$$

$$\left(x + \frac{5}{2}\right)^2 = \frac{32}{4} + \frac{25}{4}$$

$$\left(x + \frac{5}{2}\right)^2 = \frac{57}{4}$$

$$\sqrt{\left(x + \frac{5}{2}\right)^2} = \sqrt{\frac{57}{4}}$$

$$x + \frac{5}{2} = \pm \frac{\sqrt{57}}{2}$$

$$x + \frac{5}{2} = \frac{\sqrt{57}}{2} \qquad\qquad x + \frac{5}{2} = -\frac{\sqrt{57}}{2}$$

$$x = \frac{-5 + \sqrt{57}}{2} \qquad\qquad x = \frac{-5 - \sqrt{57}}{2}$$

(c) $x^2 + 4x + 3 = 0$

$$(x + 1)(x + 3) = 0$$

$$x + 1 = 0 \qquad\qquad x + 3 = 0$$

$$x = -1 \qquad\qquad x = -3$$

(d) $5x^2 + 9x = 10$

$5x^2 + 9x - 10 = 0$

$a = 5, b = 9, c = -10$

$$x = \frac{-b \pm \sqrt{b^2 - 4ac}}{2a}$$

$$x = \frac{-9 \pm \sqrt{9^2 - 4(5)(-10)}}{2(5)}$$

$$x = \frac{-9 \pm \sqrt{81 + 200}}{10}$$

$$x = \frac{-9 \pm \sqrt{281}}{10}$$

$$x_1 = \frac{-9 + \sqrt{281}}{10} \qquad\qquad x_2 = \frac{-9 - \sqrt{281}}{10}$$

26. $\dfrac{x^{-2}x^5}{x^{-3}} = \dfrac{x^5 x^3}{x^2} = \dfrac{x^8}{x^2} = x^6$

27. $\dfrac{3\pi}{8} \, \text{Rad} \cdot \dfrac{180°}{\pi \, \text{Rad}} = \dfrac{3(180°)}{8} = 67.5°$

28. $225° \cdot \dfrac{\pi \, \text{Rad}}{180°} = \dfrac{225\pi}{180} \, \text{Rad} = \dfrac{5(45)\pi}{4(45)} \, \text{Rad} = \dfrac{5\pi}{4} \, \text{Rad}$

29.

(a)

(b)

(c)

30.

(a) $x + y = -3$

$2x + 3y = -11$

Multiplying the top equation by -2 and adding:

$$-2x - 2y = 6$$

$$2x + 3y = -11$$

$$\overline{}$$

$$0 + y = -5$$

$$y = -5$$

Taking this result and inserting it into the original top equation, we find x.

$$x + y = -3$$

$$x + (-5) = -3$$

$$x = 2$$

Thus, the solution to the system is $x = 2$, $y = -5$.

(b) $2x + y = 2$

$3x - 4y = -19$

Solving the top equation for y:

$$2x + y = 2$$

$$y = 2 - 2x \qquad \boxed{A}$$

Inserting this result into the 2nd equation, we find x:

$$3x - 4y = -19$$

$$3x - 4(2 - 2x) = -19$$

$$3x - 8 + 8x = -19$$

$$11x - 8 = -19$$

$$11x = -11$$

$$x = -1$$

Inserting the result into Equation $\boxed{A}$, we find y:

$$y = 2 - 2x$$

$$y = 2 - 2(-1)$$

$$y = 2 + 2$$

$$y = 4$$

Thus, the solution to the system is $x = -1$, $y = 4$.

(c) $6x + y = 0$

$5x + 2y = -7$

$$x = \dfrac{\begin{vmatrix} 0 & 1 \\ -7 & 2 \end{vmatrix}}{\begin{vmatrix} 6 & 1 \\ 5 & 2 \end{vmatrix}} \qquad y = \dfrac{\begin{vmatrix} 6 & 0 \\ 5 & -7 \end{vmatrix}}{\begin{vmatrix} 6 & 1 \\ 5 & 2 \end{vmatrix}}$$

Solving the denominator determinant:

$$\begin{vmatrix} 6 & 1 \\ 5 & 2 \end{vmatrix} = 6(2) - 5(1) = 12 - 5 = 7$$

$$\Rightarrow \quad x = \dfrac{\begin{vmatrix} 0 & 1 \\ -7 & 2 \end{vmatrix}}{7} \qquad y = \dfrac{\begin{vmatrix} 6 & 0 \\ 5 & -7 \end{vmatrix}}{7}$$

Solving the two numerator determinants:

$$x: \quad \begin{vmatrix} 0 & 1 \\ -7 & 2 \end{vmatrix} = 0(2) - (-7)(1) = 0 + 7 = 7$$

$$y: \quad \begin{vmatrix} 6 & 0 \\ 5 & -7 \end{vmatrix} = 6(-7) - 5(0) = -42 - 0 = -42$$

Thus,

$$x = \frac{7}{7} \qquad y = \frac{-42}{7}$$

$$x = 1 \qquad y = -6$$

Thus, the solution to the system is $x = 1$, $y = -6$.

(d) $x + y - z = 9$

$2x - z = 8$

$y + 2z = -5$

We begin by constructing the augmented matrix for the system:

$$\begin{bmatrix} 1 & 1 & -1 & 9 \\ 2 & 0 & -1 & 8 \\ 0 & 1 & 2 & -5 \end{bmatrix}$$

Since we already have a 1 in Row 1, Column 1 as well as a 0 in Row 3, Column 1, we must now get a 0 in Row 2, Column 1. Multiplying the top row by −2 and adding it to the 2nd row, we get:

$$\begin{bmatrix} 1 & 1 & -1 & 9 \\ 0 & -2 & 1 & 10 \\ 0 & 1 & 2 & -5 \end{bmatrix}$$

To get a 1 in Row 2, Column 2, we interchange Rows 2 and 3.

$$\begin{bmatrix} 1 & 1 & -1 & 9 \\ 0 & 1 & 2 & -5 \\ 0 & -2 & 1 & 10 \end{bmatrix}$$

To get a 0 in Row 1, Column 2, we multiply Row 2 by -1 and add it Row 1.

$$\begin{bmatrix} 1 & 0 & -3 & 14 \\ 0 & 1 & 2 & -5 \\ 0 & -2 & 1 & -10 \end{bmatrix}$$

To get a 0 in Row 3, Column 2, we multiply Row 2 by 2 and add the result to Row 3.

$$\begin{bmatrix} 1 & 0 & -3 & 14 \\ 0 & 1 & 2 & -5 \\ 0 & 0 & 5 & -20 \end{bmatrix}$$

To get a 1 in Row 3, Column 3, we multiply Row 3 by 1/5.

$$\begin{bmatrix} 1 & 0 & -3 & 14 \\ 0 & 1 & 2 & -5 \\ 0 & 0 & 1 & -4 \end{bmatrix}$$

To get a 0 in Row 1, Column 3, we multiply Row 3 by 3 and add the result to Row 1.

$$\begin{bmatrix} 1 & 0 & 0 & 2 \\ 0 & 1 & 2 & -5 \\ 0 & 0 & 1 & -4 \end{bmatrix}$$

Lastly, to get a 0 in Row 2, Column3, we multiply Row 3 by 2 and add the result to Row 2.

$$\begin{bmatrix} 1 & 0 & 0 & 2 \\ 0 & 1 & 0 & 3 \\ 0 & 0 & 1 & -4 \end{bmatrix}$$

Thus, the solution to the system is $x = 2$, $y = 3$, $z = -4$.

31. $z = 3 + i$

$$r = \sqrt{a^2 + b^2} \qquad \theta = \tan^{-1}\left(\frac{b}{a}\right)$$

$$r = \sqrt{3^2 + 1^2} \qquad \theta = \tan^{-1}\left(\frac{1}{3}\right)$$

$$r = \sqrt{10} \qquad \theta = 18.43°$$

$$z = r\left(\cos\theta + i\sin\theta\right)$$

$$z = \sqrt{10}\left(\cos 18.43° + i\sin 18.43°\right)$$

32. $z = 3(\cos 20° + i\sin 20°)$

$z = 3[0.94 + i(0.34)]$

$z = 2.8 + 1.02i$

33. $\displaystyle\sum_{i=1}^{4} \frac{(-1)^i}{i+1} = \frac{(-1)^1}{1+1} + \frac{(-1)^2}{2+1} + \frac{(-1)^3}{3+1} + \frac{(-1)^4}{4+1}$

$\displaystyle\sum_{i=1}^{4} \frac{(-1)^i}{i+1} = \frac{-1}{2} + \frac{1}{3} - \frac{1}{4} + \frac{1}{5}$

$\displaystyle\sum_{i=1}^{4} \frac{(-1)^i}{i+1} = \frac{30}{60} + \frac{20}{60} - \frac{15}{60} + \frac{12}{60}$

$\displaystyle\sum_{i=1}^{4} \frac{(-1)^i}{i+1} = -\frac{13}{60}$

34.

(a) $\displaystyle {}_nC_r = \frac{n!}{(n-r)!\,r!}$

$\displaystyle {}_{10}C_3 = \frac{10!}{7!\,3!}$

$\displaystyle {}_{10}C_3 = 120$

(b) $\displaystyle {}_nP_r = \frac{n!}{(n-r)!}$

$\displaystyle {}_{10}P_3 = \frac{10!}{(10-3)!}$

$\displaystyle {}_{10}P_3 = \frac{10!}{7!}$

$\displaystyle {}_{10}P_3 = 720$

35.

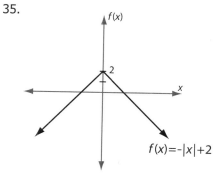

$f(x) = -|x| + 2$

36.

(a) $z_1 \cdot z_2 = 10(2)\left[\cos\left(60° + 15°\right) + i\sin\left(60° + 15°\right)\right]$

$z_1 \cdot z_2 = 20\left(\cos 75° + i\sin 75°\right)$

(b) $\dfrac{z_1}{z_2} = \dfrac{10}{2}\left[\cos\left(60° - 15°\right) + i\sin\left(60° - 15°\right)\right]$

$\dfrac{z_1}{z_2} = 5\left(\cos 45° + i\sin 45°\right)$

(c) $\left(z_2\right)^4 = 2^4\left[\cos 4\left(15°\right) + i\sin 4\left(15°\right)\right]$

$\left(z_2\right)^4 = 16\left(\cos 60° + i\sin 60°\right)$

37.

(a) $f \circ g(x) = 3(x-1)^2 + 2(x-1)$

$f \circ g(x) = 3\left(x^2 - 2x + 1\right) + 2x - 2$

$f \circ g(x) = 3x^2 - 6x + 3 + 2x - 2$

$f \circ g(x) = 3x^2 - 4x + 1$

(b) $g \circ f(x) = \left(3x^2 + 2x\right) - 1$

$g \circ f(x) = 3x^2 + 2x - 1$

(c) $f \circ g(x) = 3x^2 - 4x + 1$

$f \circ g(1) = 3(1)^2 - 4(1) + 1$

$f \circ g(1) = 3 - 4 + 1$

$f \circ g(1) = -1 + 1$

$f \circ g(1) = 0$

38.

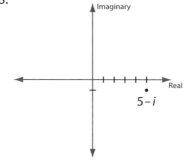

39. $a_n = (n+1)! - n$

$a_1 = (1+1)! - 1 = 2! - 1$

$a_1 = 2 - 1 = 1$

$a_2 = (2+1)! - 2 = 3! - 2$

$a_2 = 6 - 2 = 4$

$a_3 = (3+1)! - 3 = 4! - 3$

$a_3 = 24 - 3 = 21$

$a_4 = (4+1)! - 4 = 5! - 4$

$a_4 = 120 - 4 = 116$

First four terms: $\{1, 4, 21, 116\}$

40. $(-3, 45°)$

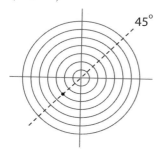

41. $(x, y) = (1, 4)$

$r = \sqrt{x^2 + y^2}$ $\qquad$ $\theta = \tan^{-1}\left(\dfrac{y}{x}\right)$

$r = \sqrt{1^2 + 4^2}$ $\qquad$ $\theta = \tan^{-1}\left(\dfrac{4}{1}\right)$

$r = \sqrt{1 + 16}$ $\qquad$ $\theta = \tan^{-1}(4)$

$r = \sqrt{17}$ $\qquad$ $\theta = 75.96°$

Thus,

$(r, \theta) = \left(\sqrt{17}, 75.96°\right)$

42. $(r, \theta) = (2, 35°)$

$x = r \cos \theta \qquad\qquad y = r \sin \theta$

$x = 2 \cos 35° \qquad\quad y = 2 \sin 35°$

$x = 2(0.82) \qquad\qquad y = 2(0.57)$

$x = 1.64 \qquad\qquad\quad y = 1.14$

Thus,

$(x, y) = (1.64, 1.14)$

43.

(a) $y = \sin x$ (b) $y = \cos x$

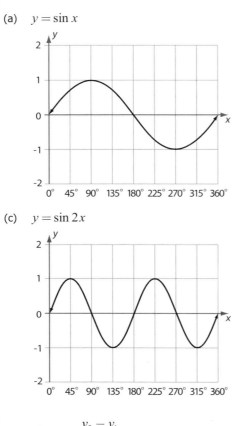 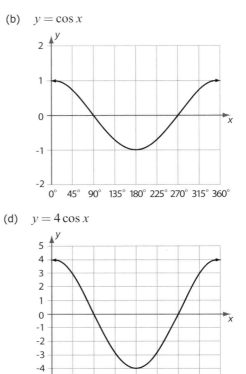

(c) $y = \sin 2x$ (d) $y = 4 \cos x$

44.

(a) $\text{Slope} = \dfrac{y_2 - y_1}{x_2 - x_1}$

$\text{Slope} = \dfrac{6 - (-4)}{1 - 3}$

$\text{Slope} = \dfrac{6 + 4}{-2}$

$\text{Slope} = \dfrac{10}{-2}$

$\text{Slope} = -5$

(b) 4

(c) 6

(d) $-\dfrac{3}{2}$

45.

(a) Using the slope-intercept form of a line, $y = mx + b$:

$$y = 5x + 2$$

(b) We begin by finding the slope:

$$(2, 4), (-1, 5)$$

$x_1 \quad y_1 \quad x_2 \quad y_2$

$$m = \frac{y_2 - y_1}{x_2 - x_1}$$

$$m = \frac{5 - 4}{-1 - 2}$$

$$m = \frac{1}{-3}$$

Inserting the slope and the coordinates (x_1, y_1) into the point-slope form of a line, we have:

$$y - y_1 = m(x - x_1)$$

$$y - 4 = -\frac{1}{3}(x - 2)$$

$$y - 4 = -\frac{1}{3}x + \frac{2}{3}$$

$$y = -\frac{1}{3}x + \frac{2}{3} + 4$$

$$y = -\frac{1}{3}x + 4\frac{2}{3}$$

(c) Since the line is parallel to the line $y = 8x - 3$, it has a slope of 8. Inserting the slope and the given y-intercept into the slope-intercept form of a line, we get:

$$y = mx + b$$

$$y = 8x + 3$$

(d) A line that is perpendicular to $y = 5x + 7$, has a slope of $-1/5$. Inserting this slope and the given coordinates into the point-slope form of a line, we get:

$$y - y_1 = m(x - x_1)$$

$$y - (-6) = -\frac{1}{5}(x - 0)$$

$$y + 6 = -\frac{1}{5}x$$

$$y = -\frac{1}{5}x - 6$$

46. $(x-h)^2 + (y+k)^2 = r^2$

$[x-(-2)]^2 + (y-6)^2 = 4^2$

$(x+2)^2 + (y-6)^2 = 16$

47. $-4x+6 < 8$

$-4x+6-6 < 8-6$

$-4x < 2$

$\dfrac{-4x}{-4} > \dfrac{2}{-4}$

$x > -\dfrac{1}{2}$

Final Examination II

Note: In this second comprehensive final exam, the topics are completely randomized so that you can see if you have fully grasped all of the material in the book.

1. Given that $\mathbf{v} = 5\mathbf{i} - \mathbf{j}$ and $\mathbf{w} = \mathbf{i} + 3\mathbf{j}$, find:

   (a) $\mathbf{v} + \mathbf{w}$

   (b) $\mathbf{v} - \mathbf{w}$

   (c) $\|\mathbf{v}\|$

   (d) $\mathbf{v} \cdot \mathbf{w}$

2. Convert the rectangular complex number $z = 2 - i$ into its polar form.

3. Convert the polar complex number $z = 5(\cos 65° + i \sin 65°)$ into its rectangular form.

4. Given that $f(x) = 3x + 1$ and $g(x) = x^2 + 4$, find:

   (a) $f \circ g(x)$

   (b) $g \circ f(x)$

   (c) $f \circ g(-1)$

5. Given that the graph of $f(x) = x^3$ is

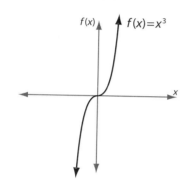

   use the shift properties to sketch a graph of $f(x) = x^3 - 1$.

6. Solve each of the following quadratic equations using the indicated method.

   (a) $5x^2 = 45$ Square Root Method

   (b) $x^2 + 9x - 1 = 0$ Completing the Square

   (c) $x^2 + 8x = 0$ Factoring

   (d) $4x^2 + 7x = 9$ Quadratic Formula

7. Plot the complex number $z = 3 + 5i$.

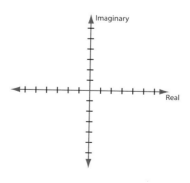

8. Plot the polar point $(r, \theta) = (2, -60°)$.

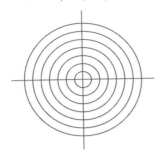

9. Sketch a graph of each of the following trigonometric functions.

   (a) $y = \cos x$

   (b) $y = 5 \cos x$

   (c) $y = \sin x$

   (d) $y = \sin 4x$

10. Given that $\cos \theta = 0.63$, find the angle θ.

11. Find the distance and midpoint between the points $(-2, 7)$ and $(4, 5)$.

12. Given that $z_1 = 2 - i$ and $z_2 = 4 + 5i$, find:

   (a) $z_1 + z_2$ (d) $\dfrac{z_1}{z_2}$

   (b) $5z_2$ (e) $(z_1)^4$

   (c) $z_1 \cdot z_2$

13. Translate each of the following logarithmic expressions into an exponential expression.

   (a) $\log_5 25 = 2$

   (b) $\text{Log } 10,000 = 4$

   (c) $\text{Ln } 2x = y$

14. Solve each of the following.

   (a) $x + 2 = 10$ (d) $\dfrac{5}{x} = 2$

   (b) $3x = 21$ (e) $6x - 1 = 13$

   (c) $\dfrac{x}{2} = 5$ (f) $\dfrac{4x + 2}{5} + 3 = 6$

15. Convert $\dfrac{2\pi}{3}$ Rad into degrees.

16. Calculate each of the following.

   (a) $_9C_2$

   (b) $_8P_4$

17. Simplify $\dfrac{x^2 \cdot x^4 \cdot x^{-5}}{x^{-3}}$ as far as possible using the properties of exponents.

18. Convert $135°$ into radians. Record you final answer in terms of π.

19. $\dfrac{\sqrt{72}}{\sqrt{2}} =$

20. Combine $\dfrac{1}{3}\operatorname{Log} x + 2\operatorname{Log} y - \dfrac{1}{2}\operatorname{Log} z - 5\operatorname{Log} w$.

21. Sketch a graph of each of the following functions.

    (a) $f(x) = 2x + 3$

    (b) $f(x) = \sqrt{x}$

    (c) $f(x) = |x|$

22. $\displaystyle\sum_{i=1}^{5} 3(i+1) =$

23. Find the center and radius of the circle whose equation is $(x+8)^2 + (y-3)^2 = 5$.

24. Given that $z_1 = 20\left(\cos 62° + i\sin 62°\right)$ and $z_2 = 4\left(\cos 17° + i\sin 17°\right)$, find:

    (a) $z_1 \cdot z_2$

    (b) $\dfrac{z_1}{z_2}$

    (c) $\left(z_2\right)^6$

25. Convert the rectangular point $(x,\, y) = (-2,\, 3)$ into polar coordinates.

26. Find the slope of each of the following lines.

    (a) The line $y = 8x + 6$.

    (b) The line that passes through the points $(-4, 1)$ and $(2, 7)$.

    (c) A line that is parallel to the line $y = -5x + 2$.

    (d) A line that is perpendicular to the line $y = 4x + 8$.

27. Write out the first four terms of the sequence $a_n = \dfrac{2(n+1)!}{n!}$.

28. Write an equation for each of the following lines.

    (a) The line with a slope of -2 and a y-intercept of 7.

    (b) The line that passes through the points $(-3,\, -6)$ and $(1,\, 8)$.

    (c) A line that is parallel to the line $y = -5x + \dfrac{1}{7}$ and passes through the point $(2,\, -5)$.

    (d) A line that is perpendicular to the line $y = 3x + 9$ and has a y-intercept of 8.

29. Solve each of the following.

    (a) $2^{3x-1} = 16$

    (b) $\text{Log}\left(\dfrac{x}{3}\right) = 2$

    (c) $\text{Ln}\left(5x+2\right) = 3$

    (d) $e^{\frac{4}{x}} = 10$

30. Factor each of the following.

    (a) $3x^5 y - 18xy^4$

    (b) $x^3 - 125$

    (c) $x^2 - 1$

31. Calculate the area of a circle of radius 5 ft.

32.

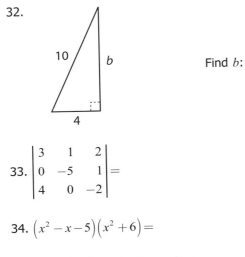

Find b:

33. $\begin{vmatrix} 3 & 1 & 2 \\ 0 & -5 & 1 \\ 4 & 0 & -2 \end{vmatrix} =$

34. $\left(x^2 - x - 5\right)\left(x^2 + 6\right) =$

35. Solve the following inequality :

$$-2 < \dfrac{x}{3} - 4 < 8$$

36. $\sec 65° =$

37. Identify the base and the exponent in the expression

$$\left(0.3\right)^6$$

38. Determine if each of the following is a function of x.

    (a) $y^4 = 6x$

    (b) $y = \sqrt{x}$

    (c) $y = \dfrac{3}{x+2}$

39. Translate each of the following exponential expressions into a logarithmic expression.

    (a) $2^6 = 64$

    (b) $e^p = x$

    (c) $10^5 = 100,000$

    (d) $\left(\dfrac{1}{4}\right)^2 = \dfrac{1}{16}$

40.

    (a)

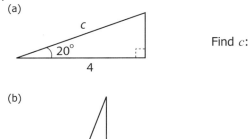

        Find c:

    (b)

        Find θ:

41. $\begin{bmatrix} 3 & -1 & 2 & 5 \end{bmatrix} \begin{bmatrix} -2 & 0 \\ 4 & -3 \\ 3 & -1 \\ 0 & 6 \end{bmatrix} =$

42. Determine if each of the following graphs is a function.

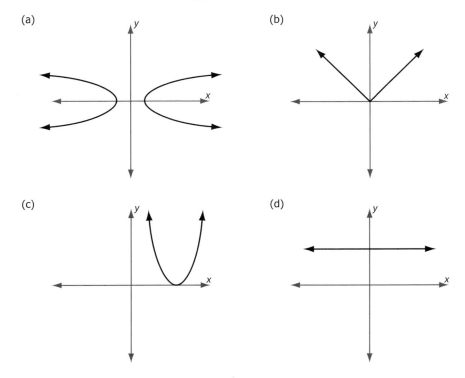

    (a)

    (b)

    (c)

    (d)

43. $-6 \begin{bmatrix} 3 & -5 \\ 2 & 1 \end{bmatrix} =$

44. $6\sqrt{3} - 9\sqrt{3} + \sqrt{3} =$

45. Convert the polar point $(r, \theta) = (3, 60°)$ into rectangular coordinates.

46. $\left(6x^3 - 9x^2 - 16\right) - \left(3x^2 - 2x - 10\right) =$

47. Solve each of the following systems of equations using the indicated method.

    (a) $5x + 2y = 8$

             $2x - y = 5$ Method of Substitution

    (b) $x + y = 3$

             $x + 2y = 5$ Method of Addition

    (c) $5x + 4y = 1$

             $3x - 6y = 2$ Cramer's Rule

    (d) $x + 3y - 2z = 14$

             $x + y - z = 6$ Gauss-Jordan Elimination

             $3x - 2y + z = -5$

1.
(a) $6\mathbf{i} + 2\mathbf{j}$

(b) $4\mathbf{i} - 4\mathbf{j}$

(c) $\sqrt{26}$

(d) 2

2. $\sqrt{5}\left[\cos\left(-26.56°\right) + i\sin\left(-26.56°\right)\right]$ or,

$\sqrt{5}\left(\cos 333.44° + i\sin 333.44°\right)$

3. $2.1 + 4.55i$

4.
(a) $3x^2 + 13$

(b) $9x^2 + 6x + 5$

(c) 16

5.

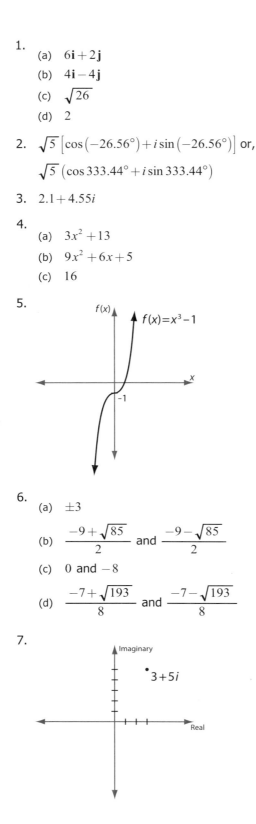

$f(x) = x^3 - 1$

6.
(a) ± 3

(b) $\dfrac{-9 + \sqrt{85}}{2}$ and $\dfrac{-9 - \sqrt{85}}{2}$

(c) 0 and -8

(d) $\dfrac{-7 + \sqrt{193}}{8}$ and $\dfrac{-7 - \sqrt{193}}{8}$

7.

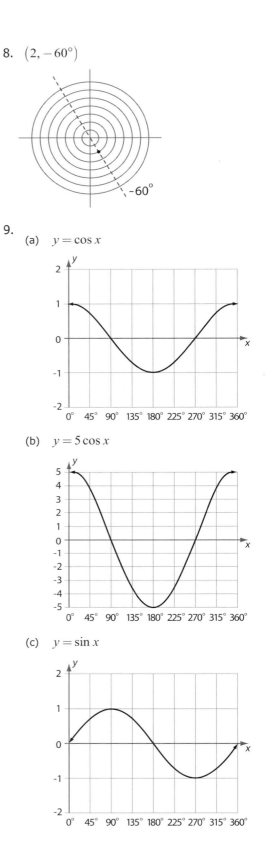

$3 + 5i$

8. $\left(2, -60°\right)$

9.
(a) $y = \cos x$

(b) $y = 5\cos x$

(c) $y = \sin x$

(d) $y = \sin 4x$

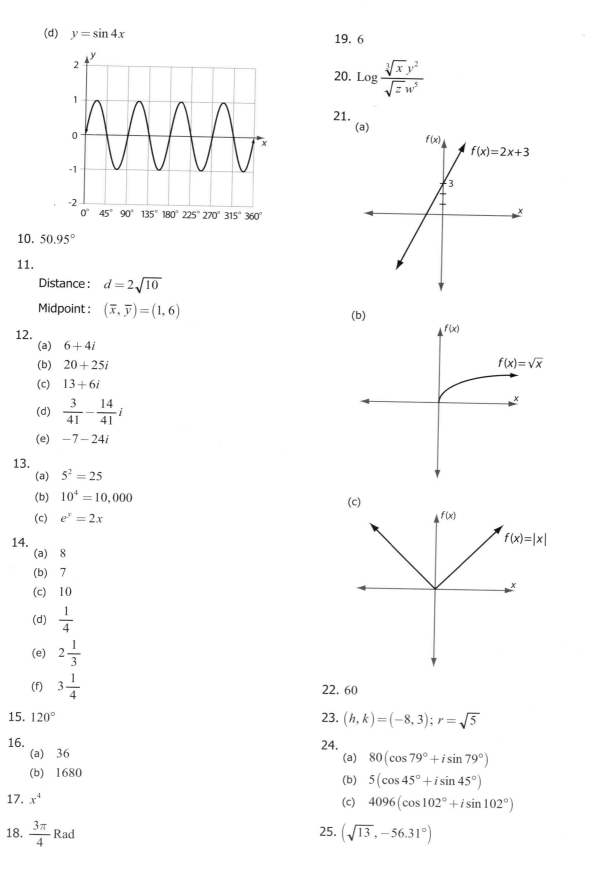

10. $50.95°$

11.

Distance: $d = 2\sqrt{10}$

Midpoint: $(\bar{x}, \bar{y}) = (1, 6)$

12.
(a) $6 + 4i$

(b) $20 + 25i$

(c) $13 + 6i$

(d) $\dfrac{3}{41} - \dfrac{14}{41}i$

(e) $-7 - 24i$

13.
(a) $5^2 = 25$

(b) $10^4 = 10,000$

(c) $e^y = 2x$

14.
(a) 8

(b) 7

(c) 10

(d) $\dfrac{1}{4}$

(e) $2\dfrac{1}{3}$

(f) $3\dfrac{1}{4}$

15. $120°$

16.
(a) 36

(b) 1680

17. x^4

18. $\dfrac{3\pi}{4}$ Rad

19. 6

20. $\operatorname{Log} \dfrac{\sqrt[3]{x}\, y^2}{\sqrt{z}\, w^5}$

21.
(a)

$f(x) = 2x + 3$

(b)

$f(x) = \sqrt{x}$

(c)

$f(x) = |x|$

22. 60

23. $(h, k) = (-8, 3);\ r = \sqrt{5}$

24.
(a) $80(\cos 79° + i \sin 79°)$

(b) $5(\cos 45° + i \sin 45°)$

(c) $4096(\cos 102° + i \sin 102°)$

25. $\left(\sqrt{13}, -56.31°\right)$

26.
(a) 8

(b) 1

(c) −5

(d) $-\dfrac{1}{4}$

27. $\{4, 6, 8, 10\}$

28.
(a) $y = -2x + 7$

(b) $y = \dfrac{7}{2}x - \dfrac{9}{2}$

(c) $y = -5x + 5$

(d) $y = -\dfrac{1}{3}x + 8$

29.
(a) $\dfrac{5}{3}$

(b) 300

(c) 3.62

(d) 1.7

30.
(a) $3xy\left(x^4 - 6y^3\right)$

(b) $(x-5)\left(x^2 + 5x + 25\right)$

(c) $(x+1)(x-1)$

31. $78.53\,\text{ft}^2$

32. 9.2

33. 74

34. $x^4 - x^3 + x^2 - 6x - 30$

35. $6 < x < 36$

36. 2.366

37. $\underbrace{(0.3)}_{\text{base}}{}^{\overset{\text{exponent}}{6}}$

38.
(a) Not a function

(b) Function

(c) Function

39.
(a) $\log_2 64 = 6$

(b) $\operatorname{Ln} x = p$

(c) $\operatorname{Log} 100{,}000 = 5$

(d) $\log_{\frac{1}{4}} \dfrac{1}{16} = 2$

40.
(a) 4.25

(b) 69.4°

41. $\begin{bmatrix} -4 & 31 \end{bmatrix}$

42.
(a) Not a function

(b) Function

(c) Function

(d) Function

43. $\begin{bmatrix} -18 & 30 \\ -12 & -6 \end{bmatrix}$

44. $-2\sqrt{3}$

45. $(1.5, 2.598)$

46. $6x^3 - 12x^2 + 2x - 6$

47.
(a) $x = 2,\ y = -1$

(b) $x = 1,\ y = 2$

(c) $x = \dfrac{1}{3},\ y = -\dfrac{1}{6}$

(d) $x = 1,\ y = 3,\ z = -2$

1.

(a) $\mathbf{v}+\mathbf{w}=(5\mathbf{i}-\mathbf{j})+(\mathbf{i}+3\mathbf{j})$

$\mathbf{v}+\mathbf{w}=5\mathbf{i}-\mathbf{j}+\mathbf{i}+3\mathbf{j}$

$\mathbf{v}+\mathbf{w}=6\mathbf{i}+2\mathbf{j}$

(b) $\mathbf{v}-\mathbf{w}=(5\mathbf{i}-\mathbf{j})-(\mathbf{i}+3\mathbf{j})$

$\mathbf{v}-\mathbf{w}=5\mathbf{i}-\mathbf{j}-\mathbf{i}-3\mathbf{j}$

$\mathbf{v}-\mathbf{w}=4\mathbf{i}-4\mathbf{j}$

(c) $\|\mathbf{v}\|=\sqrt{5^2+(-1)^2}$

$\|\mathbf{v}\|=\sqrt{25+1}$

$\|\mathbf{v}\|=\sqrt{26}$

(d) $\mathbf{v}\bullet\mathbf{w}=(5\mathbf{i}-\mathbf{j})\bullet(\mathbf{i}+3\mathbf{j})$

$\mathbf{v}\bullet\mathbf{w}=5(1)+(-1)(3)$

$\mathbf{v}\bullet\mathbf{w}=5-3$

$\mathbf{v}\bullet\mathbf{w}=2$

2. $z=2-i$

$\underset{a}{\uparrow}\quad\underset{b=-1}{\uparrow}$

$r=\sqrt{a^2+b^2}$ $\qquad$ $\theta=\tan^{-1}\left(\dfrac{b}{a}\right)$

$r=\sqrt{2^2+(-1)^2}$ $\qquad$ $\theta=\tan^{-1}\left(\dfrac{-1}{2}\right)$

$r=\sqrt{4+1}$ $\qquad$ $\theta=-26.56°$

$r=\sqrt{5}$

Thus,

$z=r(\cos\theta+i\sin\theta)$

$z=\sqrt{5}\left[\cos(-26.56°)+i\sin(-26.56°)\right]$

Or, recording $-26.56°$ as a positive angle:

$z=\sqrt{5}\left(\cos 333.44°+i\sin 333.44°\right)$

3. $z=5(\cos 65°+i\sin 65°)$

$z=5(0.423+i(0.906))$

$z=2.1+4.53i$

4.

(a) $f \circ g(x) = 3(x^2 + 4) + 1$

$f \circ g(x) = 3x^2 + 12 + 1$

$f \circ g(x) = 3x^2 + 13$

(b) $g \circ f(x) = (3x+1)^2 + 4$

$g \circ f(x) = (9x^2 + 6x + 1) + 4$

$g \circ f(x) = 9x^2 + 6x + 5$

(c) $f \circ g(x) = 3x^2 + 13$

$f \circ g(-1) = 3(-1)^2 + 13$

$f \circ g(-1) = 3 + 13$

$f \circ g(-1) = 16$

5.

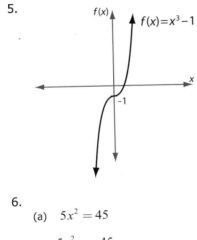

$f(x) = x^3 - 1$

6.

(a) $5x^2 = 45$

$\dfrac{5x^2}{5} = \dfrac{45}{5}$

$x^2 = 9$

$\sqrt{x^2} = \sqrt{9}$

$x = \pm 3$

(b) $x^2 + 9x - 1 = 0$

$x^2 + 9x = 1$

Finding the term that must be added to both sides:

$$\left(\frac{9}{2}\right)^2 = \frac{81}{4}$$

$\Rightarrow \qquad x^2 + 9x = 1$

$$x^2 + 9x + \frac{81}{4} = 1 + \frac{81}{4}$$

$$\left(x + \frac{9}{2}\right)^2 = \frac{85}{4}$$

$$\sqrt{\left(x + \frac{9}{2}\right)^2} = \sqrt{\frac{85}{4}}$$

$$x + \frac{9}{2} = \pm\frac{\sqrt{85}}{2}$$

$$x + \frac{9}{2} = \frac{\sqrt{85}}{2} \qquad\qquad x + \frac{9}{2} = -\frac{\sqrt{85}}{2}$$

$$x = \frac{-9 + \sqrt{85}}{2} \qquad\qquad x = \frac{-9 - \sqrt{85}}{2}$$

(c) $x^2 + 8x = 0$

$x(x + 8) = 0$

$x = 0 \qquad\qquad x + 8 = 0$

$\qquad\qquad\qquad x = -8$

(d) $4x^2 + 7x = 9$

$4x^2 + 7x - 9 = 0$

$a = 4,\ b = 7,\ c = -9$

$$x = \frac{-b \pm \sqrt{b^2 - 4ac}}{2a}$$

$$x = \frac{-7 \pm \sqrt{7^2 - 4(4)(-9)}}{2(4)}$$

$$x = \frac{-7 \pm \sqrt{49 + 144}}{8}$$

$$x = \frac{-7 \pm \sqrt{193}}{8}$$

$$x = \frac{-7 + \sqrt{193}}{8} \qquad\qquad x = \frac{-7 - \sqrt{193}}{8}$$

7.

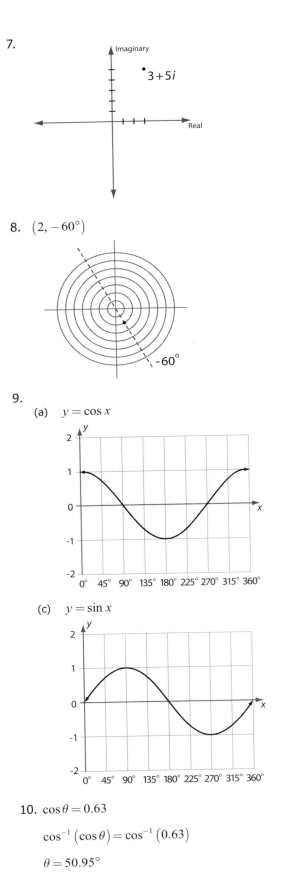

8. $(2, -60°)$

9.

(a) $y = \cos x$

(b) $y = 5\cos x$

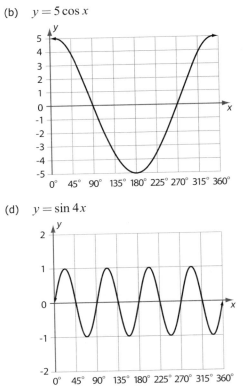

(c) $y = \sin x$

(d) $y = \sin 4x$

10. $\cos\theta = 0.63$

$\cos^{-1}(\cos\theta) = \cos^{-1}(0.63)$

$\theta = 50.95°$

11. $(-2, 7), (4, 5)$

$$x_1 \uparrow \quad \uparrow y_1 \quad x_2 \uparrow \quad \uparrow y_2$$

Distance:

$$d = \sqrt{(x_2 - x_1)^2 + (y_2 - y_1)^2}$$

$$d = \sqrt{(4 - (-2))^2 + (5 - 7)^2}$$

$$d = \sqrt{(6)^2 + (-2)^2}$$

$$d = \sqrt{36 + 4}$$

$$d = \sqrt{40}$$

$$d = 2\sqrt{10}$$

Midpoint:

$$(\bar{x}, \bar{y}) = \left(\frac{x_1 + x_2}{2}, \frac{y_1 + y_2}{2} \right)$$

$$(\bar{x}, \bar{y}) = \left(\frac{-2 + 4}{2}, \frac{7 + 5}{2} \right)$$

$$(\bar{x}, \bar{y}) = \left(\frac{2}{2}, \frac{12}{2} \right)$$

$$(\bar{x}, \bar{y}) = (1, 6)$$

12.

(a) $z_1 + z_2 = (2 - i) + (4 + 5i)$

$z_1 + z_2 = 2 - i + 4 + 5i$

$z_1 + z_2 = 6 + 4i$

(b) $5z_2 = 5(4 + 5i)$

$5z_2 = 20 + 25i$

(c) $z_1 \cdot z_2 = (2 - i)(4 + 5i)$

$z_1 \cdot z_2 = 2(4) + 2(5i) + (-i)(4) + (-i)(5i)$

$z_1 \cdot z_2 = 8 + 10i - 4i - 5i^2$

$z_1 \cdot z_2 = 8 + 6i - 5(-1)$

$z_1 \cdot z_2 = 8 + 6i + 5$

$z_1 \cdot z_2 = 13 + 6i$

(d) $\dfrac{z_1}{z_2} = \dfrac{2 - i}{4 + 5i}$

$\dfrac{z_1}{z_2} = \dfrac{2 - i}{4 + 5i} \cdot \dfrac{4 - 5i}{4 - 5i}$

$\dfrac{z_1}{z_2} = \dfrac{(2 - i)(4 - 5i)}{(4 + 5i)(4 - 5i)}$

$\dfrac{z_1}{z_2} = \dfrac{2(4) + 2(-5i) + (-i)(4) + (-i)(-5i)}{4(4) + 4(-5i) + 5i(4) + 5i(-5i)}$

$\dfrac{z_1}{z_2} = \dfrac{8 - 10i - 4i + 5i^2}{16 - 20i + 20i - 25i^5}$

calculation cont. on next page...

Solution #12(d) from previous page...

$$\frac{z_1}{z_2} = \frac{8 - 14i + 5(-1)}{16 - 25(-1)}$$

$$\frac{z_1}{z_2} = \frac{8 - 14i - 5}{16 + 25}$$

$$\frac{z_1}{z_2} = \frac{3 - 14i}{41}$$

$$\frac{z_1}{z_2} = \frac{3}{41} - \frac{14}{41}i$$

(e) $(z_1)^4 = (2 - i)^4$

First, we convert the complex number into its polar form:

$$z = 2 - i$$

$$\underset{a}{\uparrow} \quad \underset{b = -1}{\uparrow}$$

$$r = \sqrt{a^2 + b^2} \qquad \theta = \tan^{-1}\left(\frac{b}{a}\right)$$

$$r = \sqrt{2^2 + (-1)^2} \qquad \theta = \tan^{-1}\left(\frac{-1}{2}\right)$$

$$r = \sqrt{4 + 1} \qquad \theta = -26.56°$$

$$r = \sqrt{5}$$

Thus,

$$z = r(\cos\theta + i\sin\theta)$$

$$z = \sqrt{5}\left[\cos(-26.56°) + i\sin(-26.56°)\right]$$

Using DeMoivre's Theorem to incorporate the exponent of 4:

$$z = \sqrt{5}\left[\cos(-26.56°) + i\sin(-26.56°)\right]$$

$$z^4 = \left(\sqrt{5}\right)^4\left[\cos 4(-26.56°) + i\sin 4(-26.56°)\right]$$

$$z^4 = 25\left[\cos(-106.24°) + i\sin(-106.24°)\right]$$

Or, recording the angle as a positive angle:

$$z^4 = 25\left[\cos 253.76° + i\sin 253.76°\right]$$

Lastly, we convert our result back to rectangular form:

$$z^4 = 25\left[-0.28 - 0.96i\right]$$

$$z^4 = -7 - 24i$$

13.

(a) $\log_5 25 = 2 \Rightarrow 5^2 = 25$

(b) $\text{Log}\, 10,000 = 4 \Rightarrow 10^4 = 10,000$

(c) $\text{Ln}\, 2x = y \Rightarrow e^y = 2x$

14.

(a) $x + 2 = 10$

$x + 2 - 2 = 10 - 2$

$x = 8$

(b) $3x = 21$

$\dfrac{3x}{3} = \dfrac{21}{3}$

$x = 7$

(c) $\dfrac{x}{2} = 5$

$\dfrac{x}{2}(2) = 5(2)$

$x = 10$

(d) $\dfrac{5}{x} = 20$

$\dfrac{5}{x}(x) = 20(x)$

$5 = 20x$

$\dfrac{5}{20} = \dfrac{20x}{20}$

$\dfrac{1}{4} = x$

(e) $6x - 1 = 13$

$6x - 1 + 1 = 13 + 1$

$6x = 14$

$\dfrac{6x}{6} = \dfrac{14}{6}$

$x = 2\dfrac{1}{3}$

(f) $\dfrac{4x+2}{5}+3=6$

$$\dfrac{4x+2}{5}+3-3=6-3$$

$$\dfrac{4x+2}{5}=3$$

$$\dfrac{4x+2}{5}(5)=3(5)$$

$$4x+2=15$$

$$4x+2-2=15-2$$

$$4x=13$$

$$\dfrac{4x}{4}=\dfrac{13}{4}$$

$$x=3\dfrac{1}{4}$$

15. $\dfrac{2\pi}{3}\,\text{Rad}\cdot\dfrac{180}{\pi\,\text{Rad}}=\dfrac{2(180°)}{3}=120°$

16.

(a) $_nC_r=\dfrac{n!}{(n-r)!\,r!}$

$$_9C_2=\dfrac{9!}{(9-2)!\,2!}$$

$$_9C_2=\dfrac{9!}{7!\,2!}=36$$

(b) $_nP_r=\dfrac{n!}{(n-r)!}$

$$_8P_4=\dfrac{8!}{(8-4)!}$$

$$_8P_4=\dfrac{8!}{4!}$$

$$_8P_4=1680$$

17. $\dfrac{x^2\cdot x^4\cdot x^{-5}}{x^{-3}}=\dfrac{x^2\cdot x^4\cdot x^3}{x^5}=\dfrac{x^9}{x^5}=x^4$

18. $135°\cdot\dfrac{\pi\,\text{Rad}}{180°}=\dfrac{135\pi}{180}\,\text{Rad}=\dfrac{3(45)\pi}{4(45)}\,\text{Rad}=\dfrac{3\pi}{4}\,\text{Rad}$

19. $\dfrac{\sqrt{72}}{\sqrt{2}}=\sqrt{\dfrac{72}{2}}=\sqrt{36}=6$

20. $\dfrac{1}{3}\text{Log }x+2\text{Log }y-\dfrac{1}{2}\text{Log }z-5\text{Log }w=\text{Log }x^{\frac{1}{3}}+\text{Log }y^2-\text{Log }z^{\frac{1}{2}}-\text{Log }w^5$

$$=\text{Log }\sqrt[3]{x}+\text{Log }y^2-\text{Log }\sqrt{z}-\text{Log }w^5$$

$$=\text{Log }\dfrac{\sqrt[3]{x}\ y^2}{\sqrt{z}\ w^5}$$

21.

(a)

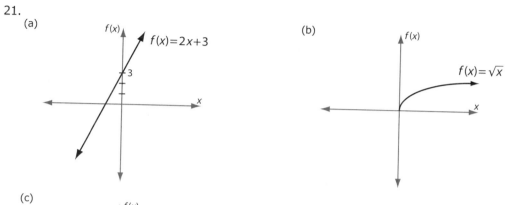

$f(x)=2x+3$

(b)

$f(x)=\sqrt{x}$

(c)

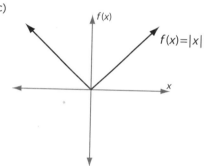

$f(x)=|x|$

22. $\displaystyle\sum_{i=1}^{5}3(i+1)=3(1+1)+3(2+1)+3(3+1)+3(4+1)+3(5+1)$

$\displaystyle\sum_{i=1}^{5}3(i+1)=3(2)+3(3)+3(4)+3(5)+3(6)$

$\displaystyle\sum_{i=1}^{5}3(i+1)=6+9+12+15+18$

$\displaystyle\sum_{i=1}^{5}3(i+1)=60$

23. $(h,k)=(-8,3);\ r=\sqrt{5}$

24.

(a) $z_1\cdot z_2=20(4)\big[\cos(62°+17°)+i\sin(62°+17°)\big]$

$z_1\cdot z_2=80(\cos 79°+i\sin 79°)$

(b) $\dfrac{z_1}{z_2}=\dfrac{20}{4}\big[\cos(62°-17°)+i\sin(62°-17°)\big]$

$\dfrac{z_1}{z_2}=5(\cos 45°+i\sin 45°)$

(c) $z_2 = 4(\cos 17^\circ + i\sin 17^\circ)$

$(z_2)^6 = 4^6\left[\cos 6\left(17^\circ\right) + i\sin 6\left(17^\circ\right)\right]$

$(z_2)^6 = 4096\left(\cos 102^\circ + i\sin 102^\circ\right)$

25. $(x, y) = (-2, 3)$

$r = \sqrt{x^2 + y^2}$ $\qquad\qquad$ $\theta = \tan^{-1}\left(\dfrac{y}{x}\right)$

$r = \sqrt{(-2)^2 + 3^2}$ $\qquad\qquad$ $\theta = \tan^{-1}\left(\dfrac{3}{-2}\right)$

$r = \sqrt{4 + 9}$ $\qquad\qquad$ $\theta = -56.31^\circ$

$r = \sqrt{13}$

Thus,

$(r, \theta) = \left(\sqrt{13}, -56.31^\circ\right)$

26.

(a)   8

(b) $(-4, 1), (2, 7)$

$\underset{x_1}{\uparrow}\ \underset{y_1}{\uparrow}\quad \underset{x_2}{\uparrow}\ \underset{y_2}{\uparrow}$

$m = \dfrac{y_2 - y_1}{x_2 - x_1}$

$m = \dfrac{7-1}{2-(-4)} = \dfrac{6}{2+4} = \dfrac{6}{6} = 1$

(c)   Since parallel lines have the same slope, the line would have a slope of –5.

(d)   Since perpendicular lines have negative reciprocal slopes, the line would have a slope of –1/4.

27. $a_n = \dfrac{2(n+1)!}{n!}$

$a_1 = \dfrac{2(1+1)!}{1!} = \dfrac{2(2)!}{1} = 2(2) = 4$

$a_2 = \dfrac{2(2+1)!}{2!} = \dfrac{2(3)!}{2} = 3! = 6$

$a_3 = \dfrac{2(3+1)!}{3!} = \dfrac{2(4)!}{3!} = 2(4) = 8$

$a_4 = \dfrac{2(4+1)!}{1!} = \dfrac{2(5)!}{4!} = 2(5) = 10$

First four terms: $\{4, 6, 8, 10\}$

28.

(a) Using the slope-intercept form of a line, $y = mx + b$:

$$y = -2x + 7$$

(b) First, we use the coordinates of the points to find the slope of the line:

$$(-3, -6), (1, 8)$$

$$m = \frac{y_2 - y_1}{x_2 - x_1}$$

$$m = \frac{8 - (-6)}{1 - (-3)}$$

$$m = \frac{14}{4}$$

$$m = \frac{7}{2}$$

Inserting the slope and the coordinates of the first point into the point-slope form of a line, we get:

$$y - y_1 = m(x - x_1)$$

$$y - (-6) = \frac{7}{2}\left[x - (-3)\right]$$

$$y + 6 = \frac{7}{2}(x + 3)$$

or,

$$y + 6 = \frac{7}{2}x + \frac{21}{2}$$

$$y = \frac{7}{2}x + \frac{21}{2} - 6$$

$$y = \frac{7}{2}x + \frac{21}{2} - \frac{12}{2}$$

$$y = \frac{7}{2}x - \frac{9}{2}$$

(c) Since parallel lines have the same slope, the line will have a slope of -5. Inserting this slope and the coordinates of the given point into the point-slope form of a line, we have:

$$y - y_1 = m(x - x_1)$$

$$y - (-5) = -5(x - 2)$$

$$y + 5 = -5x + 10$$

or,

$$y + 5 = -5x + 10$$

$$y + 5 - 5 = -5x + 10 - 5$$

$$y = -5x + 5$$

(d) Since perpendicular lines have negative reciprocal slopes, our line will have a slope of $-1/3$. Using the slope intercept form of a line, we get:

$$y = mx + b$$

$$y = -\frac{1}{3}x + 8$$

29.

(a) $2^{3x-1} = 16$

$\log_2 2^{3x-1} = \log_2 16$

$3x - 1 = 4$

$3x = 5$

$x = \dfrac{5}{3}$

(b) $\text{Log}\left(\dfrac{x}{3}\right) = 2$

$10^{\text{Log}\left(\frac{x}{3}\right)} = 10^2$

$\dfrac{x}{3} = 100$

$x = 300$

(c) $\text{Ln}(5x + 2) = 3$

$e^{\text{Ln}(5x+2)} = e^3$

$5x + 2 = 20.08$

$5x = 18.08$

$x = 3.62$

(d) $e^{\frac{4}{x}} = 10$

$\text{Ln}\, e^{\frac{4}{x}} = \text{Ln}\, 10$

$\dfrac{4}{x} = 2.3$

$4 = 2.3x$

$1.7 = x$

30.

(a) Common factors:

$$3x^5 y - 18xy^4 = 3xy\left(x^4 - 6y^3\right)$$

(b) Difference of two cubes:

$$x^3 - 125 = x^3 - 5^3 = (x - 5)\left(x^2 + 5x + 25\right)$$

(c) Difference of two squares:

$$x^2 - 1 = x^2 - 1^2 = (x + 1)(x - 1)$$

31. $A_{\text{Circle}} = \pi r^2$

$A_{\text{Circle}} = \pi \left(5\,\text{ft}\right)^2$

$A_{\text{Circle}} = 25\pi\,\text{ft}^2$

$A_{\text{Circle}} = 78.53\,\text{ft}^2$

32.

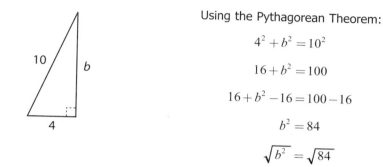

Using the Pythagorean Theorem:

$$4^2 + b^2 = 10^2$$

$$16 + b^2 = 100$$

$$16 + b^2 - 16 = 100 - 16$$

$$b^2 = 84$$

$$\sqrt{b^2} = \sqrt{84}$$

$$b = 9.2$$

33. Expanding across the top row:

$$\begin{vmatrix} 3 & 1 & 2 \\ 0 & -5 & 1 \\ 4 & 0 & -2 \end{vmatrix} = 3 \begin{vmatrix} -5 & 1 \\ 0 & -2 \end{vmatrix} - 1 \begin{vmatrix} 0 & 1 \\ 4 & -2 \end{vmatrix} + 2 \begin{vmatrix} 0 & -5 \\ 4 & 0 \end{vmatrix}$$

$$= 3\left(-5(-2) - 0(1)\right) - 1\left(0(-2) - 4(1)\right) + 2\left(0(0) - 4(-5)\right)$$

$$= 3(10 - 0) - (0 - 4) + 2(0 + 20)$$

$$= 3(10) - (-4) + 2(20)$$

$$= 30 + 4 + 40$$

$$= 74$$

34. $\left(x^2 - x - 5\right)\left(x^2 + 6\right) = x^2\left(x^2\right) + x^2(6) + (-x)\left(x^2\right) + (-x)(6) + (-5)\left(x^2\right) + (-5)(6)$

$$= x^4 + 6x^2 - x^3 - 6x - 5x^2 - 30$$

$$= x^4 - x^3 + x^2 - 6x - 30$$

35. $-2 < \dfrac{x}{3} - 4 < 8$

$-2 + 4 < \dfrac{x}{3} - 4 + 4 < 8 + 4$

$2 < \dfrac{x}{3} < 12$

$2(3) < \dfrac{x}{3}(3) < 12(3)$

$6 < x < 36$

36. $\sec 65° = \dfrac{1}{\cos 65°} = \dfrac{1}{0.423} = 2.366$

37.

exponent

$\underbrace{(0.3)}^{6}$

base

38.

(a) Not a function

(b) Function

(c) Function

39.

(a) $2^6 = 64 \Rightarrow \log_2 64 = 6$

(b) $e^p = x \Rightarrow \operatorname{Ln} x = p$

(c) $10^5 = 100,000 \Rightarrow \operatorname{Log} 100,000 = 5$

(d) $\left(\dfrac{1}{4}\right)^2 = 16 \Rightarrow \log_{\frac{1}{4}} \dfrac{1}{16} = 2$

40.

(a)

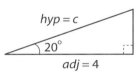

$\cos \theta = \dfrac{adj}{hyp}$

$\cos 20° = \dfrac{4}{c}$

$c \cos 20° = 4$

$c = \dfrac{4}{\cos 20°}$

$c = \dfrac{4}{0.94}$

$c = 4.25$

(b)

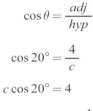

$\tan \theta = \dfrac{opp}{adj}$

$\tan \theta = \dfrac{8}{3}$

$\tan^{-1}(\tan \theta) = \tan^{-1}\left(\dfrac{8}{3}\right)$

$\theta = 69.4°$

41. $\begin{bmatrix} 3 & -1 & 2 & 5 \end{bmatrix} \begin{bmatrix} -2 & 0 \\ 4 & -3 \\ 3 & -1 \\ 0 & 6 \end{bmatrix} = \begin{bmatrix} 3(-2)+(-1)(4)+2(3)+5(0) & 3(0)+(-1)(-3)+2(-1)+5(6) \end{bmatrix}$

$$= \begin{bmatrix} -4 & 31 \end{bmatrix}$$

42.

(a)

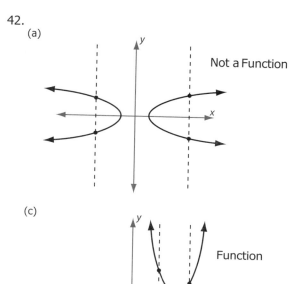

Not a Function

(b)

Function

(c)

Function

(d)

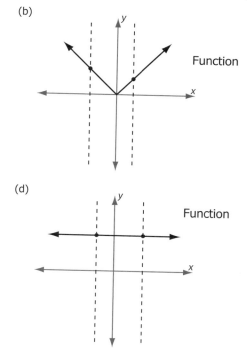

Function

43. $-6 \begin{bmatrix} 3 & -5 \\ 2 & 1 \end{bmatrix} = \begin{bmatrix} -18 & 30 \\ -12 & -6 \end{bmatrix}$

44. $6\sqrt{3} - 9\sqrt{3} + \sqrt{3} = -2\sqrt{3}$

45. $(r, \theta) = (3, 60°)$

$x = r \cos \theta \qquad\qquad y = r \sin \theta$

$x = 3 \cos 60° \qquad\qquad y = 3 \sin 60°$

$x = 3(0.5) \qquad\qquad y = 3(0.866)$

$x = 1.5 \qquad\qquad y = 2.598$

Thus,

$(x, y) = (1.5, 2.598)$

46. $\left(6x^3 - 9x^2 - 16\right) - \left(3x^2 - 2x - 10\right) = 6x^3 - 9x^2 - 16 - 3x^2 + 2x + 10$

$$= 6x^3 - 12x^2 + 2x - 6$$

47.

(a) $5x + 2y = 8$

$2x - y = 5$

Solving the 2nd equation for y:

$$2x - y = 5$$

$$-y = 5 - 2x$$

$$y = 2x - 5 \quad \boxed{A}$$

Inserting the result into the top equation, we find x:

$$5x + 2y = 8$$

$$5x + 2(2x - 5) = 8$$

$$5x + 4x - 10 = 8$$

$$9x - 10 = 8$$

$$9x - 10 + 10 = 8 + 10$$

$$9x = 18$$

$$\frac{9x}{9} = \frac{18}{9}$$

$$x = 2$$

Inserting x back into Equation $\boxed{A}$, we find y:

$$y = 2x - 5$$

$$y = 2(2) - 5$$

$$y = 4 - 5$$

$$y = -1$$

Thus, the solution to the system is $x = 2$, $y = -1$.

(b) $x + y = 3$

$x + 2y = 5$

First, we multiply the top equation by -1:

$$-x - y = -3$$

$$x + 2y = 5$$

calculation cont. on next page...

Solution #47(b) from previous page...

Next, we add the two equations and solve for y:

$$-x - y = -3$$

$$\underline{x + 2 = 5}$$

$$0 + y = 2$$

$$y = 2$$

Inserting this result into the *original* top equation, we find x:

$$x + y = 3$$

$$x + 2 = 3$$

$$x = 1$$

Thus, the solution to the system is $x = 1$, $y = 2$.

(c) $5x + 4y = 1$

  $3x - 6y = 2$

Constructing the appropriate determinants:

$$x = \frac{\begin{vmatrix} 1 & 4 \\ 2 & -6 \end{vmatrix}}{\begin{vmatrix} 5 & 4 \\ 3 & -6 \end{vmatrix}} \qquad y = \frac{\begin{vmatrix} 5 & 1 \\ 3 & 2 \end{vmatrix}}{\begin{vmatrix} 5 & 4 \\ 3 & -6 \end{vmatrix}}$$

Solving the denominator determinant:

$$\begin{vmatrix} 5 & 4 \\ 3 & -6 \end{vmatrix} = 5(-6) - 3(4) = -30 - 12 = -42$$

Thus,

$$x = \frac{\begin{vmatrix} 1 & 4 \\ 2 & -6 \end{vmatrix}}{-42} \qquad y = \frac{\begin{vmatrix} 5 & 1 \\ 3 & 2 \end{vmatrix}}{-42}$$

Solving the numerator determinants:

$$x: \quad \begin{vmatrix} 1 & 4 \\ 2 & -6 \end{vmatrix} = 1(-6) - 2(4) = -6 - 8 = -14$$

$$y: \quad \begin{vmatrix} 5 & 1 \\ 3 & 2 \end{vmatrix} = 5(2) - 3(1) = 10 - 3 = 7$$

$$\Rightarrow x = \frac{-14}{-42} \qquad y = \frac{7}{-42}$$

$$x = \frac{1}{3} \qquad y = -\frac{1}{6}$$

Thus, the solution to the system is $x = \dfrac{1}{3}$, $y = -\dfrac{1}{6}$.

(d) $x + 3y - 2z = 14$

$x + y - z = 6$

$3x - 2y + z = -5$

Constructing the augmented matrix:

$$\left[\begin{array}{ccc|c} 1 & 3 & -2 & 14 \\ 1 & 1 & -1 & 6 \\ 3 & -2 & 1 & -5 \end{array}\right]$$

Multiplying the top row by -1 and adding it to the 2nd row:

$$\left[\begin{array}{ccc|c} 1 & 3 & -2 & 14 \\ 0 & -2 & 1 & -8 \\ 3 & -2 & 1 & -5 \end{array}\right]$$

Multiplying the top row by -3 and adding it to the 3rd row:

$$\left[\begin{array}{ccc|c} 1 & 3 & -2 & 14 \\ 0 & -2 & 1 & -8 \\ 0 & -11 & 7 & -47 \end{array}\right]$$

Multiplying the 2nd row by $-1/2$:

$$\left[\begin{array}{ccc|c} 1 & 3 & -2 & 14 \\ 0 & 1 & -\dfrac{1}{2} & 4 \\ 0 & -11 & 7 & -47 \end{array}\right]$$

Multiplying the 2nd row by -3 and adding it to the 1st row:

$$\left[\begin{array}{ccc|c} 1 & 0 & -\dfrac{1}{2} & 2 \\ 0 & 1 & -\dfrac{1}{2} & 4 \\ 0 & -11 & 7 & -3 \end{array}\right]$$

Multiplying the 2nd row by 11 and adding it to the 3rd row:

$$\left[\begin{array}{ccc|c} 1 & 0 & -\dfrac{1}{2} & 2 \\ 0 & 1 & -\dfrac{1}{2} & 4 \\ 0 & 0 & \dfrac{3}{2} & -3 \end{array}\right]$$

calculation cont. on next page...

Solution #47(d) from previous page...

Multiplying the 3rd row by 2/3:

$$\begin{bmatrix} 1 & 0 & -\dfrac{1}{2} & \Big| & 2 \\ 0 & 1 & -\dfrac{1}{2} & \Big| & 4 \\ 0 & 0 & 1 & \Big| & -2 \end{bmatrix}$$

Multiplying the 3rd row by 1/2 and adding it to both the 1st and 2nd rows:

$$\begin{bmatrix} 1 & 0 & 0 & \Big| & 1 \\ 0 & 1 & 0 & \Big| & 3 \\ 0 & 0 & 1 & \Big| & -2 \end{bmatrix}$$

Thus, the solution to the system is $x = 1$, $y = 3$, $z = -2$.